THE SHARING OF POWER IN A PSYCHIATRIC HOSPITAL

The Sharing of Power in

a Psychiatric Hospital

by Robert Rubenstein and Harold D. Lasswell

with an Introduction by Stephen Fleck

New Haven and London,
Yale University Press, 1966

Rubenstein dedicates this book to
Catherine, Dirk, and Jeffrey

Lasswell dedicates it to Matthew

Preface

An analytic report of the character of this book depends on the contributions of many participants, some of whom must remain anonymous. This applies particularly to the active and often brilliant patients who have come and gone through the years at the Yale Psychiatric Institute, who left a legacy of fundamental importance to a therapeutic commonwealth.

Most directly implicated in the preparation of the manuscript were Elizabeth Bellis and Margaret Vranesh who worked intensively on the analyses of patient-staff meeting transcripts and the gathering of information from the several groups comprising the hospital community. Their devoted and creative assistance was made possible by grants from the National Institute of Mental Health and the Yale University School of Medicine, which we gratefully acknowledge.

The chore of reading and commenting on the manuscript was executed, with great benefit to the enterprise, by Yale Psychiatric Institute directors Stephen Fleck and Daniel P. Schwartz, and by Raphael Moses of Hadassah Medical School, Israel. We are especially appreciative of the willingness of directors Fleck and Schwartz to give generously of their recollections and interpretations without attempting in any way to infringe upon our responsibility for a final, independent judgment.

Vernon Lippard, dean of the Yale Medical School, Fredrick C. Redlich, chairman of the Yale department of psychiatry, and both Stephen Fleck and Theodore Lidz were of invaluable assistance in making the facilities of the Yale Psychiatric Institute fully available to us. We thank them for their unstinting cooperation. We are grateful to other of the Institute senior physicians and consulting supervisors, including Charles W. Gardner, Helen Gilmore, Roy Schafer, Alfredo Namnum, Richard Newman, Henry Wexler, Jules Coleman, Samuel Hunt, Albert Rothenberg, and David Carlson; to Gwenyth Davies, Alta Munro, Anna Baziak, and the many other Institute nurses; to Nea Norton, Institute chief social worker, Molly Brooks, and their associates; to the more than sixty psychiatrists who were resident physicians at the Institute during the eleven-year period of our study; to Carl Zimet and others who served as Institute psychologists; to G. Sarah Greer, Institute business manager; to the activities workers, teachers, and the many aides and other Institute personnel, all of whom were so cordial and helpful to us in this undertaking.

We warmly acknowledge the skillful help and encouragement of our editor, Jane Isay of the Yale University Press. Marilyn Schwartz-man has been remarkably able and conscientious in the complex task of preparing the manuscript for publication.

The particular problems with which we deal in this volume are outgrowths of exposure to many members of the intellectual community. It is impossible to touch upon any aspect of the life of the modern hospital without recognizing and paying tribute to the vision and energy of Maxwell Jones, who has done more than any other physician to crystallize awareness of the urgent importance of conceiving the therapeutic community. We desire, in addition, to underline our indebtedness in the examination of the problem of power to teachers and colleagues with whom we have had immediate association. For Rubenstein, they included Stephen Fleck, Theodore Lidz, Fredrick C. Redlich, Daniel P. Schwartz, Alfred Gross, Hans Loewald, Merton Gill, John Higgins, Richard J. Bernstein, and Robert Arnstein. Lasswell's principal teachers and colleagues in the initial efforts at the psychiatric illumination of political processes were William Alanson White, Harry Stack Sullivan, and Edward Sapir.

ROBERT RUBENSTEIN

HAROLD D. LASSWELL

New Haven
1966

Contents

Introduction by Stephen Fleck

This work is an ambitious and original attempt to bridge the two worlds of the mental hospital and of the policy sciences. If such an enterprise seems unduly venturesome, this audacity reflects the unwholesome distance between these two worlds, and Rubenstein and Lasswell examine this now much deplored isolation of mental hospitals in terms more significant than mere geographic distance. Specifically their bridge is an interdisciplinary one, a marriage of political science and clinical psychiatry, presenting the investigators with all the well-known pitfalls of interdisciplinary research. It is the authors' achievement that they have brought their work to this stage not of conclusions but of formulating precise questions and problems for further investigation, based on as solid data as can be marshaled from the process of the daily life of a mental hospital.

If this book did no more than encourage the present rapprochement between mental hospital communities and the larger community, it would deserve a wide readership; beyond this, however, it is a research document and a vivid, sensitive, microscopic description of one mental institution. The authors' approach and analysis of the mental hospital extend and render more precise the earlier sociological studies of psychiatric institutions, and they do not hesitate to force and study parallels between hospital life and our basic government institutions and beliefs. Indeed, this is the authors' venture: a juxtaposition of the organs and instruments we have developed to govern our lives and our coexistence as individuals, and the processes of healing as exemplified by the decision-making procedures in this mental hospital. The readers who undertake to follow this discourse may have varied interests; certain data are of primary importance to the researcher; some are of intense concern to the clinician; and others may engage the political scientist.

Some introductory comments on the philosophy, the aims, and the purposes of this hospital and their broader applications may be in order. As a university-based and sponsored hospital, the Yale Psychiatric Institute serves the traditional triad of treatment, teaching, and research. It should not only deliver a service of the highest order, but also experiment and innovate. As in all medical teaching, what is known should be imparted, but what is not known should be stressed, and what is practiced should be improved. As a teaching instrument, its material, the patients, should represent a wide range of psychiatric problems and afford experience in an equally broad range of treatment modalities. To the extent that paramedical professions enter into the program, these too should involve teaching and research in addition to the services they render and exemplify.

Some of these criteria and others that appropriately might be cited are not met by the Institute. Its small patient population can usually not represent all major psychiatric problems, and not all treatment modalities are practiced with equal emphasis. The reasons for this are detailed in the book, but some deserve emphasis here.

A deliberate striving for excellence cannot be reconciled with or achieved by a Cook's tour which leads around the world, however sketchily. Rather than covering the waterfront, we stress above all the learning and study of intensive psychotherapeutic involvement with patients on the part of all staff members, not only psychiatric residents. As far as the latter specifically are concerned, we not only aim to help them become competent psychotherapists for all patients —not only neurotic ones—but also to function and lead in institutional settings and in community mental health programs with expertness as well as with imagination. This requires teamwork involving several professions, and we believe it is paramount that this team share responsibilities and tasks flexibly. It is not a team of fixed roles arranged in a hierarchical order, because neither the patients nor their "illnesses" come in neat, orderly packages.

The spectrum of patient types who can be treated well on one small service, however, is not unlimited. Diagnostic variety has to be reconciled with the need for some cohesiveness of institutional life. Otherwise, staff energy can be scattered instead of intensely concentrated on doing well and therapeutically whatever is done. That the Yale Psychiatric Institute is an intensive institution is amply documented in these pages. How well the goal of excellence has been achieved is a further question, one not so readily answered here or elsewhere. To many readers, this question of the validity and effectiveness of the treatment methods described, the appraisal of the Institute, will no doubt present itself with some urgency. Yet this is not the authors' primary quest.

I would propose that to the extent that psychiatric illnesses are psychosocial disturbances, and it is this extent which almost exclusively covers the area of effective treatment at this time, any hospital activity that is designed to help patients adjust to life in the community is therapeutic and should be instituted. Most important, a mental hospital and particularly its leader must not become the servant of the community or society at large to such an extent that society's basic rejection of a mentally ill individual is reflected in the hospital atmosphere and continues to affect the individual who has been handed over to the institution for care and treatment. While medical directorship of a mental hospital does not guarantee adherence to this principle, its observance should be of paramount concern to those who take their Hippocratic oath seriously.

In the past we have, of course, sinned greatly in this regard, but these deficiencies have been generally recognized in the last decades and are in the process of being remedied at an amazingly fast pace throughout the land, although in their subtler forms these shortcomings are more difficult to discern and eradicate. However, the hospital director is given responsibility by society for the continued separation of individuals whom society has found disturbing, individuals who continue to harbor serious destructive propensities within themselves after entering the hospital; and these very characteristics which made them patients to begin with often constitute important challenges in treatment. The hospital staff must be on guard against these destructive tendencies, while the power invested in it must be used to motivate patients toward social adaptation and enable them to achieve it once they have been so motivated. Since mental patients in the United States are to return to a democratic way of life, however far below the ideals of democracy a particular community may fall, it is obviously of importance that life in the hospital reflect this democratic atmosphere when and wherever possible.

This book is concerned with degrees of institutional democracy and especially with the leadership's behavior in regard to power and democracy. The essentials and ideal ways of leadership in a democracy in general are far from solved or clearly prescribed. It is obvious that governmental forms which can be considered democratic range all the way from near anarchy, or communal living, to benign despotism. The latter occurs most often when a group has been given a new status suddenly, a liberation from above, so to speak.

This applied to our hospital. The traditional rigid and hierarchical staff organization is incompatible with the level of initiative and individual responsibility essential to around-the-clock therapeutic interaction with patients and has to be modified. Nurses' training in particular and hospital practices in general derive many of their characteristics from the requirements of the operating room suite and the out-of-date infectious disease ward. A quasi-military role stratification and job assignment may well be best suited to these tasks when technical considerations and protection of the community take precedence over individual needs and feelings. Unfortunately for those who throve under this regimented organization, the major tasks in medicine today and in psychiatry always entail a primary consideration of the individual as a person, and of his feelings toward himself, toward his impairments, and toward other people.

Thus decision-making and responsibility for patient care have to be shared and must at times rest with the individual staff members on the spot, demanding initiative and spontaneity from every staff member, tempered by his professional limitations, by the needs of the group at the time, and by an understanding of the patient's total needs and behavioral patterns. The therapeutic activity of one staff member must also be integrated with that of others on the therapeutic team, but cannot be predetermined only by fixed role limitations, such as that of a scrub nurse in the operating room. Thus a psychiatric team must rely on information-sharing, on adjusting one's role to the tasks and techniques agreed upon by all staff members, and such agreement must reflect individual attitudes and understanding, not only compliance based upon hierarchical role assignments, i.e. "taking orders."

While in service institutions the group goals or missions are clear in their broadest outlines, the day-to-day goals are usually not clear and need to be defined—one of the functions of leadership. If long-range goals or operating modes are to be revised, a group leader must also watch his timing and dosing. The public identification of new issues or goals he can discern and may consider desirable and appropriate can arouse opposition, rather than discussion and rational consideration, if this recognition is barely emergent on the part of most group members. Resistance to change within each individual, reinforced by that of his neighbor, may be called forth.

The leader of an institution with the specific mission of a service for psychiatric patients has, of course, to reconcile the accomplishment of the mission with staff competence and the procedures and attitudes with which such professionals working in the institution are comfortable. Yet, in any social arrangement, no matter how democratic, certain powers also have to be surrendered by the individual to the group and to the group-designated agent or leader. Most notable and obvious, and sometimes notorious, in this respect is police power. But democratization as such, then, is not necessarily a primary mission in a hospital. It is subordinate to the accomplishment of treatment, and only to the extent that democratic process is also therapeutic can it be a primary goal. For instance, in an army or military organization even minor degrees of democratization may prove incompatible with combat efficiency. We simply do not know to what degree democratization in a mental hospital is possible in terms of staff functions any more than we can speak with assurance about the degree of democratization that would be optimally therapeutic for the patients. This may well vary for different populations with such factors as age, social class, diagnosis, and staff attitudes.

While the book in hand concerns itself primarily with the degree of power-sharing on the part of the patients, to this observer the main task of innovation, so far at least, has been the democratization of staff procedures. First of all a change in communicative direction was involved—from vertical to horizontal. Traditionally, nurses for instance report to each other and to their own superiors, head nurses may speak to the doctors about patients, receive orders, and pass them back down to staff nurses and aides; but questions of general policy, ward or hospital-wide activities, would similarly pass up all the way to the nursing director. He or she would take it up with the clinical director and other professionals, and then a decision and change in procedure or policy would be passed down through the channels of various professional specialities, somewhat like different elevator cars running up and down in their shafts, all sent off by the same dispatcher, but with communication between individual operators occurring only through him or if he arranges for two or more operators to meet. Thus horizontal communication channels have to be established first. In larger institutions this is an essential element of "decentralization," by now a well-established policy in many state mental hospitals. Accomplishments of this type at the Yale Psychiatric Institute might have been more logically studied by scrutinizing staff meetings as such, rather than patient-staff meetings. It is true, however, that patient-staff meetings could not have occurred without at least the consent of a majority of staff members or staff groups and presumably—maybe optimistically—after a certain degree of staff democratization had been achieved. This in turn must have involved a concomitant shift in staff members' intrinsic attitudes and at least a conscious readiness in the majority of personnel for democratic staff procedures, which outweighed resistance to change. This book documents the relative ease with which some staff groups accepted the changes, but they were more troublesome to nurses and to a lesser extent to the residents. To conduct staff meetings essentially like any other group or discussion meeting is not new or original; with it come the usual problems of any group process.

A new or innovating director of an institution is apt to be met with anxiety and hostility under the best of circumstances and probably always has the choice between taking over with a firm hand, leaning toward authoritarianism and arbitrariness, or allowing feelings to come out directly in staff and other meetings which may interfere to some extent with the business at hand, namely the consideration of patients' needs. There is no question that the Yale Psychiatric Institute went through such phases in the earlier years of the decade studied, before it entered an era of possibly excessive charisma. This is another risk for leadership: once the group formation has moved from banding together against the leader to identifying with him and depending on him, the charismatic tendencies may swing toward overdependency upon his decisions, advice, and support. Most of the obstacles to staff democratization, in my belief, lie in this area of dependency and ready compliance. Naturally, those staff groups which are conditioned by their education to a position of lower rank and habitually take orders and give reports only when asked, but not otherwise, will find it most comfortable to ride the charismatic tide, to refrain from spontaneous participation, and to rationalize that it is neither desirable, proper, nor indicated. Disagreement and hostility then go underground and are only expressed to trusted colleagues on the lower hierarchical level.

Thus it is not surprising that, from the director's standpoint, the major obstacles to staff democratization have been the vertical shafts of professional responsibility and communication and the tendency of nurses to adhere to their traditional, hierarchically inferior roles. Many nurses, individually and collectively, had to overcome considerable resistance, almost forcing themselves to report spontaneously observations about which they are uncertain or afraid they cannot express in the "proper" language. This is a most important problem for general hospitals, and for mental hospitals in particular. It is also rooted in the traditional ways of hospitals and of nurses' education and has received special attention in the form of a separate, yet related, research project by the previous nursing director, Miss Anna T. Baziak. What is asked of nurses in the service of democratization is role diffusion, with all its attendant anxieties. Similar difficulties of role diffusion probably would apply to professional aides. Their situation at the Yale Psychiatric Institute is unusual. It has not been studied in detail because the majority of aides are students who are employed part-time.

The residents' role problems, differing from those of the nurses, are both more and less severe. Yet here too the hierarchical tradition represents a handicap, if not a barrier, in that by the very title resident, trainee, fellow, etc., he or she is expected to take a back seat in meetings devoted to the discussion of patients' problems and decisions pertaining to them. The residents might feel free to express themselves in a meeting clearly designated as a seminar or teaching exercise. Since in any clinical undertaking these two operations are of course combined, it is not so unusual or difficult for residents to speak up and make their views known, provided they do not have to do so *ad novum*. They need to realize that disagreements are proper topics for staff discussion and not per se equated with their superiors' disapprobation. After initial reserve, each group of residents, or most of them, participate actively and spontaneously in staff meetings, although not so readily in patient-staff meetings. Residents may be more handicapped than nurses with regard to sharing information, which their patients may consider confidential. Although patients are told that the staff works together through sharing information, the residents are expected to assume primary responsibility for their individual patients. Yet the responsibility is also a collective one, and patients often expect residents to assume responsibility on matters not considered specifically in their psychotherapy sessions. Difficulties for residents also arise because they account to superiors who carry the ultimate responsibility, but who are also the judges of the resident's performance.

Another challenge to the leader is that he serves as a model for the residents. Although much learning proceeds through identification, this must also be guarded against. The resident should learn to function in similar positions. This requires developing his own style, and it may require of him new methods and procedures in a setting both quantitatively and qualitatively different. The resident usually does not consider participation as a responsible hospital manager his main goal; his primary aim and his most difficult task are the learning of individual psychotherapy, especially psychotherapy with psychotic patients. Yet this writer would consider the operation of the Yale Psychiatric Institute a failure if at least the majority of those who passed through the training experience did not feel competent to engage themselves, at least on a part-time basis, in hospital psychiatry. It is gratifying to note that so far eighty per cent of the group under scrutiny here have done just that. Equally significant seem the questionnaire data which concern the retrospective attitudes toward the leadership at the Institute, which document their ambivalences. Complaints about arbitrariness and the authoritarian characteristics of the direction of the Institute, difficult to reconcile with the evidence of increasing power sharing, are mixed with the demand or expectation that the director and his associates devote more time and attention to the residents.

On the whole, former residents felt that they had enough decision-making power, except in the area of patient discharge. It is at this point where the director's responsibility to the community is specifically involved, and on this issue he may therefore be more retentive of power. On the other hand, residents and patients often equate discharge with successful treatment, so that they may have a unique prestige stake in this decision. Both residents and patients tend to overrate their usually very restricted experience in community living when they assess in advance the patient's ability to cope with life outside the hospital.

Other team members, social workers, group workers, and occupational therapists found much less difficulty in sharing responsibility, decision-making, and discussion. Many of these professionals have not been trained in the rigidly hierarchical medical settings with which the young physician and the student nurse have to cope and identify. The greater readiness and ability of social workers and activity therapists to participate in a more democratic process may also be related to the fact that the information they furnish was not previously available to others, while the nurses' information is always shared prior to staff meetings, through their own successive reporting or because several of them may have observed the same incident or event. That these several staff members may also be of different rank introduces apprehensions about being the first to speak and the fear of having one's account corrected, amended, or contradicted by another "witness."

The selection of patient-staff meetings as the source of the core data, then, has disadvantages, but also definite advantages. It was one of the important innovations, one that could be fixed precisely in time, involved everybody in the hospital, and lent itself readily to data collection and recording. No other change in the program during the past decade has all these attributes. The major disadvantage of this forum as the data source in an analysis of power shifts and decision-making in the Institute derives from the very purpose of these meetings. They were explicitly introduced for the purpose of exchange of information (enlightenment), for the airing and sharing of intelligence which would otherwise not become explicitly shared knowledge. They were not intended as forums for decisions and voting, and they do not parallel a parliamentary forum. The authors raise the challenging question of whether a hospital forum so constituted would be therapeutic, or more therapeutic than the one here analyzed. In this respect, the book raises important, well-defined questions for further research and experimentation.

While the question of the effect of sharing information and power on the therapeutic process remains open, we can state that the more forums further the similarity between living inside and outside the hospital, the more therapeutic they are. A further question is: Can individual therapy and treatment, probably the most private activity in which two people can engage short of affectional intimacies, be reconciled with the reduction in privacy through community-wide sharing and unhampered discussion of all topics inherent in the democratic process? This question is answered positively here, as the authors raise some pertinent issues for further evaluation.

The evidence also indicates that disturbed behavior became a much less difficult and tenacious problem after some of the innovations were begun, and patients became integrated to the level of the hospital community more readily. This evidence may be contaminated by the fact that more efficient medication was introduced, but the salutary effects were noticeable prior to the use of the modern drugs, and the staff of this Institute rated the impact of the drugs alone not very high. Yet the very knowledge of their availability raises the staff's confidence and expectations that behavioral incontinence will be controlled.

The issue of power sharing and decision-making is a two-way proposition. There are certain decisions which the management of the hospital rightly or wrongly believe their own and possibly guard jealously, some no doubt realistically, and others by virtue of rationalization. One of the outstanding examples in the Institute has been regulations concerned with fire prevention. Without blocking discussion the director brooked absolutely no interference from the staff or the patients through any democratic process, but has strictly adhered to the directions of the local fire department regardless of patients' comfort and other therapeutic needs or wishes. Other examples are to be found in the transcripts. From this writer's vantage point, however, the problem of getting rid of power and responsibility has been greater than the anxiety involved in sharing or letting it go.

The major problem, and possibly the single most important factor which detracts from effective therapy no matter what kind of treatment is used, is lack of motivation. No matter how good and skilled the therapist may be, if the patient cannot be motivated to look, strive, and search for better ways of interacting with his environment, the therapist will be ineffective, even as therapist and patient in their private sessions may glory in their successful journey toward new insights. Thus, the issue of power and decision-making seem subsidiary to this primary problem which Adolf Meyer exemplified many years ago, when he suggested the inscription over the gates of a new mental hospital, "To the will to get well." The data in this book demonstrate this point with repeated examples of avoidance of responsibility on the part of patients and staff. Many times it seems to be safe to complain about the lack of freedom, responsibility, and the like—but only as long as it is clear that they are not going to be granted. When the option can be taken up, performance and actual assumption of additional responsibility proceed slowly, if at all. One can observe over a period of time the ebbs and neaps of patients' readiness and capacity to carry on with certain responsibilities, participation in meetings or classes, or in running various aspects of their own lives collectively. This is not a function of changes in the composition of the patient population, but seems to be primarily a phenomenon of group process. However, it does not seem unique to mental hospitals; hostility, anxieties, and resistance to independent strivings are also observable in groups not composed of people severely handicapped by aberrant concept formations.

The impact of sharing information and decision-making on the technical aspects of therapy is less clear. There is no good base line for comparison with the psychotherapy of psychotic patients along the analytic model, in complete privacy, although to some extent this was practiced at the Yale Psychiatric Institute in the early 1950s. It is obvious that a community shared by patients and staff, where some staff members also are individual therapists, cannot support the same kind of relationships as the situation which exists in the office of a practicing analyst, whose private life, demeanor, and style, down to such details as how he smokes or sits in his chair, are mostly matters of which the patient cannot be aware. The office patient can only directly observe how the analyst lets him into the office and how he conducts him out, except for an occasional, usually quite accidental, glimpse of the analyst in town or at some public or social function. While the patient can acquaint himself more or less surreptitiously with certain aspects of his analyst's life and career, he is by no means acquainted with him to the degree that a patient who lives with other patients who see the same therapist and has many occasions to observe him outside their particular sessions.

Thus even if desirable, the analytic model could not be reconstructed inside the hospital. Furthermore, patients for whom it seems indicated are treated by outside therapists. The proposition, then, is not to reconstruct this particular model but to find a compromise, since the freedom of expression facilitated by the analytic model, and its privacy in particular, cannot be provided. There obviously is little sense in investigating or theorizing about the worth of an impossible situation, and the hospital has to deal with the existing milieu and move from there. Moreover, unlike the classical analytic patient, whose symptoms are essentially contained and not particularly shared with his environment, the inpatient shares most of his symptoms much of the time, and some of his symptoms all of the time, with everybody and anybody in the community. He may also share with others much of what transpires between him and his therapist. Bringing such information out in a structured forum such as patient-staff meetings is therefore not the tremendous step away from privacy it may seem to those accustomed to the private, dyadic process. On the contrary, it brings into conceivably more therapeutic channels information that has already been shared, often in ways destructive to one or another patient or to the community as a whole.

If therapy is viewed more as a learning process, which indeed it often is since some patients have to learn the simplest modes and techniques of living, the problem of sharing even intimate details becomes mainly an issue of tact, rather than of therapeutic disadvantage. Thus patients have to learn what secrets, what information, and symptoms not to share, as often as they have to overcome neurotic or antisocial needs for secrecy and privacy. Although we all use the phrase, "returning a patient to the outside," with the implication that the patient is cured and now ready to resume his "normal" life in a "normal" environment, this is a grave fallacy, for patients often have never lived in as democratic or as thoughtful an environment as the hospital. Thus a democratic atmosphere in the hospital is justified and essential because it prepares, or re-prepares, people to live in a democratic society outside the hospital. And as long as our major therapeutic instruments lie in the psychosocial sphere, any step toward democratization should therefore be therapeutically wholesome and effective. Yet the degree of democratization, and specifically the type of information open to community consideration, must be learned. Its usefulness must be evaluated in terms of therapeutic goals and the living needs in the hospital and in the larger community. Here a finding that seems to dismay the authors, does not seem particularly disturbing in this context. Whereas it is clear that the patients make primary use of the patient-staff meetings as an instrument for enlightenment, essentially in line with its goals and inception, the staff uses these meetings for admonishments and statements assigned by the researchers to the value "rectitude." It is conceivably desirable that the staff speak up primarily in the service of enlightenment, that is, enlightening patients, but it is also conceivable that in the service of the teaching function the expression of "what's right and what's wrong" may be as, or more, important. What is dismaying in perusing the transcripts is that there seems to be at times more preaching than teaching, at least on the part of the leader. But in dealing with dependent and immature people, forums such as patient-staff meetings serve more usefully as models for group living, clarifying pertinent issues, goals, and mores, rather than serving primarily for the dissemination of information, especially since other channels are available for this purpose. In general, these innovations aim—and, we believe, are effective—in preserving and enlarging patients' responsibility for their own lives to the greatest possible degree.

Another innovation not germane to this book's basic thesis must be mentioned briefly because it, too, constitutes a deviation from the traditional dyadic process of therapy. This is our therapeutic endeavor with patients' families, an outgrowth of a decade's research into the family dynamics of schizophrenia and sociopathic patients. Here also, the problem has not been the letting go of secrets, but rather exploring the sham of secrets—helping the group to talk together about topics which each member might prefer to take up "privately" with the therapist or social worker, as if the spouse, son, or father knew nothing of it. But that very family member also goes through the same "private" conversation about the same topic with some other or even with the same staff member, and the staff would only indulge this sham if they did not help the family to discuss the issue together. Work with families is essential to the issue of patients' return to the community.

Possibly the most important question for all concerned is: How applicable to other institutions are the principles and methods learned here? As we move from the large, overadministrated hospital communities to community psychiatry, the developments and experiences described seem of the utmost relevance. Even the very term "community psychiatry" implies one crucial principle, that of rendering a hospital as much as possible a stepping-stone toward living in the larger community. Equally obvious is the condition that the staff be active and community-related, instead of isolated and dependent only on the hospital community as so often is the case in outlying state hospitals. It is even more important for some patients, who move in and out of the hospital repeatedly, that the living modes outside and inside are not too discrepant. It is not necessary to wear pajamas inside, and ordinary clothes outside, to be behind locked doors inside, and to have open doors outside, to be deprived of shaving equipment and jewelry inside, and to have all these "dangerous" items available outside. All these are elements of an "open-door" philosophy, but the closed door also has value and symbolic purposes. It not only makes those patients who might feel unsafe without them feel safer, but, in another sense, it locks the staff in. The locked door obviously does not guarantee staff interaction with patients, as we know from the many examples of large government hospitals, where the staff has only the most cursory contact with severely disturbed patients and where even nurses may but rarely interact with patients, who are left almost completely to the lowest staff echelon, the aides. But if hospital psychiatrists have avoided active involvement with the patients, practicing psychiatrists in the community have avoided hospital patients almost altogether, and therewith most psychotic patients. It may be one of the important contributions of the Yale Psychiatric Institute that the residents, as well as other staff, are forced to interact with all patients, including those severely disturbed and combative, and that the staff learn to do so competently and helpfully. This demonstration is personally experienced and mastered by each psychiatrist: that one can live and work with psychotic patients; that they can be helped to live much more as they would live "outside"; that they can assume responsibilities; and that in such an atmosphere progress can be made—the "illnesses" are treated, no matter what the ultimate molecular etiology, if any, may turn out to be. Implementing this with actual competence would at least close the gap between psychiatric practices today and the level of possible practices that would be commensurate with today's knowledge. If the current activity of government-supported planning accomplishes no more than this, we should feel rewarded, but government funds in themselves do not purchase manpower know-how. Total figures of professional personnel do not reflect professional competence— competence to deal therapeutically with psychotic patients. To such a quest this volume contributes materially, but it will be of little use to those who are certain that they already know the answers, be they political scientists or psychiatrists. This book's value lies in its challenge: how to reconcile organization and goals, how to pursue professional objectives with minimal bureaucratization and with maximum homage to democratic process and human dignity, even when subordinates and patients show little inclination for, and even resistance to, practicing democratic responsibility in their daily work and life in the hospital.

THE SHARING OF POWER IN A PSYCHIATRIC HOSPITAL

1. Challenge and Innovation

The demand that the dignity of each individual be respected, that he share in shaping his destiny and that of his community, disquiets every aspect of our lives. Families, schools, churches, hospitals, and the institutions of government are affected by this transition from authoritarianism to power sharing.

The objectives and strategies of the contemporary family are ambiguous and contradictory, disrupted as they are by the uncertainties and conflicts of our epoch of transition. Paternal absolutism has been drastically curbed, deference to parental control undermined, and all family members—including children—encouraged by the prevailing ideology to assert their individuality more vigorously. Some families achieve relatively smooth but tentative success in the effort to fulfill the social function, preparing the individual for participation in the community. Gradually the dependent infant acquires skills, develops capacities, and becomes active in the life beyond family, in school, work, church, and other larger communities. The culmination of this process is the departure of the young adult, relatively independent and self-sufficient, to make his own way, pursue his own interests, and with time, to begin his own family. As he grows and develops, his power within the parental family—the extent to which he shares in the shaping of its critical decisions— gradually increases. He plays a more active part in determining the perspectives of the family (what do we care about?), their preferred outcomes (what do we want?), and their strategies (how shall we go about getting what we want?). All the passions and animosities arising among child, mother, and father, and the struggle to work them out somehow, in one's own way, for oneself, the vicissitudes of the oedipal situation, are involved: the son's love for his mother and his hatred of her for turning to another; his love of father, his wish to be his friend and to grow up to be like him, his hatred of this man who is bigger and stronger and who possesses the woman he loves, and his struggle not to be like him; the father's love and envy of his increasingly strong and able son, whose emergence heralds his own decline; the mother's complicated feelings about the transformation of her daughter into an attractive young woman. The processes mean inner conflict related to the earliest stages of psychosexual development: the child's wish to be taken care of opposing the assertion of his individuality; the wish to be more powerful than father, inhibited by the fear of his retaliation. It means conflict within the family: the parents' wish that their child remain their child, as against their wish that he become a responsible, independent adult; their wish that the child become strong and free, opposing what they now experience as a threat to their previously sanctioned positions of authority and superior power within the family.

Hopefully, the family finds a way. The parents do not experience their child's growing strength as only depleting them; the developing individual does not experience his parents' destruction as a necessary step in his maturation; growth proceeds in an atmosphere of mutual respect for the dignity and the integrity of parent and child. But struggle is a necessary and inevitable part of the process of growth. In working out these conflicts within the family and himself, the individual gains the experience and finds the strength for his own life. Ultimately his fulfillment requires that he work out for himself what he cares most about, what he wants, and how he will go about getting what he wants; he has to find a way, together with others, to build and sustain what he and those in the communities of which he chooses to become a part care about and believe in. The disadvantaged child has, in short, emerged into the roles and positions of power. For some, however, this transition does not occur.

The great social movements of our time concern the demand for full participation as equals in the affairs of the community by the disadvantaged. Sermons and speeches have long acknowledged the justice of this demand, but the insistence that we take the democratic ideology seriously and live by it is revolutionary. All of us may be viewed in some context as disadvantaged. Two prominent examples are Negroes and women; two groups less aware of being deprived are students and patients.

The exploitation of Negroes and women is sustained because it is experienced as politically, economically, and socially gratifying to others in the community. Their struggles involve conflicts similar to those of the maturing adolescent as he emerges from a dependent child into an independent, responsible adult. Those opposing full citizenship and equal opportunity for women and Negroes rationalize their opposition, as do parents seeking to hold onto their children: they are fragile, unable to survive in the adult world without special protection, primitive, childlike, and hyperemotional, underdeveloped biologically and intellectually, and content with their passive, dependent, and subordinate position. It is only when Negroes, women, and children convincingly demonstrate the adequacy of their resources and their ability to handle responsibility, when they have resolved their inner resistance to moving beyond being taken care of and effectively voice their dissatisfaction, that a conflict of conscience is evoked within those opposing their fulfillment. Only then are attitudes supporting their growth and development as equals mobilized within those from whom freedom is sought; only then does change occur.

Students and their school and college communities are subject to extraordinary control by administrators and teachers. They are encouraged to assume the role of passive recipients of the ministrations of experts. Students are rarely invited to share in the making of critical decisions or substantially in the continuing dialogue that determines the perspectives, preferred outcomes, and strategies of their schools. They are offered few opportunities to participate in such a way as to prepare themselves for full, successful participation in the communities of which they choose to be a part beyond graduation.

The rituals of prescribed courses, majors, examinations, and the authoritarian atmosphere of the classroom separate the school experience from the student's needs. Mock student councils and anemic student governments suggest only a limited awareness of the need for substantial student participation in the determination of the affairs of his community. What the student cares about and wants becomes increasingly remote in institutions directed by others with very different values and perspectives and in which he has no voice. The position of the student is rationalized, like that of child, Negro, and woman: he is immature and irresponsible, he requires and prefers direction and control.

To be meaningful to students and responsive to their needs, schools must become communities in which all the participants—faculty, administrators, and students—actively share in the shaping of what they together believe in and want and the means by which they will seek to fulfill their objectives together. Only recently have students as a group begun to assert the capacity to handle the greater responsibilities of such participation and the clear preference for a stronger voice; conflicts of conscience are only just being evoked in administrators and teachers; schools remain remarkably unaffected by the great social transformation of our time.

Patients are also among the disadvantaged. It is customary to view them as having to be taken care of because they are ill, incapacitated, or defective. Hospitalized psychiatric patients, the subgroup we shall focus upon, have been defeated in long, protracted, at times subtle, at times violent, power struggles within their families, and by friends and colleagues in school, work, and the other communities in which they have unsuccessfully sought to participate. Unable to find a way to share effectively in the decision-making processes of the family, they remain in unresolved conflict with those exercising power and at odds with their critical decisions, their perspectives, preferred outcomes, and strategies.

The patient is a target of severe sanction in the family decision process and is finally ejected as so burdensome, threatening, and disruptive that the life of the family cannot proceed without his removal. The deprivations experienced in this struggle may have been so overwhelming that he responded with intense pain and suffering, apathy, a sense of depletion, estrangement, and withdrawal; he may have taken refuge in psychosis, the elaboration of a more congenial, indulgent private world. The deprivation may have been intensified intrapsychically and expressed in depression, characterized by unrelenting self-flagellation, or externalized and expressed in sociopathic behavior, rebellion against the prescriptions of the larger society.

Specialized environments may reprocess the behavior and the inner perspectives of individuals whose needs have not been met by the family: institutions which may serve this function, including schools, monasteries, utopian work communities, prisons, and psychiatric hospitals have appeared, prospered, and been displaced by one another in different eras. While each has special advantages, all are alike in offering an opportunity for participation in a new community. They vary in the level of respect accorded the members and in the power exercised over losers in the family struggle. The expellees may be objects of contempt and fear and be subjected to physical abuse. A loser may present himself to the new environment as "misguided" and become the object of reeducation and rehabilitation. He may take advantage of a revolutionary mood in society, seeing himself as exploited and victimized by powerful, malignant social forces whose great impact dwarfs the deprivations sustained within the family. If the strategies employed by losers involve their becoming "sufferers" or emphasize physical and mental incapacitation, they may be perceived as "sick" and be provided with medical treatment.

The success of a loser in obtaining access to medical institutions depends upon being perceived as within the category of persons for whom medical treatment is regarded as appropriate. Since most expellees present behavioral problems which cannot be treated by the therapies customarily applied to organic disorders, they have not always been well-received by ordinary physicians, who find the peculiar difficulties of diagnosis and treatment an affront. Many of these "ill" have therefore been rejected as "legitimate" patients by the power figures of strictly medical hospitals. Within psychiatry, however, the problem-solving roles, institutions, and functions elaborated for the physically ill were applied by psychiatrists to relieve the exigencies of their predicament. This provided the defeated and expelled with the advantages of being dealt with in the relatively humane way appropriate for the sick; in addition, it protected them from possible abuses by nonpsychiatrist physicians, who might not differentiate them from other sufferers. However, it has become increasingly clear that this mode of solution is not well adapted to the problems of those subjected to severe family-imposed power deprivations, even when it is applied by psychiatrists.

Conventional psychiatric institutions reinforce the self-image of the hospitalized as losers, sufferers, and victims. Decisions about fundamental and pressing issues in the lives of patients are decided by others; the individuals most concerned participate not at all. In an authoritarian hospital, the roles of doctors, nurses, and patients are clearly defined. The "good patient" is compliant, cooperative, accepting, unquestioning, the recipient of the good, established, known care from doctors, nurses, and other staff members. He is regarded as a troublemaker, uncooperative, and cantankerous if he questions procedures, seeks information about why this is being done and that isn't, or presumes to take a more active position by volunteering judgments about what is wrong with him and what should be done, or the nature of the difficulties and the treatment of other patients. One part of the hospital—the staff—does things to that other part of the hospital—the patients—"to get 'them' well." The patients comply with these implicit expectations by assuming the passive role of those to whom things are done by others.

Once more, society and the doctors, experts with extraordinary authority over the lives of others, justify such exemptions from democratic practices and drastic usurpation of rights by describing the mentally ill as fragile, childlike, irresponsible, and dangerous to themselves and others. Not protecting them, failing to administer their affairs as dependents, would be a breach of professional obligation. But now the possibility is being considered that the traditional medical model is not appropriate for reprocessing these defeated and disadvantaged, and new institutions specifically elaborated in response to their needs are developing. This shift was prompted both by convincing demonstrations of the beneficial effects of patients participating actively with staff in determining and assessing what happens in the hospital[1] and by conflicts of conscience among those exercising power, the doctors, who knew, but had not previously been forced to acknowledge, the necessity of extending throughout the patient's experience the dignity, respect, responsibility, autonomy, and self-determination long acknowledged as central to psychoanalytic treatment. As will be demonstrated, patients respond competently and responsibly to such opportunities and expectations; in such an atmosphere they assert their dissatisfaction with being the passive recipients of the ministrations of others. That fact renders the doctor's authoritarian position uncertain and conflictful. He cannot continue to violate the canons of shared power and fulfill his obligations as a physician, for these deviations from democratic practice are no longer justifiable on therapeutic grounds.

The "therapeutic community" has emerged. The patient is invited to prepare himself for successful participation in the larger community by learning realistic techniques and strategies within the hospital community. The symptoms so dramatically exhibited by the sufferer are increasingly coming to be viewed as strategies for influencing the social environment, desperation devices used by those individuals who have lost their power struggle in the family and whose symptoms are so disturbing that the family no longer finds it possible to cope with them. In the hospital to which they are, in effect, expelled, they continue to rely on their symptoms, however unsatisfactory, to gain the net advantage of exemption from the responsibilities of full participation in the everyday life of society. If the mental hospital fails to return them to responsible participation, the patient will remain stranded in a noncontributory role.

The Changing Perspective in Psychiatry

How can the hospital environment be modified to permit those who are perceived as patients to alter their approach to life so that they are willing and able to act more responsibly? Psychiatrists who ask this question must make a total inventory of the traditional hospital and confront its every specific feature with the challenge "But is it therapeutic?" This volume presents a study of the effects of such an effort, the introduction in 1956 of a series of changes designed to draw patients into more active participation in the deci-

1. Maxwell Jones, *The Therapeutic Community, A New Treatment Method in Psychiatry* (New York, Basic Books, 1953).

sion process of the Yale Psychiatric Institute (YPI), a small treatment, training, and research hospital operated by the Yale Medical School.

Patient-staff conferences, the major innovation, were introduced in 1956 to provide an opportunity for patients to examine themselves and others in a realistic situation. But not only were the patients faced by a recurring opportunity and challenge. Every participant was enabled to see himself in the broader context, the senior physicians, the residents (the psychiatrists in training), the nurses, and all other members of the hospital community.

While the present report is addressed in part to psychiatrists and others concerned with the study and treatment of the psychoses, the YPI innovation is of interest and importance to specialists in many other fields. Political scientists and jurists can learn from YPI experience, since a fundamental problem of political science and jurisprudence is the sharing of power, which is the enlarging of authoritative and controlling participation in decision processes. Throughout the United States, institutions of government and law are moving in the direction required by democratic norms. Discrimination against all members of disadvantaged groups is, as we have seen, being severely questioned, and attempts to counteract this are being made.

These macroscopic cases should be reconsidered in the light of microchanges, such as the ones at the YPI; the general significance of the YPI innovation can be of value to political scientists, jurists, and neighboring scientists and scholars. This report will make more explicit the characteristics of contextual, problem-solving psychiatry that shares in the orientation of the policy sciences.

Contextualism and the Sciences of Man

The emphasis on the larger social setting at the YPI is part of a comprehensive trend toward contextualism in all the sciences of man. The formation of the Social Science Research Council in the 1920s provides a bench mark for interdisciplinary cooperation. The Council was initiated and guided by a political scientist, the late Charles E. Merriam of the University of Chicago. Merriam encouraged the study of psychiatry and psychology in the hope of obtaining from modern advances in the study of human nature insights comparable with the contributions made in the past when political theorists became acquainted with new developments in psychology.[2] Graham Wallas, of the London School of Economics and Political Science,

2. For Merriam's viewpoint at the time see his *New Aspects of Politics* (Chicago, University of Chicago Press, 1925).

had previously taken the lead among contemporary scholars in rejuvenating the interest in "human nature" which had been so fruitful in the hands of Hobbes, Locke, and Bentham.

In the United States, psychoanalysis influenced the first distinctive school of jurisprudence, the "American realists." The realists were chiefly concerned with transforming the traditional approach to law by emphasizing the social and psychological factors that played upon the judge and other participants in the decision process of the community. A realist such as the late Jerome Frank took from psychoanalysis its appreciation of unconscious forces in determining human conduct and sought to assess the significance of such factors for the theory and practice of law.[3]

Social and behavioral scientists emphasize the bearing of their speciality on public policy and stress the connection between their contributions to knowledge and the overriding goals, traditionally formulated in such slogans as "life, liberty and pursuit of happiness" and "the right of all men to equal opportunity." So far as law, government, and politics are concerned, the goal of human dignity (or freedom) unmistakably includes democracy, or the sharing of power in the community decision process.[4] Since patient-staff meetings at the YPI are devices by which power is presumably shared, the study of this innovation, conducted under circumstances favorable to rather full recording, may disclose the finer structure of the democratizing process and enrich the data available to political science and jurisprudence.[5]

The YPI case is an example of "democracy from above" since the top administrative officers of the hospital voluntarily delegated some degree of authority and control to the patients. Technically, this is an act of "devolution." It is in obvious contrast to situations in which power is shared as a response to revolutionary and radical "movements from below." In political history "territorial" devolu-

---

3. Jerome Frank, *Law and the Modern Mind* (New York, Coward-McCann, 1949). On American legal realism, consult many articles found in Morris R. Cohen and Felix S. Cohen, *Readings in Jurisprudence and Legal Philosophy* (New York, Prentice-Hall, 1952). In general, Edgar Bodenheimer, *Jurisprudence; The Philosophy and Method of Law* (Cambridge, Mass., Harvard University Press, 1962).

4. A fundamental guide to the theory of democracy in the context of political theory in general is George H. Sabine, *History of Political Theory* (New York, Holt, 1937 [and later editions]).

5. The trend of political science is toward detailed empirical inquiry, guided by systematic theory. See Karl W. Deutsch, *The Nerves of Government* (Glencoe, Illinois, The Free Press, 1963); Austin Ranney, ed., *Essays on the Behavioral Study of Politics* (Urbana, University of Illinois Press, 1962).

tion is exemplified on a grand scale by the cultivation of self-government in the overseas colonies of the British.[6] "Pluralistic" devolution
occurs when corporate bodies, organized along occupational lines,
for example, receive a recognized place in the decision process of a
larger territorial community. The Yale Psychiatric Institute is no
city ward, congressional district, or nation-state. Hence in the
larger setting of American life the YPI is a pluralistic, rather than a
territorial, unit. If we examine its structure in finer detail, however,
the territorial basis of the YPI regains importance. The patients
may be restricted in their freedom of movement to the buildings
and grounds of the Institute and are at all times subject to the jurisdiction of hospital authorities. The patient-staff meetings provided greater recognition in the decision process to patients, a result
akin to the pluralization of power inside a territorial unit along
occupational or other lines of special activity.

The relationship between a contemporary psychiatric hospital
in the United States and the surrounding community with which it
perpetually interacts is distinctive in that the hospital is an island
of exemption from the democratic standards emphasized in the
larger society. Hence the innovations at the YPI are partly intelligi-
ble if we view them as an effort to bring decision-making and execution within the hospital into closer harmony with the norms of the
American environment.

The Demand to Conform

Although psychiatric hospitals are among the most widely accepted
instances of restrictive treatment of individuals within our society, it
is pertinent to challenge and possibly reconsider the wisdom of
the degree to which exemptions from democratic practice have
been authorized. Should the traditional policy be modified? How
much? By what technique?

The advent of patient-staff meetings at the YPI was a move toward reducing the discrepancy between a relatively nondemocratic
decision process and the articulate norms of the larger American
community. How did this come about? The reply may seem obvious.
The stability of any community depends upon adherence to the
prescriptions of the public and civic order; any exception to conformity is a threat to the established system and an eligible target
of criticism or of more severe measures of deprivation to bring it

6. Strategies of devolution are examined in H. Duncan Hall, *Mandates,
Dependencies and Trusteeship* (Washington, D.C.), Carnegie Endowment for
International Peace, 1948.

into line. It is therefore plausible to assert that the YPI would eventually take measures to conform with community-wide norms.

On further reflection, however, the answer is inadequate. How can the timing be explained? The policy of exempting mental hospitals from ordinary standards is well rooted in American practice. Some identifiable factors must have become active, or some previously dynamic influences must have failed to continue to operate.

The hypothesis might be entertained that YPI directors and staff had been the target of outside pressure, perhaps from political parties or pressure organizations. This conjecture does not survive factual inquiry. The YPI was not a target of public protest; on the contrary, the initiative for the sharing of power with patients came from inside the Institute, and more specifically from within the staff.

When we look at the YPI case in the context of recent intellectual currents among the professions, it begins to be comprehensible. In the fields of education, criminology, military law, and psychiatry, for example, recent movements have much in common with the innovations at the Yale Psychiatric Institute.

Members of the teaching profession have wondered whether it is possible to reconcile the objective of educating for adult citizenship with the degree and methods of control often exercised in the classroom, a concern which had much to do with the original drive toward "progressive education" and with some more recent tendencies.[7] Similarly, those charged with responsibility for rehabilitating prisoners have persistently questioned whether the policies put into effect by custodial and correctional agencies do in fact prepare the individual to rejoin his fellow citizens in the larger community.[8] Psychiatrists, too, have raised telling questions about their work.

In this connection, one of the first questions that arises in reference to any alleged power-sharing activity is whether the facts warrant the claims. Investigation of the various phases of the decision process should reveal the extent to which power is genuinely shared. Political scientists and jurists are beginning to invent and apply relatively objective techniques for the study of decision. The patient-staff meetings took no formal votes. Hence the problem of assessing the degree to which power was shared is far from simple

7. See B. Bailyn, *Education in the Forming of American Society* (New York, Vintage Books, 1960).
8. For example, George Dession, "The Technique of Public Order: Evolving Concepts of Criminal Law," *Buffalo Law Review*, 22 (1955), 5.

and raises many novel questions of definition and procedure that are broached in this report.

A Problem-Solving Orientation

The research reported in the following pages is perhaps best understood in the frame of reference of the contextual, problem-solving approach characteristic of the policy sciences and evident in the behavior of the principal innovators at the YPI. This orientation emphasizes the importance of examining any particular detail in relation to the context of which it is part. It calls for the performance of the five intellectual tasks pertinent to coping with any problem: clarification of goal, description of trend, analysis of conditions, projection of development, and the invention, evaluation, and selection of policy alternatives.

The principle value goal of YPI physicians was clear: they were committed to pursuing enlightenment and skill in the service of the well-being of their patients. Their frame of reference demanded the clarification of issues that are often allowed to remain vague and confused. The recurring question, "But is it therapeutic?," made it necessary for all concerned to scan the hospital situation as a whole and, in so doing, to discover latent value conflicts and conflicts between specific practices and comprehensive value goals. As we shall see, most physicians were committed to the democratic goal of wide, rather than narrow, power sharing. In keeping with medical tradition, they were accustomed to exempting their work from the demands of the democratic ideology because they were convinced that the welfare of patients was best served when physicians took responsibility for making their important decisions. But the new scientific developments which cast doubt on this assumption reveal hitherto unrecognized value conflicts and consequently cast doubt upon established practices of hospital management and treatment. For example, do existing therapeutic procedures provide enough opportunities to "learn by doing," especially by learning how to participate in the decision process of the community?

A conspicuous fact about these movements is that they originated inside the professional groups responsible for education, correction, or therapy. These groups, like the YPI itself, were relatively free at the time from organized outside pressure. How are we to account for this phenomenon?

Conscious factors appear insufficiently strong to account for the intensity of this response; it is appropriate to explore the possible role of unconscious determinants. Physicians, educators, and other professional men and women reared in American society acquire the conscious perspectives, the myth, of a democratic social system. These consciously held political perspectives are reinforced by the introjection of democratic demands and expectations during the formative years which, as components of the superego, press for the support of the social practice of widespread participation in all social values, including power. The proposition, then, is that *individuals who are reared in societies that make articulate the demand for power sharing mature into persons who suffer conflicts of conscience when they behave in ways that they perceive as contradicting the norm.*

The unconscious reinforcement of democratic attitudes may be potent enough to generate guilt and shame, or diffuse discomfort and anxiety, when an individual finds himself or his group playing a role that appears to violate the democratic imperative. Indeed, to the extent that the development of such a "democratic conscience" is fostered within an individual, he is the more confused and troubled by the abundant evidence of practices contradicting these pronouncements. He must somehow come to terms with these discrepancies: striving not to see, to minimize, to deny that practice is discrepant from spoken norm; rationalizing exemptions from democratic practice on special grounds ("Negroes are fragile, incompetent, irresponsible, require protection and control"); cynically viewing parents, teachers, adults as corrupt hypocrites and dismissing what they say; struggling to live out and fulfill the democratic ideology, in conflict with those who proclaim but do not practice it. It is plausible in this perspective, for example, to accept James Baldwin's interpretation of the white man's guilt for his conduct toward the Negro.[9]

The Value-Institution Approach

Of direct concern to psychiatrists, political scientists, and all students of culture and personality are the dynamics of change. The psychiatrist is primarily concerned with the individual sufferer, seeking to comprehend and expedite basic changes in the patient's system of identity, value demands, and expectations. Political scientists and jurists also pay heed to individuals, especially those who perform a discernible role in public affairs. The stable patterns exhibited by an individual in relation to himself and others comprise

9. James Baldwin, *The Fire Next Time* (New York, Dial Press, 1963).

the personality system. The analysts of politics and law have the problem of accounting for relatively profound, as well as comparatively superficial, changes, for example when a seeming conformist suddenly turns into a revolutionary agitator. But political scientists and jurists are primarily preoccupied with the social process as a whole in territorial or pluralistic groups. The stable patterns exhibited by the members of a group in reference to one another and to the members of other groups comprise the culture. Cultures, too, may change radically or very little; and a major intellectual task is to explain what happens.

Psychiatrists are becoming aware that they are necessarily concerned with culture. A psychiatric hospital, for instance, is a subculture within the general culture of the locality, the region, the nation, "Western European civilization," and the "universalizing culture of science." Patients and staff enter the hospital after years of exposure to, and interaction with, cultures having many degrees of likeness and difference. The personality system of each individual, viewed at any cross section in time, shows degrees of intense (or slack) adherence to the patterns presented by antecedent environments or strategies invented to cope with the environment.

A most promising way to look at man is to see him as seeking to maximize (optimize) his values. This implies that he moves into the ever receding future in pursuit of clearly, or dimly, perceived preferred events (values). Psychiatrists and political scientists are equally concerned with improving their methods of discovering the orientation of individuals who act alone or collectively in concrete situations. To what extent are such specific situations as a patient-staff meeting regarded as a source of net value indulgence or deprivation by the participants? A fundamental and inclusive hypothesis is that *participants are disposed to continue in situations that are expected to yield net advantages and to turn away from situations that are not.* We take seriously the task of examining YPI innovations from this point of view, emphasizing the potentialities and limitations of present techniques of observation and analysis when applied to any problem in the investigation of man and society. We apply a systematic, contextual method to the analysis of value shaping and sharing and to the relatively specialized patterns in particular circumstances to each major value.

The Strategy of Prototyping

Patient-staff meetings and other forums developed at the YPI are, if they prove successful, social institutions eligible for transfer to "real-world" situations outside psychiatric hospitals. They are potential models for transforming the power process for individuals perceived by the larger community as falling below the minimum standard of capability necessary for a fully responsible role in group policy. The research upon which this book reports illustrates the investigational technique of prototyping, as contrasted with experimentation or intervention, for the innovations deal directly with social practices, and the accepted criteria of true experimentation are applicable only in part. Experiments proceed by identifying, measuring, and modifying variables according to plan; the results are amenable to succinct, usually mathematical, summary and precise replication. Experimental procedures are valued in premedical and medical curricula and continue to be emphasized by psychiatrists, for example, in psycho-physiological and psycho-pharmacological research. The enrichment of understanding the therapist derives from learning to live with the mentally ill and paying attention to the entire context of interaction lacks the orderly, cumulative, manageable quality of an experiment. The psychiatrist may nevertheless apply the term "experiment" to the more elusive situation.

Prototyping consists in innovating social practices for the purpose of discovering factors that condition their occurrence and consequences. A prototype is launched in a context which is only partially controlled by the innovators. A social practice is studied in direct relation to other social practices. In a true experiment, on the other hand, patterns of practice are dissolved into variables which may appear as components of many institutional practices. Such an experiment may, for instance, examine the response of the retina of the eye to variations in the intensity of light. The experimenter's modes of measurement may be transferred to functioning "real-world" situations if, for instance, it can be shown that the variables—such as involuntary muscle movements—correctly predict role selection in such settings. If persons who are predisposed to play agitational or administrative roles can be identified, the personnel practices of the larger context may eventually be modified. Personnel practices might figure in prototypical innovations, and a major strategic task would be to mobilize enough effective motivation to bring conformity to the pattern to be introduced and studied. The most appropriate strategies take the whole value-institution context into consideration.

Prototypes are distinguished from "interventions," as well as experiments. An intervention is an innovation which, despite opposition, is officially introduced by the decision-makers of the larger community. If a city is the scene of controversies over the introduction of psychiatrists into the schools, the innovation is part of the arena of power, and concessions must be made to political expediency. The enlightenment goal, or even the goal of well-being, may be somewhat compromised. The YPI innovation was not involved in general controversy; rather, the staff took the initiative in order to realize their goals.

Despite the absence of the degree of control appropriate to an experiment, the innovators of a prototype adhere to the same scrupulous standards of objectivity in reporting and assessing results that ideally prevail in laboratory work.

Although past innovations in psychiatry—such as the use of occupational therapy—can be classified as prototypes, the literature contains few discussions of the strategies best adapted to prototyping. Hence we are on comparatively new ground when we generalize the YPI experience.

The description of the "trend phase" of problem solving was central at the YPI; as at most psychiatric hospitals, attention was riveted upon the examination of the clinical course of each patient and of the hospital as a whole.

The scientific question, the search for knowledge of factors affecting psychiatric illness and recovery, played a prominent part at the YPI in its role as a research institution within a university. The innovation with which we are concerned was adopted as a broad hypothesis about the significance of power sharing for the onset and alleviation of mental disorganization. The projection of future events was always prominent: the staff was obligated to assess the likelihood that a patient, if discharged from the hospital, would be able to carry on effectively. Similarly, the invention, evaluation, and selection of policy options were unavoidable aspects of the conduct of hospital affairs. The patient-staff meeting was a significant departure from past practice, and it will be illuminating to examine the origin and acceptance of this policy.

The Social Process as a Whole

Our approach is explicitly contextual. We hope to discover the significance of the innovation for every category of participant whose interactions with one another comprise the therapeutic community. We deal extensively with the senior staff, residents, nurses, and patients by examining their pre- and post-innovation relationships to one another and to themselves. In what frame of mind were the innovations approached by all concerned? What happened as a result of attempted change? In a word, what difference did it make in anything of any importance to anybody?

The hospital is viewed as a sample of human associations anywhere and under any conditions whatever. In this fundamental sense the fact that the YPI is a "hospital," or a "mental hospital," is less significant than that it is a situation where, for better or worse, human beings interact with one another. Hence we characterize the YPI as a "social process." In the broadest sense the "participants" "interact" both with one another and with the social and physical environment. The interactions are not random; on the contrary they are attempts on the part of everyone involved to gratify what are variously called "wants," "desires," "wishes," and "needs," which we shall here refer to and categorize as "values." To achieve gratification is to achieve "preferred events" or "outcomes"; these are the values whose shaping and sharing give direction to any social process.

How shall we classify the values in a social process? Since our purpose is to bring out their similarities and their uniqueness in any specific context, we adopt a set of categories which can be conveniently applied to any civilization or folk society, contemporary or historical. It is also useful for comparative purposes to adopt terms that are as close as possible to current usage in the community of scholars, since factual information is classified to serve the purposes of specialists. A further consideration is brevity; the human mind cannot easily handle many more than ten categories at the same level of abstraction. In analyzing the YPI we shall employ eight value categories, characterized briefly below.

AFFECTION: Love is expressed or withheld, received or rejected; investment of love inaugurates a continuing friendship or family grouping; people may be rated in a given community as occupying high, middle, or low levels of popularity.

RESPECT: Polite or impolite greetings are exchanged; admiration or contempt is expressed; ranks are recognized according to upper, middle, or lower distinction in the context.

RECTITUDE: An act or actor is characterized as ethically responsible or irresponsible; criteria are formulated for assessing responsible conduct.

POWER: Decisions are agreed to or opposed, often tacitly or after combat.

ENLIGHTENMENT: Information is reported or withheld; estimates of future events are offered or retained.

SKILL: An opportunity is given to achieve a high score for excellence; criteria are formulated and applied in assessing levels of performance.

WEALTH: Dollars are exchanged for goods and services; goods and services are bartered; income is saved or given to others.

WELL-BEING: Care is given or retained, received or rejected; safety is endangered or protected; anxiety is intensified or reduced.

Although the foregoing characterizations are far from comprehensive, they provide clues to the outcome events in the social process which are classified as values (culminating interactions). Each participant can be described as "indulged" or "deprived" in varying degree of each value, and the indulgence or deprivation can be an act of others or of the individual. The patients and doctors who interact with one another at the YPI are not only affecting one another's well-being (health, safety, and comfort), but influencing one another's flow of affection, respect, and all other values.

Having located any value outcomes, it is possible to describe the interactions that lead up to each culmination and to assess subsequent effects. Pre-outcome events, for example, involve the subjectivities ("perspectives") of all who influence the result. Hence the degree to which patients consciously desire to be well and the level of optimism they entertain are relevant pre-outcome events. The influence on the result exercised by any participant depends on the assets or liabilities at his disposal. A physician determined to help his patient may or may not possess skill adequate to the challenge; his "base values" may be meager. Hence the strategies he employs may be ineffective in realizing his "cherished perspective" (goal), improving the patient's health (the doctor cannot indulge the patient in terms of well-being). The value outcomes sought by a doctor are not restricted to indulgences or deprivations of his own ego. His perspective may identify his "ego" with others to constitute a larger self, whose improved value position is sought. Psychiatrists identified with the YPI want to improve their own enlightenment, skill, wealth, and respect positions, and the well-being of their patients.

The contextual viewpoint implies that all interactions shape and share all values to some extent. By analyzing every specific interaction in terms of all eight value categories, we become aware of ordinarily overlooked value consequences. If we explore the significance of an entire situation for a particular value, we make similar discoveries. This is the importance of the question asked of every detail of hospital life, "Is it therapeutic?" (does it contribute to the well-being of patients?), which eventually led to the innovations.

The YPI buildings and grounds, available as a base value (wealth), were assessed in this frame of reference. The professional competence of the staff (skill and enlightenment), and community esteem for the hospital and Yale (affection) were similarly evaluated. So, too, for each base value.

The YPI is distinguished from many other social processes by the priority given well-being. The goal perspectives held by the participants, especially the staff, led them to try to utilize the available base values in every situation in strategies which held promise of maximizing the well-being of patients.

Our model of social process includes another set of major categories which refer to patterns specialized to the shaping and sharing of a particular value. Each pattern is composed of "perspectives" and "operations"; the whole pattern is a "practice." A common therapeutic practice at a mental hospital is the administration of drugs on prescription. The salient perspectives of doctors, nurses, and patients, the writing of orders, and the obtaining and injection of the drug, are all part of this practice. A pattern of practices relatively specialized to a given value constitute an "institution." The YPI is classified as an institution specialized to well-being; government, law, and politics are institutions of power; industries specialized to production, distribution, and consumption are among the wealth institutions; television, radio, newspapers, books, and other mass media are enlightenment institutions; schools are skill institutions; churches are among rectitude institutions; the family and groups of friends belong to the institutions of affection. Focusing intensively on the YPI context, the delineation of the practices relatively specialized to each value makes it possible to see how the flow of values is interconnected.[10]

The Decision Process

The YPI innovations were explicit changes introduced into the policy making and executing institutions of the Institute. Patients joined together with staff in meetings where all were encouraged to speak out on any topic of common interest. The innovations were power changes; they purported to widen the degree of participation in the power process or, synonymously, the decision process.

The specialized institutions of the decision process in any social

10. The categories summarized in the preceding pages are set forth in more detail in Harold D. Lasswell and Abraham Kaplan, *Power and Society: A Framework for Political Inquiry* (New Haven, Yale University Press, 1950), and Harold D. Lasswell, *Power and Personality* (New York, Norton, 1948).

context are usually readily identified. The participants refer to "governors," "rulers," "bosses," or to the "organs of government." In the national community, the Presidency, Congress, the Supreme Court, and the executive departments and commissions are promptly enumerated as institutions of government. The list may be extended to include political parties and the hundreds of pressure groups that seek to influence policy. And the government is characterized as democratic because power is very widely shared in the American body politic.

Persons familiar with the YPI quickly identify the most important figures as those who make the key decisions. The situations relatively specialized to formulating and applying YPI policy are also easily identified. The director and chief resident are clearly among the principal figures, and their discussions are among the significant power situations.

In conventional usage a distinction is drawn, however vaguely, between official authority and effective power. Patient government, for example, was long recognized as having some sort of official authority, but at the same time it was discounted as an effective influence.

Political and social scientists make corresponding distinctions which they define more carefully for purposes of research. "Functional" definitions are distinguished from "conventional" usages in any given context. The task of research is to assess in functional terms the realism and completeness of conventional perspectives. Hence we confront usage at the YPI with functional conceptions of power and other values.

It will be useful to introduce some of the distinctions made in analyzing the decision process at the YPI. We have hinted at the significant characteristics of a decision outcome: value consequences are at stake which importantly affect the context as a whole; the conclusion which is made is expected to be enforced against most, if not all, who challenge it; the enforcement will employ severely deprivational sanctions if necessary; expectations of enforcement are confirmed in fact.

We are most accustomed to recognizing these characteristics in the national context. When Congress passes and the President signs a tax statute, important values are at stake for all Americans. Wealth values will be directly affected by this exercise of power, and the ramifications for health, education, and other values are wide and deep. It is expected that the statute will be enforced against all who neglect or seek to evade its prescriptions, that severe fines or imprisonment will be imposed against offenders. And, as time passes, it will be possible to confirm these expectations.

In the YPI context it is possible to apply the same criteria in identifying decisions. If the medical director made a rule against receiving visitors on certain days or hours of the day, the rule would unquestionably affect the patients' value position. Moreover, enforcement by doctors and nurses and the employing of severe sanctions against offenders, such as total denial of access by visitors, would be expected. And these expectations may be verified by subsequent hospital events.

The authority of Congress to enact tax legislation or of the director to promulgate a rule regulating visiting hours may not be challenged by anyone. However, specific provisions of a tax statute may be assailed as beyond the authority of Congress. They may, for example, be denounced as discriminatory. The Supreme Court may agree; thus the Congress may have sought to exercise a degree of "naked power"; otherwise it exercised "lawful power." Sometimes tax legislation contains provisions which are neither expected to be enforcible nor are in fact enforced. Such provisions are "pretended power"—they are not power at all. The relevant distinctions are: power is controlling when effective; power is lawful when authoritative and controlling; power is naked if control is not joined with authority; power is pretended if authority is divorced from control.

The same categories are applicable to the study of any context. The authority of the director to regulate visitors is rarely challenged; such an effective rule is a law, not an exhibition of naked or pretended power. The classification of any decision as lawful depends upon expectations in the relevant social context. In large national communities, the distribution of expectations may vary enormously from one time to another and from one region or pluralized group to another. Scientific observers seek to clarify the minimum frequencies and other conditions that must be met before a given decision may be called a law or lawful. Careful empirical work can disclose the genuine complexity of the decision process; it can challenge dogmatic rigidities of view about what is or is not lawful or what value consequences follow from a given law or legal system.

The "public order" of the national community includes the preferred pattern of important institutions and of value distribution. In the United States we are committed to widespread participation in value shaping and sharing. Hence our public order aspires toward and approximates a democratic, rather than an undemocratic, order of society. Our public order also includes the protection of certain institutions specialized to value shaping and sharing. In power we are committed to such institutions as majority rule, minority protection, judicial review, and a competitive (typically two-party) party system. Our protected wealth institutions include a mixed system of private and public property, limited liability corporations, and freedom of job selection and transfer. Enlightenment institutions include freedom of competition among public media, free public instruction during the early years, freedom of research and publication. Among institutions relating to affection are monogamous marriage (or at least serial monogamy), freedom of choice of marriage partners (subject to ethnic exceptions in some jurisdictions), and limited community guardianship of children. Respect institutions include freedom from discrimination (subject to many ethnic restrictions), protection of privacy, barriers against degrading punishments, and limitations upon slander and libel. Among rectitude institutions we recognize freedom of worship and separation of church and state. Skill institutions include the provision of schooling beyond minimum enlightenment requirements and freedom to organize for the improvement of excellence in arts, crafts, and professions. The well-being institutions encompass basic policies for the protection and improvement of health, safety, and comfort.

We use the term "civic order" to describe the features of the social process which are protected by the use of relatively mild, rather than severely deprivational, sanctions. Conventionally, all congressional statutes are part of the public order; functionally, many statutes are part of the civic order because they refrain from authorizing severe sanctions. In regard to the YPI it is relevant to distinguish between public order and civic order. As implied, however, these distinctions occur only in rudimentary form in conventional usage.

Americans are trained to think of decision processes in the tripartite categories well known to constitutional law and civic education: "legislative," "executive," and "judicial." Although these terms are serviceable, there are advantages to employing a more refined set of conceptions. The accumulating body of information on the process of decision that is going forward rapidly in the social and behavioral sciences can be most conveniently dealt with by more than three categories. The following questions give a preliminary idea of the intended scope of the seven categories, or phases, of the decision process to which we shall refer:

INTELLIGENCE: What are the sources of information concerning recent and past events which are used by those who participate in decision? What estimates of the future are used? Who invents and tentatively evaluates the policies by which value goals can be realized?

PROMOTING: Who engages in the active promotion of broad innovations of policy?

PRESCRIBING: What agencies lay down general policies?

INVOKING: Who provisionally characterizes a concrete act as violating or harmonizing with prescriptions?

APPLYING: Which individuals or agencies make final judgments of the correctness of invocations and carry out the prescriptions involved?

APPRAISING: Who reviews the acts of those charged with responsibility for articulating and implementing the goals of policy and evaluates their success?

TERMINATING: How are prescriptions or arrangements that execute prescriptions ended?

Examples of how these categories are used in analyzing the decision process of the United States may provide clarification. As these examples indicate, decision activities are not limited to organs conventionally called "the government." Many informal or semiformal organizations are involved.

INTELLIGENCE: The obtaining and processing of information by the Census Bureau and the Central Intelligence Agency; the planning of metropolitan redevelopment programs; the gathering and dissemination of news and comment by the mass media of communication.

PROMOTING: The formation of party programs and the conduct of campaigns; the attempts by pressure organizations to obtain or block the passage of statutes or the adoption of regulations.

PRESCRIBING: The enactment of legislation by Congress and state legislative bodies; the amendment of the Constitution; the adoption of tax regulations by the Treasury Department.

INVOKING: The indictment, arrest, and prosecution of alleged offenders; the initiating of programs alleged to execute a statute.

APPLYING: The administering of programs by governmental agencies; the decision of courts or administrative bodies regarding alleged violations.

APPRAISING: The review by auditors of aggregate expenditures; reports by inspectors of aggregate efficiency of performance; review of records of administrative departments and agencies by Congress.

TERMINATING: The repeal of statutes and rescinding of regulations; the compensation of owners for expropriation of property for public use.[11]

We speak of the United States as democratic because of the widespread sharing of power at every phase of the decision process. The media of public intelligence are not monopolized by governmental or private power; political party and pressure organizations enjoy great freedom of competitive propaganda; legislatures and chief executives are chosen by popular vote for comparatively short terms and keep in close contact with constituencies; police and prosecutors are accountable to elected officials and operate within a framework of "due process of law"; judges, chosen by methods that give direct or indirect voice to the voters, operate within a frame of law; appraisers are able to criticize officials without running serious danger of reprisal; limits are recognized upon the degree to which one group can bind its successors (there are flexible arrangements for termination). Although the seven categories are primarily concerned with the comparative study of the decision process in community-wide organizations they are equally applicable to the decision process of any group, whether territorial or pluralistic. We use these distinctions in analyzing the YPI and specify as precisely as possible the operational indices that we choose for each term.

The Emerging Theoretical Approach

Certain basic postulates about the psychotherapy of the psychoses have important implications for their overall hospital treatment. Psychoanalysis as a therapy of the psychoneuroses emphasizes the effort to regain contact with the unconscious, to bring the wishes, needs, and impulses of the unconscious into awareness, and to facilitate the extent to which the ego can work with the unconscious in attaining gratification. A major objective of psychoanalytic treatment in the neuroses is the shift from conflict between ego and id to a more harmonious cooperation between these psychic agencies, the ego respecting and working for the fulfillment of id strivings rather than struggling against them.

11. These categories are utilized in the analysis of large-scale decisions by Myres S. McDougal and associates in a series of volumes, the most recent of which is Myres S. McDougal, Harold D. Lasswell, and Ivan A. Vlasic, *Law and Public Order in Space* (New Haven, Yale University Press, 1963).

The psychoanalytic psychotherapy of the psychoses shares these goals, but important technical differences are necessitated by differences between the psychoneuroses and the psychoses.[12] Important among these differences is the more advanced growth, development, and strength which has been achieved by the ego in the neuroses, and the greater availability to consciousness and to direct expression in behavior of id strivings in the psychoses. In the treatment of the neuroses, emphasis is placed on broadening the ego's awareness of the id, making the unconscious conscious, and bringing id strivings for gratification under the direction and mastery of the ego. The problems and the emphasis required in the treatment of the psychoses focus attention upon the relative weakness and inadequate development of the ego and its great limitations in the effort to cope with id pressures and forces. Whereas certain achieved levels of ego development, strength, and mastery are a criterion for the undertaking of psychoanalysis, the psychotherapy of the psychoses must work toward achieving that degree of ego integration and strength which has already been achieved in the neuroses before those id pressures experienced as threatening, and indeed overwhelming, can begin to be brought under the ego's direction and control. Unless the synthesizing and integrating functions of the ego become strong enough to participate actively in this investigatory process, explorations into the strivings and forces of the unconscious can only serve to heighten the stress experienced by the patient.

Every patient, however troubled and incapacitated on admission to the hospital, has managed to retain some of his resources and strengths, his base values, intact. The hospital—the people who live and work with the patient, those whose perspectives and value

12. The following are basic sources on the psychoanalytically oriented psychotherapy of the psychoses: Victor Tausk, "On the Origin of the 'Influencing Machine' in Schizophrenia," *Psychoanalytic Quarterly*, 2 (1933), 519; Frieda Fromm-Reichmann, *Principles of Intensive Psychotherapy* (Chicago, University of Chicago Press, 1950); Heinz Hartmann, "Contribution to the Metapsychology of Schizophrenia," *The Psychoanalytic Study of the Child* (New York, International Universities Press, 1953) 8, 177–97; D. M. Bullard, ed., *Psychoanalysis and Psychotherapy: Selected Papers of Frieda Fromm-Reichmann* (Chicago, University of Chicago Press, 1959); Eugene Brody and Fredrick Redlich, eds., *Psychotherapy With Schizophrenics* (New York, International Universities Press, 1952); Silvano Arieti, *Interpretation of Schizophrenia* (New York, Robert Brunner, 1955); Lewis B. Hill, *Psychotherapeutic Intervention in Schizophrenia* (Chicago, University of Chicago Press, 1955); Don D. Jackson, ed., *The Etiology of Schizophrenia* (New York, Basic Books, 1960); Arthur Burton, ed., *Psychotherapy of the Psychoses* (New York, Basic Books, 1961); Beulah Parker, *My Language Is Me* (New York, Basic Books, 1962).

assets collectively constitute the environment in which the effort to restore the patient's health is undertaken—can respond to him in a number of alternative ways. They can invite him to regress even further, regarding it as necessary and useful for unconscious strivings to find direct and relatively uninhibited expression in behavior; they can busy him with a series of routines which, in combination with his removal from the demands and stresses of his prior environment, serve to help him reorganize himself in some way; they can offer him the opportunity to continue to exercise and pursue the further development of those ego capacities which are relatively unimpaired and intact (for example, in school, work, and physical activity); they can discourage regressive behavior and demand that the patient do what he can, protected as necessary from trying to do what he cannot. When their expectations of the patient are informed by an appreciation of his capacities and resources, and when their patience and understanding are motivated by an appreciation of the intensity of the patient's struggle, the demand that the individual be "crazy" becomes unnecessary.

All too often, a premium has been given to "craziness." A troubled person is traditionally required to introduce himself as crazy in order to gain admission to a mental hospital and must remain crazy in order to stay in the hospital. He must demonstrate clearly to those who treat him that he is incapable of functioning outside the hospital. When a commitment to the position of being crazy is implicitly encouraged as a necessary stage in the unfolding of a psychotic process, or when such a position is implicitly required as a justification for care and for a moratorium from the ongoing responsibilities and demands of life, the treatment process is severely handicapped.

With these considerations in mind, the staff of the YPI sought to make clear their recognition that the patient was troubled and continued to require treatment even when he did not behave crazily, to make evident to the patient that his conduct was valued and encouraged if he exercised those ego capacities which continued to function relatively well in the face of illness, and if he struggled to exercise other capacities which functioned less well, in no way did he jeopardize the continuation of treatment in the hospital by abandoning his craziness. This step freed the patient from the "lunatic's burden" and encouraged him to exercise certain ego capacities, including the synthesizing and integrating functions essential to effective psychotherapeutic work. It now became possible for the healthy part of the patient to show itself and to work as the therapist's ally in psychotherapy. To this end, the staff also sought to provide greatly increased opportunities for the patient to continue education, physical activity, and work.

The Sequence of Innovation

It is important to emphasize that the changes at the YPI were in harmony with the psychoanalytic orientation of the hospital. The innovators were all psychoanalysts and remained committed to the application and development of the psychoanalytic treatment of the psychoses. Psychoanalytic psychotherapy remained the core experience in the hospital for both the physician and his patient. The new changes were not intended to modify the formal psychotherapeutic interaction between doctor and patient. They focused upon the other hours of the patient's day and sought to make the total experience of hospitalization therapeutic.

We have seen how this new concern with the patient's overall hospital experience emerged as the YPI stabilized its position as a psychoanalytic hospital which emphasized individual psychotherapy in the treatment of the psychoses. It was stimulated by the investigatory and interdisciplinary emphasis, by the careful examination of communication between doctors, nurses, and patients, by interest in the families of patients, by insistence upon the primacy of therapeutic considerations in all hospital planning, by an increasing degree of involvement of residents in the patient community, and by the view that the patient has a responsible share in his treatment. Ensuing changes in the patient's experience in the hospital reflected the recognition of the need to release the patient from the burden of having to "act crazy" and the desire to provide increasing opportunities for education, physical activity, and work. The objective of these changing strategies was to create an environment in which the patient was aware that value indulgences could be obtained by exercising his ego capacities to the full extent of his capability. In this way, by strengthening the synthesizing and integrating functions of the ego and accelerating the patient's active, responsible participation in effective psychotherapeutic work, recovery could proceed.

The first of the formal innovations was the introduction of group psychotherapy in 1953.[13] Residents led groups of seven or eight

13. On the background of group psychotherapy: S. R. Slavson, ed., *The Fields of Group Psychotherapy* (New York, International Universities Press, 1956); Florence Powdermaker and Jerome D. Frank, *Group Psychotherapy: Studies in Methodology of Research and Therapy* (Cambridge, Mass., Harvard University Press, 1953).

patients and a nurse or social worker which met weekly at first and twice each week later. Patients were not assigned to groups led by their own resident therapist. Competent supervisors of group therapy later became available, but in the beginning the leaders floundered about with little or no prior training and no ongoing supervision. As a result, the character and usefulness of group psychotherapy varied sharply, depending upon the interests and skills of the group leader. As training and supervision were made available and the functions of group psychotherapy were clarified in relation to other forums in the hospital, group therapy tended to stabilize its position somewhere between individual therapy and the larger group meetings to be described.

The introduction of patient-staff meetings in 1956 was the next major change and the one which concerns us most in this study. Precisely how these meetings began remains unclear. They seem to have been initiated as a result of simultaneous and independent pressures for such a forum originating with patients, residents, social workers (especially the group worker), the chief resident, and the medical director. Perhaps such a development was possible only when these different participants in the hospital all saw that an institution of the kind would serve their needs. In talking with patients and members of the staff who were in the hospital when patient-staff meetings began, one is convinced that the initiative came in turn from certain key patients, a particular patient, the patients as a group, the chief resident, the medical director, the assistant director, the residents as a group, certain key residents, a particular resident, a social worker, or the social workers as a group.

Patients were dissatisfied with the restrictions on their freedom that resulted from the fact that the staff had little available time to accompany patients when they went out. The idea of a "buddy system" emerged, a plan under which less disturbed patients would accompany and assume responsibility for patients who at the time were not permitted outside the hospital unless escorted by an aide, a nurse, or some other staff member. This plan was supported enthusiastically by many patients who began to press for its adoption. Among its most articulate proponents was a patient who had been raised in a democratic work-community and was intensely interested in democratic process and in social and political questions. He agitated for the proposal and lobbied for the opportunity to discuss it directly with the staff, to argue it out with them, and to get a clear-cut decision about it. The medical director had frequently responded to these proposals in staff meetings by suggesting that perhaps the patients and the staff ought to get together and talk about it. The chief resident, one or more of the residents, and one or more of the social workers were very interested in Maxwell Jones' reports; they wanted something of this kind introduced at the YPI. The ground work had to some extent been laid in patient government meetings at which chief residents had discussed similar problems and proposals with the patients, usually observing that the patients had not adequately thought out what they wanted to do and how they wanted to do it; the chief residents also emphasized the necessity of staff deliberation before such plans could be introduced.

The patient-staff meetings began in 1956, at first irregularly, then weekly, then twice weekly, and in 1960, three times each week. From the beginning they were chaired by the medical director. He called on people who raised their hand, giving them the floor, and he occasionally offered comments. The meetings were usually attended by about sixty people, including all patients, residents, social workers, activities workers, nurses, and aides on duty, the assistant medical director, chief resident, business manager, student nurses and medical students working in the hospital, and by occasional visitors. At first "post-mortems" were held by the staff convening as a group immediately after each meeting. They reviewed the character and content of the conference, discussed patients who had come to their attention in the course of the meeting, and offered comments and suggestions that, with time, staff members found it possible to present directly in the patient-staff meetings themselves.

When patient-staff meetings were set at a regular time each week, one of the staff meetings, previously held each morning, was replaced by the patient-staff meeting of that day and its post-mortem. Gradually more matters brought up in staff meeting were responded to with the resolution, "this should be discussed in patient-staff meeting," instead of being decided in the staff meeting or by the director, assistant director, or chief resident acting alone. In 1959, when patient-staff meetings were held twice each week, two staff meetings were dropped, and eventually post-mortems were also discontinued, except for the first weeks of each hospital year, when new residents and other personnel were oriented to these peculiar forums.

Staff meetings traditionally began with a report from the doctor on duty in the hospital the previous night. As patient-staff replaced staff meetings and the staff developed a language for discussing matters previously deemed unsuitable for discussion in the presence of patients, the patient-staff meeting also began with such a report. Gradually patient-staff meetings came to include regular reports from patient government, the functions of which changed decisively as the patient-staff institution developed, and from patient-staff advisory committee, the next forum to evolve.

Unlike patient-staff meetings, the patient-staff advisory committee was deliberately suggested and planned by the chief resident and assistant director in collaboration with the medical director. The idea came from a visit to the Austen Riggs Center, an open psychiatric hospital in Stockbridge, Massachusetts, where patient participation in running the hospital had been encouraged for some time. At Riggs the character and arrangement of meetings in which patients participate had developed out of the distinctive features of their situation. The Riggs Center shared with other therapeutic communities (including the one which had begun to develop at Yale) features which permitted and encouraged greater patient participation in, and enlarged patient responsibility for, the affairs of the entire hospital. Some basic differences between the Riggs Center and the Psychiatric Institute at Yale led to specific differences in community structure. Although working with about the same number of patients, Austen Riggs is a completely open hospital whereas the Institute has both open and closed sections. There are few nurses and no aides in attendance at Stockbridge. The contrast reflects the greater range of pathology at the Institute, where some patients are more disturbed than any at Riggs.

Patient-staff meetings were held only three or four times a year at Austen Riggs. Their regular forums consisted of four groups of about ten patients each who met weekly with one or two staff members. A central committee, composed of representatives from each small group of patients and staff members had decision-making power for the entire community. They considered and made proposals about a great range of affairs concerning the Riggs hospital community. This central committee was the model for the patient-staff advisory committee at the YPI.

In the beginning patient-staff advisory committee operated awkwardly and under close staff supervision. Gradually, however, much of the decision-making entailed in patient management shifted from staff meetings to the new patient-staff advisory committee, and this forum drastically altered the conduct of hospital affairs. All decisions by advisory committee were offered in the form of recommendations to the staff and subject to staff veto. Although their proposals were subject to further scrutiny in staff and patient-staff meetings, recommendations usually went into effect promptly. The sober and thoughtful way in which matters were discussed in the committee by its members, including eight to ten patients, a physician (usually the chief resident), two nurses (usually the director of nursing and a chief nurse), and a social or group worker, was impressive to all who observed the deliberations. Issues formerly directed to individual therapists or to staff meetings were now brought to this committee for consideration: whether a given patient should be moved from the closed to the open ward; whether a patient should be permitted to go out of the hospital in groups, accompanied by a staff member, by another patient, or left unaccompanied; whether or not a patient should undertake steps toward leaving the hospital; the failure of a patient to attend patient-staff meetings, adult education classes, calisthenics, high school classes or some other hospital activity. The advisory committee also considered urgent problems concerning particularly troubled or annoying patients and made recommendations to the patient involved and others in the community for coping with the situation. The best-integrated patients in the hospital were consistently elected to the committee; membership enjoyed high prestige among patients, and the responsibility of serving on the committee was taken seriously.

During visits to other hospitals, members of the YPI Staff were impressed with the frequency with which the administrators and members of the staffs of hospitals located in rural districts emphasized their remoteness and complained about the unavailability to their patients of the many activities at hand in cities. Similarly, those at hospitals located within cities regretted being cramped in an urban community without grounds for adequate outdoor programs. The YPI staff was impressed with how infrequently the opportunities in the local setting of a given hospital were fully utilized. They reexamined the setting of the YPI: New Haven, a city of manageable size, the Yale University community, the Yale medical center, including the adjacent general hospital and medical school, and the hospital's limited outdoor space. They decided to take advantage of being within a university by inaugurating an adult education program in the hospital, to augment the opportunity for physical exercise with a calisthenics program directed by the Yale athletic staff, and to utilize the hospital's location in a medical center as the focus for a work program for patients. These programs were introduced in 1957.

The patient's day was carefully scrutinized. The period between the evening meal and the activities scheduled for later evening hours was found especially barren and lonely: the day staff, including all doctors except the doctor on duty for the evening, had left the hospital, and the small evening nurse shift was on. Particularly in winter months when it got dark early and activities outside on the hospital's terrace were impractical, patients tended to drift about aimlessly. Four one-hour classes were scheduled, one for each weekday evening, with one evening reserved for a patient-government meeting. A list of available instructors and courses they might offer was prepared, and the patients periodically elected four of them. The courses were taught by members of the Yale faculty, paid from the hospital's budget. They included instruction in literature, poetry, politics, art, anthropology, sociology, history, and philosophy. The program was set up on a required basis, each patient being expected to enroll in and attend at least one class every week. Many enrolled in more than one class, and some regularly attended all four. Gradually the patient-staff advisory committee took over enforcement of compulsory attendance.

Aside from evening classes, other special-interest courses were organized, paid for out of the hospital budget when possible, or by the students. Such courses included instruction on constructing electronic equipment and automobile repair—a local mechanic brought a disassembled automobile to the hospital which was systematically studied and reassembled by adolescent male patients. This education program augmented the existing painting class, play reading group, and individual music instruction, which continued under the direction of the occupational therapy and activities workers.

Under the supervision of an instructor on the Yale athletics staff, half-hour calisthenics classes were scheduled in the hospital's small gymnasium four times each week for men, three times each week for women. The patient-staff advisory committee decided to insist on both attendance and active participation because some patients were consistently absent or attended the class as observers. Although calisthenics rarely arouses much popular support in any group, its imaginative instructor succeeded in winning the interest of many patients and the participation of some staff members.

Although some patients were involved in jobs and schooling outside of the hospital earlier, a systematic work program for patients was first organized in 1957 in cooperation with the director of volunteer services in the adjacent general hospital. Patients undertook anywhere from a few hours to an almost full-time schedule

of work in a great variety of capacities in the medical center, including jobs in the mail room, messenger service, and the accounting
office. They served as orderlies, secretaries, laboratory assistants,
helped in the hospital's gift shop, played with children on pediat-
rics, ushered patients through medical and surgical out-patient
clinics, and helped admit patients to the general hospital. Some
performed more specialized jobs; for example, a patient who had
been a contractor worked at estimating costs on hospital construc-
tion projects. Patients gradually increased their working time per
week, and the character of their jobs was upgraded as they gained
mastery; some moved into paid jobs in the medical center, the
university, and the larger community. This program lent substance
and reality to hours formerly spent in make-work projects or
meaningless inactivity about the wards and helped patients to deal
with problems involved in resuming work and responsibility.

In 1960 a high school classroom was set up on the closed ward of
the YPI. A teacher was provided by the New Haven school system,
her salary augmented in recognition of the special demands involved in such a setting. Adolescent patients whose schooling had
been interrupted by hospitalization undertook from one course to a
more complete program of high school instruction. Certain courses
were not available, including those which require laboratory facilities. Students in increasing numbers were prepared to attend
schools in the larger community while remaining patients in the
hospital.

Patient government continued to meet each week. Its functions
became clearer and more circumscribed: the election of members of
the patient-staff advisory and activities committees; the preparation of a written constitution and the consideration of proposed
amendments; the discussion of maintenance problems; the planning
of the hospital social program.

Informal and exceptional forums, including assemblies of the
patients on a ward, a floor, or all the patients in the hospital when
some issue demanded prompt action, were held with increasing frequency. For example, during a critical period when a patient on a
ward was particularly troubled, agitated, or irritating, ad hoc ward
meetings were held, often with only patients present, occasionally
with the doctor or nurse on duty invited to participate, and these
meetings were sometimes convened every morning and evening
until the end of the crisis. They were without formal organization
and were held only when regularly scheduled patient-staff meetings
or advisory committee meetings were not sufficient.

Innovations rarely occurred by acclamation. Wherever the suggestion originated, whether with staff or patients, it was certain to arouse less than sanguine expectations on the part of some members of the staff or patient group. The lines of division were not necessarily along patient-staff lines; nor did they always coincide with some easily identifiable element in the community. All were concerned about possible deprivational effects upon their life and work when patient-staff meetings were introduced, when the patient-staff advisory committee was established, when each new forum began to meet more frequently, when the number of staff meetings was decreased, when functions previously carried out by staff members and issues previously discussed and decided exclusively within the staff were considered by forums which included patients, and upon the inauguration of a substantial education and work program. Each innovation meant disturbing shifts in role for patients, physicians, nurses, and social workers.

The Sequence of Presentation

The chapters to follow characterize the pre-innovation hospital, the innovation itself, and the post-innovation hospital, in that order. The predispositions with which all major participants entered the period of relatively rapid change are described, including the range of their orientations to a program of enlarged power sharing.

The innovations have been enumerated in the preceding pages. In order to bring out their possible significance, we will focus upon the most conspicuous change, the patient-staff meeting, and provide sufficient detail to examine what it was like when partially stabilized. Verbatim reports of six meetings distributed over the first year of the new practice have been studied. Some meetings show the character of the sessions in predictably stressful times in the hospital year; others are contrasting examples.

The post-innovation chapters undertake to assess the impact of the new hospital, giving particular attention to the patient-staff meeting as a decision process. Its task is to examine precisely what differences the new practices made.

The report is derived from the detailed examination of hospital records and transcripts of staff meetings, patient-staff meetings, other hospital forums, interviews with key participants, questionnaires, and participant observation. One author (Rubenstein) worked at the Yale Psychiatric Institute as a resident physician for two years, served as its assistant director for four years, was a consulting supervisor on its staff for five years, and is presently its

co-director. In addition to interviews conducted for basic orientation with senior staff members and supervisors, residents, nurses,
social workers, and aides, five different questionnaires were prepared, one for each of these categories of participants, and sent to
all who were associated with the YPI during the eleven year period
with which we are primarily concerned (July 1, 1950 to June 30,
1961).

Since it is understood that patient-staff meetings involve the
sharing of power among all who participate in the life of the hospital, including patients, it is appropriate to examine in detail the
grounds upon which such claims rest. Modern political science
and jurisprudence are bringing refined methods of empirical study
to their tasks. The patient-staff meeting is a situation that raises
some exceptionally challenging questions which, if satisfactorily
dealt with, will widen the repertory of methods by which semiformal institutions are described. We have remarked on the fact
that the patient-staff meetings did not take votes. Can it be demonstrated that they performed any decision role whatever? The answer
will be affirmative, and qualified in detail.

The verbatim records confirm one major possibility and put to
rest a galaxy of fears that spring to mind in thinking about the conduct of mental hospitals. It is convincingly demonstrated that the
traditional coercive practices of psychiatric hospitals and the atmosphere of dependency, isolation, hostility, and suspicion they foster
are drastically unnecessary and in opposition to treatment objectives. YPI experience warrants the firm conclusion that the conventional modes of psychiatric hospital administration and treatment
require revision. The conduct of patients at every step of the sequence of innovation disclosed a potential for responsible participation in the process of treatment that cannot but quiet the conventional fears with which "craziness" has been approached. The
experience of the YPI strongly confirms the view that unless the
power process of a psychiatric hospital is genuinely and realistically
shared, the damaged and defeated young cannot become responsible, contributing participants in the larger community.

The Yale Background

After World War I, the Rockefeller Foundation decided to devote a
major part of its resources to the development of the sciences concerned with the study of man and society. Made at a time when the
possibility of orderly social evolution was dramatically challenged

by the emergence of the Soviet Union and its struggle for survival and expansion, this important decision was aimed at applying to the social sciences the empirical techniques so successful in the physical sciences. An important result of this decision was the establishment in 1930 of the Institute of Human Relations at Yale, where cooperative research by investigators from a wide range of theoretical and empirical viewpoints was encouraged. This was in contrast to the traditional isolation of university departments. Psychiatric research and training were given a central position in the Institute of Human Relations, and a psychiatric hospital, the Yale Psychiatric Institute, was established within it.

Between 1930 and the early 1940s the Yale Psychiatric Institute sought to provide a humane environment in which disease processes were to be identified. Expectations of positive therapeutic results were neither entertained nor encouraged. Competent psychiatric diagnosticians concentrated upon establishing an accurate and complete characterization of the patient. Physical therapies, including electric shock and insulin treatment, were sometimes employed, but a skeptical attitude regarding their usefulness prevailed, and the broad use of these treatments, which at that time was characteristic of most psychiatric hospitals, was limited by very strict criteria of application. Diagnosis and evaluation were emphasized. It was by and large taken for granted that seriously ill patients would remain seriously ill, subject to rare but welcome spontaneous remissions. The dossiers on each patient were large and detailed: for instance, the patient was said to show more or less facial mobility, to speak more or less distinctly, to try to get out of bed or not. The "work-up" was the focus for the talents of the entire professional staff.

In 1945, an era of new personalities, theories, methods, and excitement began in the department of psychiatry and the YPI. The change was characterized primarily by a turn toward psychoanalysis as the foundation for theoretical and clinical investigation and practice. A group of psychoanalysts, including Lawrence Kubie, Rudolph Lowenstein, Robert Knight, Erik Erikson, William Pious, Alfred Gross, and later Merton Gill, Charles Brenner, and Hans Loewald, lent their talents and energies to these new efforts. The task of organizing and developing the new department and hospital was undertaken by Fredrick Redlich, a psychoanalyst committed to the application of psychoanalytic insights to psychiatric training and treatment, particularly in the therapy of the psychoses, and to the pursuit of psychiatric investigation and research. The emphasis within the YPI shifted from classical diagnosis and evaluation to an optimistic, thoroughgoing application of psychoanalytic psychotherapy. The doctors struggled in a new atmosphere of enthusiasm and therapeutic hope to comprehend and master the ideas, techniques, and clinical problems, investigatory questions, and methods which this change stimulated. The application of psychoanalysis in the treatment of the psychoses was in the early stages of its development, and in the United States the concept of a psychoanalytic hospital had only begun to emerge, most notably in the work of Harry Stack Sullivan and Frieda Fromm-Reichmann at Chestnut Lodge, of Karl and William Menninger at the Menninger Clinic, and of Robert Knight at the Austen Riggs Center.

In addition to the emphasis upon psychoanalysis, the department became increasingly involved with neighboring fields of investigation. The sharing of ideas and joint research were encouraged among psychiatrists, psychoanalysts, anthropologists, sociologists, psychologists, lawyers, political scientists, and researchers in the basic medical sciences. Redlich devoted his attention to developing a comprehensive training and research program in psychiatry. He participated in the founding of an autonomous, research-oriented psychoanalytic institute which provided members of the department an opportunity for training in psychoanalysis.[14] As the department's activities greatly expanded in volume and diversification, the YPI became one of several treatment facilities used for training and research, and the clinical activities of the department and its chairman were no longer concentrated exclusively in the YPI.

An important stimulus to the changes in the hospital with which we are here concerned were the researches undertaken by an anthropologist, William Caudill, in part in association with Edward Stainbrook.[15] These studies focused upon interactions between patients, doctors, and nurses and conceptualized the hospital as a small so-

14. The Western New England Institute For Psychoanalysis, founded in 1953. A comprehensive description of psychoanalytic training is offered in Bertram D. Lewin and Helen Ross, *Psychoanalytic Education in the United States* (New York, Norton, 1960).

15. William Caudill, F. C. Redlich, H. R. Gilmore, and E. B. Brody, "Social Structure and Interaction Processes on a Psychiatric Ward," *American Journal of Orthopsychiatry*, 22 (1952), 314–34; William Caudill and Edward Stainbrook, "Some Covert Effects of Communication Difficulties in a Psychiatric Hospital," *Psychiatry*, 17 (1954), 27–40; William Caudill, "Social Process in a Collective Disturbance on a Psychiatric Ward," in M. Greenblatt, D. S. Levinson, and R. H. Williams, eds. *The Patient and the Mental Hospital* (Glencoe, The Free Press, 1957); William Caudill, *The Psychiatric Hospital as a Small Society* (Cambridge, Mass., Harvard University Press, 1958).

ciety. The distinctive challenge arising from these investigations was the demand that the hospital staff move beyond the restricted view of what took place during the formal psychotherapeutic hour to the complex experience of being a patient. Stainbrook, director of the hospital during 1951–52, consistently sought to arouse interest in the patient's overall hospital experience. He added a group worker, a social worker with special training in working with groups of hospitalized patients, to the staff. Her reports at staff meetings accustomed resident physicians to the importance of being informed about the patients' entire day. Stainbrook also sought to bring the nurses a richer understanding of the importance of interactions occurring in the patient community and of their role in treatment and emphasized the need for improved communications among the staff, particularly between nurses and residents. The example of his own respect for and attentiveness to the nurses in staff meetings and on the wards had an observable effect on the residents' attitudes.

It was at this time (1952) that Maxwell Jones' *Social Psychiatry* appeared.[16] Jones described an exciting attempt to use the entire hospital experience in a thoroughgoing therapeutic program with patients diagnosed as severe character disorders. Its central feature was a meeting of patients and staff in which everyone was encouraged to participate in free discussions of all issues affecting members of the hospital community. Remarkable therapeutic results with severely disturbed patients were reported; in Jones' opinion these could not have been obtained by relying on individual psychotherapy alone.[17]

The only forum in which YPI patients then participated was patient government, an anemic institution with sporadic existence in the hospital. Brief evening meetings of patients were held weekly or monthly with elected officers presiding. At times the chief resident or the resident on duty participated regularly; at other times physicians and nurses attended but refrained from active participation. That acutely disturbed patients were sometimes elected to office expressed the patients' apathy, contempt for what they regarded as pro forma government, and feeling that the staff alone exercised

16. *The Therapeutic Community.*
17. Subsequent studies show the influence of Jones and others: A. H. Stanton and M. S. Schwartz, *The Mental Hospital* (New York, Basic Books, 1954); Ivan Belnap, *Human Problems of a State Mental Hospital* (New York, Blakiston, 1956); M. Greenblatt, D. J. Levinson, R. H. Williams, eds., *The Patient and the Mental Hospital;* A. J. Leighton, J. A. Clausen, R. N. Wilson, eds., *Explorations in Social Psychiatry* (New York, Basic Books, 1957).

power and made all important decisions in the hospital. Voting was a frequent operation at patient-government meetings, but just what issues were being voted upon was often far from clear. Discussion was generally limited to complaints about meals, the physical maintenance of the hospital, and the activities program. The meetings were used primarily to express the dissatisfactions of people who identified themselves and were identified by others as "patients," the passive recipients of the active efforts of doctors and nurses, the "expert" staff which "treated" them.

During this period, the hospital director, Theodore Lidz, was interested in using the YPI for his studies of the families of schizophrenic patients, exploring the contribution of interactions within the family to the occurrence and the specific character of emotional illness.[18] Lidz's concern with social units, rather than the lone individual, tended to enlarge the residents' field of interest. Contact with the patients' families had been the social worker's obligation and prerogative. This division of labor contributed to the isolation of the resident, an isolation which he had gratefully accepted as a means of avoiding distractions from individual psychotherapy. The residents' avoidance of contact with the patients' families was believed to enhance his role as a therapist.

18. The published reports on this work by Lidz, Fleck, and their associates include: T. Lidz, B. Parker, and A. Cornelison, "The Role of the Father in the Family Environment of the Schizophrenic Patient," *American Journal of Psychiatry*, *113* (1956), 126–32; T. Lidz, A. Cornelison, et al., "The Intrafamilial Environment of the Schizophrenic Patient. I: The Father," *Psychiatry*, *20* (1957), 329–42; T. Lidz, A. Cornelison, S. Fleck, and D. Terry, "The Intrafamilial Environment of the Schizophrenic Patient. II: Marital Schism and Marital Skew," *American Journal of Psychiatry*, *114* (1957), 241–48; T. Lidz, A. Cornelison, et al., "The Intrafamilial Environment of the Schizophrenic Patient. IV: Parental Personalities and Family Interaction," *American Journal of Orthopsychiatry*, *28* (1958), 764–76, S. Fleck, D. Freedman, A. Cornelison, D. Terry, and T. Lidz, "The Intrafamilial Environment of the Schizophrenic Patient. V: The Understanding of Symptomatology Through the Study of Family Interaction," Read at the Annual Meeting of the American Psychiatric Association, May, 1957; T. Lidz, A. Cornelison, et al., "The Intrafamilial Environment of the Schizophrenic Patient. VI: The Transmission of Irrationality," *Arch. Neurol. Psychiat.*, *79* (1958), 305–16; S. Fleck, T. Lidz, A. Cornelison, S. Schafer, and D. Terry, "The Intrafamilial Environment of the Schizophrenic Patient. Incestuous and Homosexual Problems," in J. H. Masserman, ed., *Individual and Familial Dynamics* (New York, Grune and Stratton, 1958); T. Lidz, S. Schafer, S. Fleck, A. Cornelison, D. Terry, "Ego Differentiation and Schizophrenic Symptom Formation in Identical Twins," *Journal of The American Psychoanalytic Association*, *10* (1962); T. Lidz, S. Fleck, A Cornelison, *Schizophrenia and the Family* (New York, International Universities Press, 1966).

In 1952–53 Lidz reintroduced formal weekly ward rounds, during which the director visited each patient in his own room and talked briefly with him. A daily occurrence in the early days, they had fallen into disuse when individual psychotherapy became the hospital's primary emphasis. The residents were initially apprehensive that ward rounds would disrupt individual therapy. They met with the director prior to his rounds and told him what they thought he should and should not say to each patient. There was great concern afterward about the content and the effects of these encounters. Gradually, less fuss was made. Rounds did not prove disruptive. Meetings prior to rounds were dropped. This commotion about ward rounds foreshadowed the apprehension with which residents viewed every formal innovation; they feared that their therapeutic role and, implicitly, their power position in the hospital community would be undermined.

Lidz also revamped the run-down and poorly adapted hospital building. Individual rooms were redesigned to function as sitting rooms; ward dining rooms which put an end to the practice of nurses serving meal trays to patients were constructed; lounges and a terrace facilitated a more active social and recreational program; the dreary seclusion area, "special," was reconstructed to include a small, pleasant lounge for isolated patients. Later the hospital's small gymnasium was adapted to serve as a classroom; a small combined classroom and study hall on the closed ward was constructed; music rooms appeared on each ward; and a large conference room adjacent to the wards in which the entire hospital population could assemble. These alterations, made over a period of five years, reflected, accompanied, and confirmed the changing perspectives and operational routines of the hospital.

During 1953–54 Stephen Fleck joined Lidz in directing the hospital and gradually assumed full responsibility. His term as YPI director continued through the remaining years covered by this study. Certain early influences and approaches of Fleck and his associates (including Charles Gardner, Edwin Wood, Nea Norton, Daniel Freedman, Daniel Schwartz, and Rubenstein) were of particular importance in paving the way for the formal innovations of 1956:

1. They insisted that so-called administrative and therapeutic considerations could not validly be separated because every aspect of hospital life affected the patient's clinical course and the effectiveness of treatment. Whereas "administrative reasons" and "that's the way we do things here" had previously been acceptable in account-

ing for established procedures, all practices were now open to reappraisal and often modified in the light of the question, "Is it therapeutic?"

2. Among the practices reexamined was the avoidance of contact between residents and patients outside of psychotherapeutic hours. Residents were encouraged to have more informal contact with patients. The aim was to make the psychotherapeutic contact more meaningful, not to detract from it in any way. They emphasized the need to establish genuine contact with the patient, observing that meaningful communication sometimes began with previously isolated, withdrawn, and provocative psychotic patients after the physician and patient took a walk together, played ping-pong, drank coffee, or chatted informally in the hallway or in the dining room over supper.

3. They conceived of the patient and the staff as entering into a tacit contractual agreement: on its part, the staff contracted to do all that it could to aid the patient in solving the problems that made his hospitalization necessary and to facilitate his return to health and the community; on his part, the patient also contracted to facilitate conscientiously—to the limit of his capacity at any given time—this movement toward health. Just as the patient could reproach the staff for not working effectively with him in his efforts to get well, the staff could demand of the patient that he too participate actively in this effort. The patient's responsibility now replaced his previous position as a passive recipient of staff effort.

Part I
The Conventional Psychiatric Hospital

2. The Social and Physical Environment

Recognizing the influence upon the YPI of its location within a series of concentric, overlapping, and disparate circles is analogous to the child's discovery that the address of his house on Bayberry Lane may be expanded to include his town, state, U.S.A., Western Hemisphere, Earth and Universe. Each localization of the hospital brings important characterizing factors into consideration. New Haven: a city of 150,000 people, including a vigorous mixture of ethnic groups, engaged primarily in commerce and light industry, with Yale occupying much of its center. New Haven has been studied intensively; a detailed sociological characterization is contained in Redlich and Hollingshead's *Social Class and Mental Illness*.[1] Connecticut: a small, prosperous, industrialized eastern state oriented toward the larger cities of neighboring states, Boston, and New York. Its people are in greater contact with international political, economic, and intellectual currents than in other sections of the United States. New England traditions contribute to a philosophical position, reflected in the development of the hospital and its ideology, which emphasizes self-reliance and communal responsibility for those who cannot help themselves.

Among psychiatric hospitals, the Yale Psychiatric Institute, as a small, private psychoanalytically oriented psychiatric hospital, operated by a university medical school, is distinguished from state, community, and veterans hospitals, in which the great majority of hospitalized psychiatric patients are treated, and also from the nonuniversity private psychiatric hospitals which care for most of the others. The hospital's patients are few in number (a maximum of forty-four) and capable of affording relatively expensive, individualized care. The characterization "psychoanalytically oriented" indicates reliance upon psychotherapy as a treatment method, guided and informed in theory and technique by psychoanalysis. As part of its being operated by a medical school within a university, the hospital is committed not only to the treatment of patients but also to both training in the professional disciplines related to the mentally ill and research. The YPI participates in the training of psychiatrists,

1. F. C. Redlich and A. B. Hollingshead, *Social Class and Mental Illness* (New York, Wiley, 1958).

medical students, psychiatric nurses and nursing students, psychologists, and social workers; it functions as a research facility for students of psychoanalysis, psychiatry, psychology, sociology, law, and anthropology. The Yale Medical Center includes the Yale Psychiatric Institute, the medical school, a large community hospital, and a complex of related research and treatment facilities.

The hospital is also involved with the larger worlds of psychiatry and psychoanalysis; members of its staff participate in the scientific undertakings and the policy determinations of professional organizations, foundations, and government agencies.

The staff of the Institute has persistently attempted to put the treatment of its patients first in the hierarchy of its three primary functions, treatment, training, and research.

The hospital occupies two floors of a wing of the main building of the Yale Medical School which also houses the University's departments of psychiatry, psychology, sociology, anthropology, and the Child Study Center (collectively, the Institute of Human Relations). Each floor of the hospital consists of an L-shaped corridor lined with individual rooms arranged as studies or sitting rooms, two lounges, and a dining room. The first floor constitutes an open ward; the second floor is locked. Male and female sections are separated on the second floor by doors which are usually left open during the day but closed at night; they are contiguous and unseparated on the first floor. "Special," the hospital's isolation area, consists of a series of individual rooms on the second floor for acutely disturbed patients. Its windows are heavily screened; the doors have small windows and are locked. The gradual renovation of this section of the hospital has been described. A small fenced-in terrace off the first floor includes a garden and areas for playing volleyball and pitching horseshoes. A small gymnasium and an occupational therapy shop are located on a lower level of the building. A treatment room on the second floor has been converted to a classroom and the gymnasium has been modified for use as a classroom as well as calisthenics and sports. The residents' offices are in a corridor off the open ward, conference rooms and senior staff offices are on the second floor off the wards and on the third floor of the building.

The Social Environment

The Yale Psychiatric Institute is a group of people of diversified roles who strive for a variety of goals, including the primary treatment, training, and research objectives. The conventional role designations include members of the hospital board, senior staff physicians and administrators (medical director, assistant medical director, chief resident, supervisors of psychotherapy), residents (physicians in the third year of psychiatric training beyond internship), nurses, aides, medical students, nursing students, psychologists, social workers (including group workers), activities workers (occupational therapists and teachers), and patients.

The board of directors, including the dean of the medical school, the director of the medical center's general hospital, the chairman of the department of psychiatry, the psychiatrist-in-chief of the medical center, and the YPI director, has assumed an unobtrusive, increasingly nominal position in the overseeing of the affairs of the YPI. It appraises the hospital's financial position and ratifies the budget and policies offered for approval by the director. Only five of the sixty-one physicians who worked as YPI residents during the eleven years of this study were aware that the board existed. The board's relatively passive position reflects contentment with the hospital's currently untroubled financial state and confidence in the direction given the hospital by its professional staff, particularly the director. Its role is in marked contrast to the boards of some private psychiatric hospitals, where power is clearly retained by the trustees, and where the director must consult with them constantly and often defer to their judgment on matters of personnel selection, policy, and finance. The inconspicuous role of the Yale Board reflects, in part, its entirely professional membership—in contrast with the lay composition of some hospital boards—and the relatively limited segments of the larger community with which the hospital is most directly concerned and to whose interests it is most responsive: the university, the medical center, the medical school, and the department of psychiatry.

The senior medical staff of the YPI consists in that group of faculty members of the department of psychiatry concerned with management of the treatment program in the hospital, the training of the hospital's residents, and research involving its facilities and patients. The chairman of the department is kept informed about the hospital but in large measure leaves control and responsibility to the YPI director.

The medical director of the YPI is the central figure in the hospital. He is most important in the management and treatment of patients and in the training of residents; it is very clearly *his* hospital, reflecting his personality, his interests, his values, and his conception of psychiatric illness and its treatment. During the period studied, 1950 through 1961, there were four medical directors. The terms of the first three ranged from one to two years; the fourth served from 1953 to 1963. Since he was the director during so much of the period covered by this study, including the innovation and post-innovation years, he is often referred to as the "present director" in this book. In addition to his work at the YPI, the director is usually concerned with a wide range of activities in the larger community, the medical school, and other sections of the department of psychiatry. For example, the director of the hospital through the last eight years of this study served on the boards of the Mental Health and Visiting Nurse Associations and on the advisory committee of the Council of Social Agencies, and was active in, and had been president of, the Parent Teacher Associations of his children's schools and his church. He taught in the department of public health, supervised psychiatric residents in the veterans hospital during their initial year of inpatient work, was in charge of the overall resident training program of the department of psychiatry, treated some patients in individual psychotherapy and psychoanalysis, and worked with department colleagues in research on the families of psychotic patients.

The director's activities involve every aspect of hospital life. Because the YPI is small, with relatively few patients and staff, he exerts an immediate, personal impact on every individual and activity in the hospital community. A detailed account of his interactions with other senior staff members, residents, nurses, patients, patients' families, and students will emerge in this study.

The assistant director serves primarily as an aide to the medical director, assisting in his many administrative and teaching tasks, helping to develop hospital policy, and constantly reviewing with him and the chief resident the work of each resident and the therapy and overall management of each patient. He serves the director by critically assessing his management of hospital affairs and by acting as an extension of the director with residents, nurses, other members of the hospital staff, and patients. He participates in many of the director's contacts with staff and patients and alternates in some tasks with him, chairing some staff meetings, making rounds on the wards, supervising residents, and consulting with patients' families and key staff figures. He relieves the director of some administrative burdens and participates in a continuing dialogue on the affairs of the hospital.

There are usually six supervisors of psychotherapy on the YPI staff. They are psychoanalysts in private practice, most of whom have previously served in the full-time department staff. These unpaid members of the clinical faculty devote two to three hours a week to the task of meeting individually with two residents for one hour of supervision. Each resident has two such supervisors. Since each supervisor usually works with a resident for six months, shifting midway through the year, the resident works with four different supervisors during a year. Supervisory hours are usually devoted to the resident's work with one or two patients. The resident reports on the therapeutic hours during the previous week. The discussion, while focusing on therapy, may include any topic concerned with patients, therapy, and sometimes the professional and emotional life of the resident. Such supervision is distinguished from "administrative supervision," the weekly individual meeting with the director or assistant director in which the resident briefly reviews the status of each of his patients and his current work with them.

The supervisors meet in conference with the director and assistant director four times a year to appraise the work of each resident. Information is shared about the supervisors' contact with residents, including assessments of the residents' resources and problems, and the status and treatment of patients. Otherwise, supervisors have no direct contact with patients and do not participate in the life of the hospital community.

The chief resident is usually appointed for a one-year term, on the completion of his three years of training, the last of which was spent in the YPI. His appointment is an honor bestowed in recognition of his superiority as a resident. The job is sometimes turned down by the selected resident, however, because he wishes to pursue other training or because he must leave the university for military service. On assuming the job of chief resident, a sudden shift occurs. On June 30, he is one of the resident physicians, eagerly seeking the approval of teachers and bosses, often disgruntled by their decisions which he condemns as arbitrary and unwise; on July 1, he is a member of the senior staff, no longer a part of the resident group, not yet comfortable as a colleague of his former teachers and bosses, but identified with them by new residents and the rest of the hospital community. As a colleague of the director and assistant director, he is expected to appraise the residents' work in a thoroughgoing, critical way. With his seniors, he weighs a resident's resources and deficiencies, including his capacities and difficulties in seeing, understanding, and being useful, with reference to the resident's personal problems, the nature of his blind spots, and his defenses. To participate in such a discussion requires drastic shifts of role on the part of a chief resident. He must also assume new responsibilities toward patients. For example, some whom he treated during the preceding year are now in therapy with others; he must find new ways of relating to these patients and his junior colleagues now assigned to them.

These shifting relationships with residents, with the director and assistant director, and with patients are accompanied by other changes. His salary is abruptly increased more than twofold. Other staff members, particularly nurses, now perceive him as one of the bosses.

The activities and interactions within the hospital of the senior staff will emerge more clearly as we proceed in the following three chapters to characterize patients, nurses, and resident physicians in the pre-innovation period.

3. The Patient as Ward

For the patient, admission to a psychiatric hospital is a climactic deprivation in a sequence of failures. A history of increasing alienation and estrangement has led him to view the world as confronting him only with obstinate misunderstanding, indifference, contempt, and condemnation. He feels that he cannot act for himself, is dominated by others, who make arbitrary and erratic decisions without reference to his wishes and needs. He and his family, friends, colleagues in work, school, church, the larger community—his social environment—are at odds. Their common problems can no longer be solved within the permissible limits of the social order. The initiative for hospitalization comes directly or indirectly from others; the patient is, in effect, ejected from his social setting, the communities in which he has unsuccessfully sought to participate. In the power struggle which culminates in this outcome, the patient obtained gratification from a pattern of living which imposed deprivations upon those around him, provoking them to defend themselves by a formidable counter-deprivation, confinement in a hospital. This severe sanction was invoked by the group to protect its value patterns and institutions.

The hospital is used to remove a menace to the public order of the family or other environment. The expulsion of the individual is an exercise of power which concedes that the consensus necessary for group life has broken down, that the effective decision-makers in the collectivity can no longer tolerate the presence and participation of the patient in ordering their lives. The YPI receives the loser of this prolonged power struggle.

Examined in this light, prehospital events take on added significance. All interactions in some way modify predispositions to handle future problems. Any family behavior at a cross section in time is an interplay between predispositions and the confrontations which constitute a current environment. When a child is born or any member is added to a group, the task at hand is to enable the new member to acquire appropriate perspectives and operational capabilities. The group is composed of persons who seek to maximize values; the culture of the collectivity is made up of the stable patterns of value shaping and sharing. The pattern is comparatively stable when a value participation arrangement is roughly fixed.

The family operates as an institution in which helpless infants are socialized into more or less competent adults. Within it, huge inequalities of power are gradually modified into stable equalities or inequalities. Outcomes of this power distribution relate to degrees of participation in power itself and to every other value outcome. They also include the settlement of controversies arrived at by the group and usually enforced by the most severe deprivations at the disposal of the collectivity. Sending a member of the family to a psychiatric hospital imposes such a sanction. As a rule, only a small percentage of the flow of choices and decisions involved in daily interaction within the family become matters of controversy which involve severe sanction.

The prehospital history of a patient may also be described by exploring the constellation of forces which result in his inability to function within the family power system. It may not be enough to identify the incapacities of the expellee, for the effective power figures (parents, one parent, coalitions of parents and siblings) may be so constituted that they cannot permit others to join in decision-making and, at the same time, are incapable of acting in ways that would extirpate the demand to participate. Conflicting tendencies are fostered in the developing person; he oscillates between renunciation of self-assertion and rebellion against limitation.

The pre-innovation hospital undertook to rehabilitate the patient causing disruption of family life; the staff sought to restore him to his environment in such a way that he would not disrupt the family again. The hospital catered to the family demands, executing and sustaining the power deprivation imposed upon the patient. The family is not uninvolved once the patient has been admitted to the hospital. They must deal with a sense of responsibility for the plight of the patient, and they may have no frame of reference in which to comprehend what has happened. Although they usually believe that the respect position of everyone concerned has been damaged and that, in some obscure way, moral culpability is involved, the act of hospitalization is basically perceived as a means of improving the position of all effective decision-makers in all values at stake, including self-perceptions of respect, rectitude, and other values.

At the beginning of the pre-innovation period, the YPI was still known as primarily an evaluation and diagnostic center. Although physical treatments were sometimes used, the restoration of the patient's premorbid state was not a prominent expectation on the part of referring physicians, the patient, his family, or the hospital staff. As the YPI gained a reputation for intensive psychotherapy, the expectation that an effort would be made to restore health through definitive treatment gradually developed, and admission was sought for many more patients than the YPI could accommodate. As the only private psychiatric hospital in New Haven, the YPI served the local community; as part of the university, it was obligated to meet the needs for hospitalization of Yale students, faculty members, and their families; as its reputation as a psychotherapeutic hospital for severely disturbed patients was established, psychoanalysts and psychiatrists across the United States referred patients; a few were admitted because their problems were of special interest to researchers working in the hospital.

The pre-innovation patient group was accordingly diverse. However, it increasingly consisted of patients most likely to benefit from psychotherapeutic treatment. Occasional neurological problems and organic psychoses were encountered, but most patients were in the schizophrenic, depressed, and psychopathic categories. A small but increasing number described as severely neurotic or "borderline," rather than psychotic, were also hospitalized. Patients ranged in age from twelve to sixty-five, including high school, college, and graduate school students, faculty members, and older men and women with established social and professional positions. Some had been unsuccessfully treated in a series of hospitals for years, some had no prior treatment, and for others hospitalization was necessary because outpatient psychotherapy had proved inadequate.

Prior to the period of this study, patients remained in the YPI for a short time. When hospitalization was diagnostic and evaluatory, most remained for two months or less; when electroshock or insulin treatments were administered, they usually stayed less than six months. As the psychotherapeutic emphasis took hold, the length of stay gradually increased, and most patients entered the hospital aware that they would probably remain for a year or longer.

Because of the great expense of hospitalization and limited insurance coverage, lengthening the stay tended to limit the hospital to patients of higher socioeconomic status, although some were supported by research funds or the pooled resources of an extended family. The funds necessary to maintain psychiatric hospitalization over a period of months or years may have a severe impact upon the financial position and, secondarily, the social position of the family. Few upper-middle class families can afford lengthy psychiatric hospitalization without major sacrifice; already strained emotional relationships within the family are severely burdened, particularly where financial position is an important basis for status and prestige. This financial deprivation arouses guilt in the patient and frequently serves to expiate guilt for the illness felt by members of the family.

Private psychiatric hospital patients feel guilty about their relatively elegant care compared to that of public institutions. When a patient must be transferred to a state hospital for financial reasons, intense feeling is often aroused among patients. Some, often patients concerned about the financial burden suffered by their own families as a result of hospitalization, may come forward with well-meaning, though ineffective, offers of financial assistance. Concern about money is then freely expressed, but money is otherwise rarely a topic of conversation or public discussion in the hospital.

The patient has usually suffered severe deprivations of well-being immediately prior to hospitalization. Frightening thoughts and feelings preoccupy and estrange him. He is severely deprived in affection, convinced that those important to him do not care; he is unable to accept concern and tenderness, unable to feel or express love for anyone. Fears and longings consume him. He is deprived in power, enlightenment, skill, and wealth; assertive, definitive action has become impossible; attention to the external world, the turning away from inner demands, cannot be sustained; work is disrupted. When designated "psychiatrically ill," he is subjected to further deprivations of respect and rectitude. Such illness is viewed by patient, family, and friends as undermining his status in the community and conveys ethical implications which reflect against the patient and all who are close to him. Value deprivations suffered by family members arise from their identification with him: puzzled inadequacy in trying to understand and help (enlightenment and skill), the undermining of their respect position as a family (respect and power), emotional distress (well-being), self-blame (rectitude), a sense of being estranged from him (affection). They may react with counter-hostility, anger, and blame, further depriving the patient of affection, respect, rectitude, and well-being. In attempting to cope with the patient's "illness," they consult and "put him in the care of" an expert, depriving him of power, and to the extent that they avoid being helpful to him directly themselves, of affection.

In his work with the psychiatric expert thus engaged, the patient is indulged in affection and respect (becoming an object of the psychiatrist's attentiveness, interest, and concern) and in enlightenment and skill (through the investigatory effort and in the acquisition of strategies for coping with his feelings and thoughts and those of others). The objective is to restore the patient's emotional well-being. Work with the psychiatrist may further deprive the family in wealth, rectitude (if the patient uses the understanding gained to blame them), and power (if he now, reinforced by his psychiatrist-ally, is more assertive and demanding).

If his illness persists or gets worse, despite the psychiatrist with whom he worked as an out-patient, hospitalization is the result of the incapacity of the patient, the family, or the psychiatrist to sustain these multiple value deprivations. In the pre-innovation period, the act of hospitalization subjected the patient to a multiplicity of new value deprivations: isolation from family, friends, and familiar psychiatrist (affection), withdrawal from ongoing events in the outside world, local community, and family (enlightenment), vulnerability to the social stigma attached to entering a psychiatric institution (respect and rectitude), removal from the possibility of gainful employment and liability for the financial burden of care (wealth and skill), deprivation of his autonomy and rights as a responsible citizen, and subordination to the direction and surveillance of the hospital staff (power). This compounding of deprivations was in part alleviated by affection, respect, enlightenment, and well-being indulgences: the doctors' and nurses' concern with his emotional health and ongoing psychological growth; asylum from pressures, responsibilities, and involvements which had proved too burdensome; efforts to respect his needs and respond with thoughtfulness; protection from self-hate and the intolerance and aggression of others. In the hospital he might find in doctors and others warmth and compassion, a readiness to share and understand his experience, without the intensity of involvement and conflict experienced with parents; he might find a maternal tenderness and care in relationships with nurses and social workers that he could not find or accept from mother or wife; he might gain respect and tolerance from other patients not found with siblings and friends.

But, as always, the problems which made hospitalization necessary quickly find expression in these new relationships. Nevertheless, it is different in the hospital: old animosities are not present on both sides; his development as a person is genuinely sought and at least superficially threatens no one. When his provocations do not succeed in diverting others from the important issues, the patient is forced to turn his attention to productive work. The more terrible struggle within himself must now be engaged, hopefully with those around him as allies rather than as convenient external foes to whom he may impute responsibility for his difficulties.

It is also possible that the referring psychiatrist and hospital staff may be experienced as agents of his disappointed, angry, and critical family who punish, humiliate, and subject him to new deprivations on their behalf. The pre-innovation mode of hospitalization not infrequently confirmed such a view. Disillusionment with the hospital may have been encouraged by its having been idealized by referring psychiatrist, admitting physician, or the family in their efforts to deal with the patient's resistance and their own feelings about participating in the act of hospitalization. The new patient sometimes arrived completely uninformed about what was happening to him. He was told by his family that he was going to a general hospital for a check-up, that he would remain in the hospital for only a few days, or even that he was being admitted to Yale as a student. In accepting a patient who had been so misinformed or deceived, the hospital participated in his victimization and could hardly be experienced subsequently as benign and concerned with his interests.

Among his predispositions on entering the hospital, the wish to get away and be taken care of was, at least in part, gratified. But the patient had little reason to anticipate basic or long-term indulgences in well-being. Hospitalization was consistent with and tended to compound and sustain his role as a victim and the severe deprivations that taken together constitute "illness."

The YPI Experience

Confined to the hospital at the instigation of his family and the experts they consulted, the patient perceived it as a place where the direction of his life was usurped by others. His day consisted in sitting, listening to radio or television, reading, and talking with other patients, nurses, and aides. Time on the wards was relieved by an occasional hour in occupational therapy, where he would weave, paint, or model ashtrays out of clay. A movie was shown one night each week. The hospital's small terrace was used for sunning, volleyball, and pitching horseshoes in warm months. As permission was granted, patients took walks and shopped accompanied by aides, were escorted in small groups to theater and beach, and occasionally went to concerts and restaurants together without being accompanied. Patients saw families and close friends during scheduled visiting hours and might later visit at home with staff approval.

Patients told one another their secrets and commiserated about their predicament in the hospital and circumstances which led to hospitalization. In their common confinement, they often became good friends, tolerant and understanding of the behavior to which they felt driven. They were bound together as fellow victims of the indifference and rejection of their families and the arbitrariness and manipulation of the hospital staff. They were mischievous children together, trying to avoid the intrusions, judgments, and control of the staff.

Aides were perceived as similarly powerless figures with whom some thoughts and feelings could be shared. There was little expectation of deriving any advantage beyond the exchange, although what a patient said to the aides was often passed on to the nurses.

The nurses were clearly part of the opposition, the "they" and "them" against whom the patient strove to maintain his dignity, privacy, and integrity. Nurses were always about, checking at regular intervals through the night, awakening patients, nagging about getting dressed and to breakfast, collecting laundry, serving meals, writing endless notes, handing out medications, enforcing rules, and calling the doctor. Although members of the opposition, nurses in their crisp, uniformed efficiency were comforting to have around.

The remote senior doctors sat in offices in other sections of the building away from the wards. The patient felt that they were ultimately in charge of his destiny, made all the decisions, determined when he was ready for "privileges" or discharge, and yet had rarely said more than a few words to him. It was all too easy to attribute great power to senior doctors, to assume they determined every aspect of his life and that decisions were based on inadequate information and grounds having little relation to the patient's view of his best interests. Fantasies about the director and chief resident were fostered by the patient's wish for omniscient, omnipotent figures concerned with his welfare and responsible for his destiny, facilitated by the absence of contradictory data, and abetted by residents' and nurses' needs for a similar powerful, higher force who assumed responsibility and took care of them, too.

Although psychotherapy was the emphasized treatment, insulin and electric shock treatments were sometimes administered. The aura of mystery and punishment associated with them was intimidating, and it intensified the patients' sense of helplessness and victimization.

Each patient was assigned a resident as his doctor. They met together in individual psychotherapeutic sessions three to five hours each week and sought to clarify the problems and concerns that brought him to the hospital. It was important to the patient to have more freedom, live on the open ward, come and go from the hospital (preferably unescorted and frequently); he tried to win the agreement of his doctor that he was ready for these "privileges." But the doctor often seemed noncommital and evasive about these issues. He was seldom encountered outside of treatment hours, except when walking through the wards or on duty at night or weekends.

Patients talked incessantly among themselves about the doctors, comparing and rating them, and complaining. They assumed that doctors were interested and wanted to be helpful, but were skeptical of what could be accomplished through talks which often seemed removed from issues which occupied much of their time.

These hours of psychotherapy, though sometimes remote from pressing matters, were the central experience of hospitalization. On undertaking therapy with the resident assigned him, the patient cautiously and distrustfully sought the interest and concern he did not expect to get; he employed a variety of strategies to convince himself that his therapist had a genuine and deep personal interest in him and to confirm his suspicion that the doctor did not really care at all. Gradually, if his doctor listened and tried to understand, he confided in him, tried to examine what life had been for him, looked closely at the people he cared about and those who had been important to him, and began to consider the possibility that the doctor understood and appreciated what he felt. But the doctor made comparable investments in others, others whom one lived with, cared about, and envied, and the doctor was reluctant to extend greater freedoms, despite the patient's expectation that such freedom would be forthcoming when the doctor understood him. The doctor's reluctance disappointed the patient, caused him to question whether his doctor really understood, and appeared determined by forces outside their relationship.

As their work together continued, the patient found himself increasingly preoccupied with what he and his doctor said to one another, feelings about the doctor, and uncertainty about how the doctor felt about him. During this one hour of the day the patient worked directly on his problems. The rest of the day was often experienced as a neutral, interim period of waiting for the next therapeutic hour. It was time to be killed, thinking about what had been and might be talked about with the doctor; more commonly, the patient tried to avoid thinking by passive absorption in television or magazines, playing bridge, pounding out metal ashtrays, or weaving. He tried harder to please his doctor, striving to recapture earlier and more complete memories, to pursue the investigation of his symptoms and dreams more vigorously, and to demonstrate his compliance with the psychotherapeutic ideology. He sought his doctor's direction and advice but learned that he had to request it subtly or indirectly, for he was reminded that the doctor was participating in an investigation with him and not telling him what to do. He became sensitive to less obvious indicators of his doctor's preferences and complied with them in his effort to be respected and loved. In their work together, feelings and behavior toward the doctor were inspected and identified as originating in and being appropriate to other relationships. Gradually more freedom was granted him. Some problems began to appear less impossible of solution; the relationship with the doctor was acknowledged as useful and important.

But as he began to think seriously about leaving the hospital and returning to home and work, earlier feelings that it was all impossible returned. At times the patient felt sure that he could be heard and understood only in his relationship with his doctor. The task of transposing what had been found in that one relationship to the people and predicaments to be faced again outside seemed beyond him. Although his doctor seemed at times to understand, in visits with family and in exchanges with other patients and nurses, it was hard to keep alive the feeling that it was worth it. Conflict and suffering seemed intrinsic to his experience. Making a go of it in the world seemed a giant step from the relationship now established with his doctor.

His Power Position

Beyond the isolated hours spent with the doctor, the hospital seemed barren to the patient, a microcosm reflecting the emptiness of the outside world. Neither in the hospital nor the world could the patient find a way to participate with other suitable persons in creating and sustaining something useful and important. The beginnings of such an opportunity for constructive participation were experienced in psychotherapeutic hours. In work with the doctor, he became aware of obstacles within himself to such sharing and began to struggle with how to do something about them.

This effort with the therapist was isolated from the rest of his experience. A crucial step in the psychotherapeutic task was shifting from a position in which he felt helpless, a passive victim of external forces which made it impossible to take responsibility for the course of his life, to a perspective in which he began to see himself as able to make an affirmative choice and to act upon what he wanted for himself. Such a shift was contradicted and opposed by his experience in the hospital. He fitted into the environment by assuming the passive role of those to whom things are done by others.

While he began to consider with his doctor the possibility that he had actively participated in determining his life experience, that he contributed to much of his suffering, that he could no longer abdicate responsibility, the rest of his hospital experience reinforced the view that his life was determined by others. His tentative efforts to determine for himself what he wanted and to act upon such decisions were often responded to as challenging provocations which those around him sought to thwart and undermine. Under such circumstances, the patient sometimes settled for the tangible, if second-best, gratifications available to him. He exploited the readiness of those around him to provide care and attention when he continued to present himself as childlike, needful, and incapable of caring for himself. He found excitement and evidence of concern when, by assuming the posture of the naughty or lazy incompetent, he provoked their wrath.

Because the relationship with his resident therapist was so important and he had no comparable relationships with others in the staff, the disappearance of the resident at the end of the training year and the shift to working in treatment with a new resident was painful. It confirmed his distrustfulness and revived doubts about whether the doctor cared, appreciated his feelings, and understood. If the doctor really cared and understood, how could he leave him?

On contemplating discharge, the patient abruptly faced the resumption of relationships and tasks in family and community for which he felt ill-prepared by the hospital experience. His "adjustment" to the hospital required him to assume functions and roles maladapted to the outside world; leaving meant a shift from months of lounging, artificial work, and indulgent psychotherapeutic hours to the demands and responsibilities of work, school, and family.

The pre-innovation patient was indulged in respect, affection, skill, enlightenment, and well-being in the psychotherapeutic relationship with his doctor. The overall hospital experience deprived him in wealth and power. Rectitude demands made in psychotherapy were in unacknowledged conflict with those put forward outside the psychotherapeutic interview. Whereas the doctor, in keeping with the psychotherapeutic ideology, encouraged the patient to pursue enlightenment, skill, and power objectives in quest of improved well-being, others deprived him in such values. They indulged him in rectitude and well-being in response to his passive compliance, a deprivation of power. When the resident therapist left at the end of his training year, the patient was sharply deprived in all values, especially affection. Discharge from the pre-innovation hospital entailed shifting from a society in which power deprivations were endured in the name of well-being to the larger community where the assumption of responsibility (fuller indulgence in power) is prerequisite for indulgences in respect, affection, rectitude, and well-being. The patient had come to the hospital in flight from victimization, which meant being deprived in all values. In the pre-innovation hospital this victimization was perpetuated, and in some ways reinforced, by a flow of compensating partial indulgences in rectitude and affection. In psychotherapy the effort was made to examine the patient's own responsibility for being victimized (hence to foster his enlightenment) and to find ways of altering his predicament (skill); but these experiences were isolated from the rest of his hospital experience, which opposed any shift of power arising from such insight. The patient's total hospital experience tended to consolidate his adverse power position (as a passive victim) in return for providing moderate indulgences in affection.

4. The Traditional Nurse

Predispositions and Perspectives[1]

The nurses, the durable staff members who have most contact with patients, have been around for a very long time watching doctors, patients, theories, diagnoses, therapies, and procedures come and go. There are eighteen nurses on the staff, twelve of whom constitute a core group, "the old timers," all of whom have worked at the hospital for more than nine years, seven for more than twenty years. All chief nurses are members of the core group. Nurses other than core group members have usually worked at the hospital for at least two years, although many transient nurses have served for brief trial periods or temporarily during vacations and leaves-of-absence.

The nurses work in three shifts: the day shift (7 A.M. to 3 P.M.) includes a chief nurse on each floor and five staff nurses; the evening (3 P.M. to 11 P.M.) and night (11 P.M. to 7 A.M.) shifts are each covered by a chief and two staff nurses. On weekends, the day shift includes fewer nurses. Because of the rotation of days off, the full roster of nurses is never on duty during any single 24-hour period.

The contrast between most of the nurses' long familiarity with the hospital and the relatively shorter stays of residents and patients is important. One of the reassuring defenses which they may employ in coping with difficult patients and residents is to remind themselves and each other that they will remain in the hospital long after the others have left. Because of this strong sense of security they do not have to please patients or residents, although it is important that their own superiors (the chief nurses and director of nursing) and the senior doctors regard them as capable.

Unlike doctors and social workers, nurses view their work as a job; this designation is important and differentiating. Other members of the professional staff work with a sense of challenge and see

1. An effort was made to send questionnaires to the forty-five nurses who had worked at the Yale Psychiatric Institute for six months or longer between July 1, 1950 and June 30, 1961; many could not be located. Questionnaires were filled out and returned by twenty-six of these nurses: four who worked at the hospital only during the pre-innovation period (prior to July 1, 1956), eleven who worked at the YPI in both the pre- and post-innovation periods (11 of the 12 "core-group nurses" who worked at the YPI for 9 years or longer), and eleven who served only in the post-innovation period.

themselves as confronting difficult problems and making the effort required to master them; experience at the hospital is one stage in their professional growth and development. The nurse remains in the same position year after year, and opportunities for modifying the character of her work are very limited.

Members of the professional staff may derive social status (respect) from being part of a university; training and work at Yale will remain a source of prestige throughout their professional careers. The senior staff and social workers are members of the medical school faculty (the chief resident, for example, is an instructor); residents are postdoctoral fellows, a status between that of student and faculty member. The aides as graduate students also enjoy increments of prestige from their Yale affiliation. The nurses, however, are employees of the university, not students or faculty members. The modest self-appraisal implied in the nurses' view of their work as a job is emphatically confirmed by the way in which they are classified by the university.

The time-clock rhythm of the nurse's day, which invites her to perceive her work as a job rather than a profession, and her designation as an employee, militate against the growth of an image of the self as a professional person who is expected to master and contribute to a field of knowledge. It is therefore not surprising that enlightenment is a much less important value to nurses. As a nonstudent, a nurse experiences the hospital context and her activities with relatively little intellectualization. She does not abstract her experience or try to relate it to a conceptual model. Her view of patients, for example, tends to be very personal; her informal talk about them shows no deliberate effort to put aside the conventional assumptions of a lay person. In this highly specialized professional environment, she is relatively unprepared to discuss problems of dynamics and diagnosis or to absorb the insights of her colleagues. A nurse's view of hospital interactions selects the concrete, the practical, the "common sense." This pragmatic, nonintellectual orientation often permits the nurse to respond in a spontaneous and genuine way, participating in a relatively unguarded and unselfconscious emotional give-and-take with patients which may be experienced by them as more vital and meaningful than contacts and exchanges with other staff.

These preliminary characterizations of the nurse will gain in dimension as we examine data specifically from and about nurses who worked at the YPI in pre-innovation years. Many of the pre-innovation staff were also functioning in the post-innovation period, and some characteristics of the nurses have remained substantially unmodified by subsequent developments.

Who are the nurses? Where do they come from? What values do they pursue in the hospital context? The most conspicuous facts are that all the nurses are women, most of them middle-aged, and most of them married.[2] Most of the noncore group had no children, in contrast to core group members, most of whom had two or more children.[3]

The YPI nurse was usually of the middle or lower middle class. The majority described their parents' socio-economic standing as the same as their own.[4]

The image of the conservative nurses is strengthened by an examination of their professed political perspectives: in contrast to overwhelmingly "liberal Democratic" senior and resident physicians, most nurses identified themselves as Republicans or conservative Democrats,[5] and the majority opposed government-supported medical care.[6] Although a majority (twelve of twenty) of all nurses favored government-supported hospital and outpatient psychiatric care, only a minority in the core group (four of eleven) took this position. These differences between the nurses' and doctors' political orientation alert us to anticipate differences in attitudes toward power sharing and new modes of decision-making in the hospital community.

When asked about participation in medical, psychiatric, civic, political, social, and fraternal groups, the largest number belonged to religious organizations. The nurses tend to be active churchgoers, and members of the core group sometimes attend church together.[7] They are the most actively religious staff members, and the only

2. Ten (7 of the 11 core group respondents) were married; six (2 in the core group) were single; two widowed (both in the core group); two separated; and none divorced.

3. Eleven of twenty-one had no children (3 in the core group); four (3 in the core group) had two children, six (5 in the core group) had three or more children.

4. Ten of nineteen said "the same" (5 of 11 in the core group); five (2 in the core group) stated that their parents were of higher, and four (3 in the core group) of lower socio-economic status.

5. Six of twenty (3 of 11 in the core group) described themselves as "liberal Republicans," one as a "conservative Republican," three (1 in the core group) as "conservative Democrats," five (3 in the core group) as "liberal Democrats"; five (4 in the core group) stated that they were "uncommitted."

6. Fifteen of twenty (10 of 11 in the core group).

7. Nine stated their religious affiliation as Protestant, eight as Catholic, one as Jewish; two had no religious affiliation. Seven of the twelve core group members are Catholics.

group in the hospital community which includes many Catholics. They tend to take religion seriously and sometimes join aides (divinity students) in encouraging patients to attend church.

The nurses' religiosity at times comes into conflict with attitudes regarded as intrinsic to psychotherapeutic work. For example, the emphasis in psychotherapy upon the extent to which the individual is in control of his own destiny conflicts with some religious attitudes emphasizing reliance upon external forces and supernatural powers. Conflicts may also be evident in attitudes toward sexual behavior, between what is to be sanctioned as healthy and what one regards as sinful (a juxtaposition of terms revealing the rectitude element in such ostensibly value-free characterizations as "healthy," "normal," "sick"); between understanding and informative responses to expressions of concern or ignorance about sexual matters and the inclination to be moralistic and restrictive.

When they began work at the YPI, most nurses were not specifically prepared for service in a conventional psychiatric hospital, and very few had any prior exposures in training that would facilitate their work in a hospital emphasizing psychoanalytic psychotherapy. The great majority were prepared only for nursing in a general hospital.[8]

The nurses join their professional colleagues in being optimistic about psychotherapy and the attainability of its goals. This is a shift from the perspectives they originally brought with them to the hospital, providing evidence of their flexibility and capacity for change. Their earlier pessimism reflected views then prevalent about the chronicity and hopelessness of schizophrenia.[9]

The nurses thus emerge as a stable and relatively conservative element. Their value demands, expectations, and image of themselves stand in remarkable contrast to the perspectives of physicians and social workers. Nurses do not see themselves as satisfying in-

8. Most YPI nurses decided to go into psychiatric nursing during their nursing training (9 of 17). Most had only the limited training in psychiatric nursing provided as part of conventional nursing training (15 out of 22); five had no training for psychiatric nursing; only two had specialized psychiatric-nursing training beyond nursing school.

9. They placed themselves on the optimistic end of an optimism–pessimism continuum about the effectiveness of psychotherapeutic treatment in schizophrenia (19 out of 22). This contrasts with positions they held earlier; in their first year of psychiatric nursing, the majority (12 of 22) say they were pessimistic about the effectiveness of psychotherapy in schizophrenia. When asked how they felt about the possibility of effecting something approximating a cure in schizophrenia, the majority again were optimistic (13 of 18, 7 of 8 in the core group); and again, during their first year of psychiatric nursing, the majority had been pessimistic (13 of 20, 6 out of 8 in the core group).

tellectual interests or pursuing a complex path of professional development in their work. They are predisposed to find their value indulgences and deprivations in the day-to-day life of the hospital, particularly with patients and with one another.

The YPI Experience

The nurse's role in the YPI was well defined in pre-innovation years when the "management" of patients closely approximated the general hospital. Her tasks and position were clear: she administered medications, aided the doctors in carrying out physical treatments, observed patients and reported about them to the doctors, used the aides as assistants and directed their activities, and oversaw the physical maintenance of her ward. She occupied a clear hierarchical position, subservient to the doctors but exercising unquestioned authority over aides, student nurses, auxiliary hospital personnel (maids, kitchen helpers, janitors), and over patients. She was active, directing, certain of what she had to do (the doctor had written orders, and she carried them out; the hospital had established treatment and management policies, and she carried them out). She belonged to that part of the hospital—the staff—which did things to that other part of the hospital—the patients—"to get 'them' well."

The nurse arrived for duty in her crisp white uniform, conferred with nurses who had been on the previous shift about what they (the patients) had been up to, and got to work. She was mistress of her domain, subject only to the guidance of the doctors, and the doctors were not there very much. The doctors were occupied with scientific and intellectual aspects of problems presented by patients; studying these, they arrived at recommendations, "what 'they' needed," which were then transmitted verbally and in written orders; thus guided, the nurse proceeded to do her job. She gave patients pills at prescribed times, helped with their insulin and electric shock treatments, restrained them when necessary with wet sheet packs, continuous baths, and camisoles, isolated them when, in her judgment, their behavior required it, and reprimanded them when they disobeyed. She reproached, and in effect punished, patients when they stayed up too late, made an unauthorized telephone call, returned late from a visit, or were guilty of any infringement of rules or orders. She was also occupied with policing the safety of patients, counting silverware and sharp instruments, closely supervising the use of razors and scissors, keeping closets locked, and locking away radios, lamps, and other appliances during the night.

Important to the nurse's status was her possession of secrets: confidential information about patients, including diagnoses and the circumstances which led to hospitalization. One of the nurse's primary tasks was observing and taking notes on patients' behavior through the day. These notes, carefully withheld from the eyes of patients, were read daily by residents, chief resident, and director, and gave the nurses a direct line to the most powerful hospital figures. The nurses' observations were also reported at staff meetings not attended by patients. As a keeper of secrets, including the doctors' assessments of the patients, the nurse was the physician's associate and confidante; she was the primary source of enlightenment about the every-day stream of hospital events.

The nurse's position as doctor's helpmate was based in part upon her skill in the physical care of patients and proficiency in specialized techniques. She assisted in initial and periodic physical examinations of patients. When electric shock or insulin coma therapy was administered, the nurse carried through most of the procedure under the resident's nominal supervision; she remained with the patient throughout the treatments and was usually more experienced and knowledgeable about them than the resident. In these tasks her work was much like that of medical and surgical nurses; they afforded her an opportunity to be of service in a clear, socially valued performance about which she felt confident. There was little conflict about the fulfillment of her preferred professional image as she conscientiously helped the doctor, followed his orders, observed and reported, administered medications and physical treatments, and protected and cared for patients.

When nurses were asked to assess the relative importance of their duties at the YPI, "being available to patients" was viewed as clearly the most important.[10] "Overseeing procedures which protect patients from hurting themselves or others" was seen as next most important.[11] Other tasks most emphasized were giving medication, assessing with doctors how a patient is doing, participating in activities with patients, giving oral reports to doctors, participating with

10. Of twenty-one of their duties, "being available to patients" was rated most important by twenty-one of twenty-two respondents (10 of 11 in the core group said, "very important"; the remaining one said, "important").

11. "Very important," said thirteen; "important," said nine (in the core group, this protection of patients was regarded as "very important" by 7 and "important" by 4).

staff in making decisions about patients, recording observations, and reporting in staff meetings. These responses emphasize the importance to the nurse of her work with patients and give prominence to those operations of patient care and protection which must closely overlap the duties of a general hospital nurse. The tasks assessed by nurses as least significant were suggesting that a doctor change his order on a given patient, stating ward procedure, and recommending changes in ward procedure to staff. These require more assertiveness with doctors and a degree of responsibility and initiative uncharacteristic of the nurse's conventional position.

Asked what they most like to do, the favorite task was participating with doctors in assessing how a patient is doing, i.e. their gratification in being the doctors' helpmate.[12]

When nurses were asked what was the most rewarding aspect of their YPI service, the majority of the core group emphasized their gratification at the improvement of a patient.[13] This reply contrasts oddly with the residents', who emphasized instead the training opportunities enjoyed at the YPI. None of the residents referred to a patient's improvement as a rewarding aspect of their work (the psychotherapeutic ideology, to which residents adhere, disparages "helping" as a source of gratification for the therapist).

Differences in emphasis between core-group members and other nurses suggest that those who remain in the hospital for long periods of service are likely to see their gratification as coming from patients and from helping patients get well rather than from intellectual or other sources. However, nurses prefer to exercise therapeutic impact through their work with the doctors rather than by interacting directly with the patients; whereas participating with doctors in assessing how a patient is doing was the favored task, being

12. This task was chosen by eleven nurses (7 of the core group). Although spending time on the ward with patients and being available to patients were next most favored (both chosen by 8 respondents), members of the core group were not as strongly in favor of them (selected by 4 and 3 members of the core group respectively). Stating ward procedure and suggesting that a doctor change his orders on a given patient were the tasks they least liked to do (both designated by 8 nurses, including 4 core group members). These least-favored tasks were also rated least important.

13. Eight core group nurses referred to their pleasure on seeing a patient who had been severely ill recover, leave the hospital, and return to his family and work. Three core group members said the most rewarding aspect of their work was "being with" and cultivating "relationships" with patients. Nurses other than core group members also mentioned the rewards of seeing patients improve (3), but their replies put more emphasis on other aspects of their work: five spoke of the opportunity to offer individualized care to patients, four emphasized what they learned about human relations and psychology, and four stressed their relations with others in the staff as part of the treatment team.

available to patients and spending time on the ward with patients were not among duties nurses like most.

When asked what was "the least satisfactory aspect" of YPI service, the nurses replied with general complaints. Most emphasized irritating conditions of work: low pay, too much routine bookwork, having to act as policemen, limited opportunities for advancement, hours of work not scheduled conveniently (night and weekend duty being particularly irregular), and not enough personnel on duty during the night.[14] As with residents, nurses' complaints emphasized difficult working conditions, most particularly low salaries and the inconvenience of their work schedule. They were more vocal than residents in expressing concern about lack of communication and teamwork, especially with doctors and within the nursing group.[15]

Nurses were asked to assess the amount of stress involved in their work at the YPI. Three groups of equal size offered three different replies: "great," "moderate," and "less than that." This varied assessment contrasts with the residents' agreement in characterizing the stress of their work as great. Asked how the nurses as a group and they personally felt about their work at the YPI, most described nurses as a group as "contented" and themselves as "enthusiastic."[16]

The Nurse and the Patient

The pre-innovation nurse's activity centered on the ward to which she was assigned, especially its nursing station and kitchen. Male

14. Twelve (5 of the core group). Six nurses (2 in the core group) expressed concerns about patients when asked about the least satisfactory aspect of their work: "patients are too isolated and alone in the hospital," "some patients simply don't get well," and "patients are sometimes encouraged to express their feelings in ways which would not be tolerated outside the hospital." Five nurses, including two in the core group, singled out the residents' failure to communicate and work together with them in the treatment of patients.

15. When asked, "Are there any complaints you did not feel free to bring up?," sixteen replied, "no" (5 of the 6 who said "yes" were core-group members). The single complaint they did not feel free to express concerned working conditions (the hours of their shifts). Other complaints involved inadequate communication with doctors and other nurses, and the doctors' improper conduct: they sometimes "analyzed" nurses and revealed nurses' confidences to patients. The nurses reiterated their wish for more communication within the staff, particularly with doctors, when asked, "What aspects of the YPI would you change?

16. Fourteen of twenty-two (7 of 11 in the core group) described the nurses as a group as "contented." Twelve of twenty-two said they themselves were "enthusiastic" (5 of 11 in the core group). Only two (none in the core group) said nurses as a group were "discontented," and none viewed them as "very dissatisfied." One nurse (a member of the core group) said she was "discontented"; none were "very dissatisfied."

and female patients were housed on separate wings of the L-shaped, closed ward. The one nursing station on the closed ward was a simple, bare room with a desk and cabinets for medicines and supplies. Here nurses wrote down observations and prepared medications, doctors wrote orders, and doctors conferred with nurses, usually behind closed doors. The station was located in the middle of the women's side, well away from male patients with whom nurses were clearly much less comfortable. The male aides on the closed ward spent almost all their time on the men's side; nurses appeared there infrequently.

The nurse was usually involved with set tasks: she assisted kitchen helpers in serving meal trays to patients, checked patients confined to the isolation area and all patients throughout the night at regular intervals, escorted patients to occupational therapy and occasionally outside the hospital, and, as described, restrained patients and helped with physical treatment. In intervals between these tasks, nurses conferred informally with one another or with the resident on duty over coffee in the kitchen or in the nursing station. The kitchen or office door was usually locked, but patients with a request or complaint could knock and attract the nurse's attention. At the beginning and end of each shift the nurses reviewed the status of all patients on the ward, handed on any special instructions, and chatted briefly. The nurses left the wards only to attend the daily staff meeting and to escort patients.

Patients chatted informally with nurses standing together in the hallway or sometimes sitting with them in the nursing station. The most intense contact occurred when, in the course of a physical treatment, a nurse stayed with a patient to check his physical status regularly. Most nurse-patient contacts were incidental to the nurse's execution of a set task. Any less formal contact was usually initiated by a patient. In many of their interactions the nurse directed, reproached, or disciplined the patient. She pressed him to keep his room as orderly as the maid had left it, to keep out of other patients' rooms, to lower the volume of his phonograph. When patients were agitated or uncontrolled, the nurse subdued, restrained, and isolated them with the help of residents and aides. These encounters and interventions were often frightening.[17]

17. When asked, "Were you ever physically afraid of patients in the YPI?," sixteen nurses (6 in the core group) said "yes." Six replied, "no" (5 in the core group). Thirteen nurses (6 in the core group) described having been physically attacked by a YPI patient. Nine (5 in the core group) said that they had never been attacked.

In the pre-innovation period, then, interactions of patients and nurses were highly structured and authoritarian; informal contact was not encouraged, nor was its possible importance appreciated. The emphasis was upon the nurse performing clear-cut, prescribed tasks, to which direct interactions between nurses and patients were incidental.

There was no possibility of confusing nurses with patients. Nurses wore clearly differentiating white uniforms, patients wore informal street clothes. The nurse, a busy member of the staff who clearly shared its authority and control, was occupied with doing things to and for patients. It was obvious that the nurse was "well" and able to be of use, and that the patient was "sick," needful, and in an inferior position. There were other less emphasized differences: the economic, social, and educational level of patients tended to be higher than nurses', and this set limits on their common experiences and their capacity to communicate. Nurses sometimes felt sensitive and vulnerable about these differences and adopted strategies which helped them cope with these feelings. Among these were emphasizing their superior professional status by wearing a uniform, avoiding informal contact, and referring to patients as "they." Nurses and patients, however, appeared oblivious to the differences, did not acknowledge them, and focused upon their roles as dispensers and recipients of help. Nurses experienced patients as children to be taken care of, cantankerous younger siblings requiring control, sick friends, burdened people requiring a respite with special care for a time in order to "make a go" of their lives, and also as employers and elderly, now dependent parents. Nurses were sometimes nurturing and maternal but rarely recognized the mutual gratification in such bonds. In these complex relationships, nurses perceived themselves as parents, servants, nursemaids, friends, teachers, and as professionals performing medical services.

Asked the relative importance of ten aspects of the treatment program in determining whether or not a patient in the YPI gets better, nurses agreed with residents in ranking individual psychotherapy first.[18] Whereas residents viewed nursing care as clearly second in importance and rated all other aspects of the hospital program much below psychotherapy and nursing care, nurses themselves viewed nursing care as less important, on a par with occupa-

18. Of "great importance" said eighteen nurses (9 in the core group); three (one core group member) said "of moderate importance"; none rated individual psychotherapy as of little or no importance.

tional therapy, recreational activities, and other secondary components of the hospital program.

When asked to rate the success of the hospital in its treatment of patients, most replied "good" (15 of 21 nurses, including 8 in the core group) rather than "excellent" (only 3, including the other 2 core group respondents), "fair" (3), or "poor" (none).

Asked to assess relative influence over whether or not patients get better, nurses rated residents most influential (13, including 7 in the core group). They ranked themselves next most influential, and the chief nurses, director, and chief resident as close behind. They concurred with residents that the department chairman exerted little or no influence, and viewed the director of nursing as much less influential than the nurses as a group or the chief nurses.

Nurses' perspectives about how they should conduct themselves are reflected in their answers to the question, "What are the most frequent mistakes that inexperienced nurses make in their relationships with patients?" They answered, "getting too involved," "becoming too social," and "being too eager to please patients," in that order. In contrast, only one nurse (not in the core group) mentioned remaining too distant from patients as an error, and only three (none in the core group) chose to cite the mistake of not being social enough. Respondents, particularly core-group members, saw lack of proper concern for the rules as a frequent mistake. Old-timers, in observing their less experienced colleagues, were critical of conduct which decreased the distance between nurses and patients.

The Nurse and other Staff Members

Just as nurses may perceive patients as cantankerous, needy, or promising children, sick friends, and occasionally as elderly, now dependent parents, they may reestablish emotional relationships with other staff members similar to those experienced in their earlier family lives. The nurse may find in the director a benign or stern father; in residents competent or ineffectual brothers and husbands; and with other nurses and social workers the companionship, cooperation, competition, feelings of loyalty and closeness, and the animosities and feelings of distance characteristic of relationships with siblings and friends.

The nurse tends to view her position in the staff as relatively inferior, in part because of her employee status and her perception of her work as a job. In practice, however, aspects of her administrative and teaching responsibilities give her a superior role. The resident leans heavily upon her experience for advice in managing patients and procedures and in administering physical treatments. The resident is especially dependent on the nurse early in his training year at the YPI when problems arise and he is the only physician on duty on evenings and weekends. The nurse supervises aides, kitchen helpers, and maintenance personnel and is responsible for instructing and guiding the work of student nurses. Despite these and still greater responsibilities with patients, the pre-innovation nurse saw herself as deprived in respect, power, wealth, skill, and enlightenment, when compared with colleagues.

The relationship between nurses and residents undergoes a cyclic transition in the course of a year. It begins with the arrival of new residents each July 1. The nurses teach these neophytes discretely and tactfully; the doctors, however uninformed, enjoy a traditionally superior status. As the year progresses, camaraderie develops between nurses and residents. Residents gradually assume more responsibility and authority and direct the nurses more actively. On June 30, when this phase of the residents' development reaches its culmination, they depart and are replaced by the new residents, and the cycle begins over again. Just as nurses harden themselves to losses they face as a result of recovery, transfer, discharge, or death of patients, they become hardened to the repetitive losses they experience with young doctors. As the years pass their readiness to get close to these transient doctors decreases; relatively shallow interaction is sometimes all they will tolerate.

From the beginning of his work in the hospital the resident is in a position of authority over the nurse; she carries out his orders. The nurse, aware of her wider experience, must find some basis for accepting this hierarchical arrangement. She may emphasize a traditional image of the physician or think of the resident as a specialized technician in the work of psychotherapy, who possesses mysterious skills beyond her grasp. In the pre-innovation period, when the YPI was consolidating its identity as a psychotherapeutic hospital, psychotherapy was indeed a new and mysterious development for nurses.[19] They had little awareness of any overlap between

19. Few had any personal experience with psychotherapy. Seventeen nurses (9 in the core group) stated they had received no personal psychotherapy, psychoanalysis, or other psychiatric treatment; only three nurses (one in the core group) had been in psychotherapy. None had received any other psychiatric treatment. When asked, "Do you think personal therapy is a help or a hindrance in psychiatric nursing?," twelve (5 core group members) replied, "a help"; five (4 in the core group) stated that psychotherapy is "a hindrance" in psychiatric nursing; three nurses were undecided. One core group nurse said, "It depends on how great the need is."

the residents' psychotherapeutic work and their own interactions with patients. They tended at times to be dismissive, suspicious, and curious about psychotherapy.

The nurses' preference for working with doctors as helpmates reflects both their wanting to be important and useful to the doctors and the secondary position they assign to direct interactions with patients.[20] Although nurses described their favorite task as participating with doctors in assessing the progress of a patient, their responses when asked, "How important do you think you are to the residents?" in nine common, specific hospital situations, suggest that they did not see themselves as important to residents in the very aspect of their work which they prefer. They saw themselves as most important to residents in dealing with patients during acute upsets, in preventing patients from hurting themselves or each other, and in recording observations on patients, in that order. They also rated telling the resident about his patient among their most useful functions. They perceived themselves as least important to the resident in arriving at decisions about a patient's treatment, and in assessing whether or not a patient is getting better.

In response to questions about how they saw their interactions with residents, nurses felt free to talk with residents about patients, and saw them as receptive to their ideas, but felt that the doctors did not adequately share with them information about patients.[21]

The nurses in the pre-innovation period had much more overall contact with, and opportunity to observe, patients on the ward than the residents. They tended to think that residents had an incomplete picture of what patients were really like and what they were up to. This was especially so if they failed to avail themselves of the information the nurse had to offer.[22] The nurses' view of how they

20. Asked about their importance to residents in helping with patients, ten (2 in the core group) said "very important"; eleven (8 core nurses) said "important"; none said of some or no importance. The oldtimers appeared less impressed with their importance to residents than newer nurses, but they may have been reporting their impressions of doctors' view of their importance rather than their own assessments.

21. Twenty-one nurses (10 in the core group) "do feel free to talk to residents about their patients"; only one nurse (a member of the core group) said that she did not feel this freedom. Thirteen said that the residents do chat with them enough about how their patients are doing (6 in the core group); however, nine (5 in the core group) replied in the negative. Fifteen said that the residents are generally receptive to nurses' ideas about their patients (7 in the core group); five (3 in the core group) replied that the residents were not receptive.

22. When asked, "Do you think the residents really know what their patients are like on the wards?," nine (5 in the core group) said, "No"; eight

should relate to doctors is reflected in what they saw as the most frequent mistakes that inexperienced nurses make in their relationships with doctors: too eager to please (7), too intellectual (7), not social enough (6), and too distant (5).

The nurses' social contact with one another was not intensive; however, core-group members had more contact than other members of the nursing staff.[23]

The Nurse and Her Seniors

Nurses are more inclined than other members of the professional staff to respect hierarchical relationships within the hospital as a rigid table of organization. The chain of command places maintenance workers, kitchen helpers, student nurses, and aides below nurses, and newer nurses below members of the core group. Nurses are, in turn, responsible to their chief nurses and view the director of nursing as their boss. Residents and senior doctors also exercise authority over them, but nurses see themselves as primarily responsible to seniors within the nursing staff. In keeping with traditional general hospital nursing practice, the nurses tend to view bringing complaints to anyone other than their own chiefs or nursing director as improper.[24] They view the director of nursing as the most powerful figure in their work, and the chief nurses as next

---

nurses (only 2 in the core group) replied, "yes"; five (4 in the core group) emphasized a wide range in residents' knowledge of their patients. When asked, "Do you think the residents tend to overestimate or underestimate the patients' difficulties?," nurses replied that residents tend to see patients as less disturbed: nine nurses said, "less disturbed" (including 5 in the core group); only three (none in the core group) said residents see patients as more disturbed than nurses do, and "easier to manage" than they really are; ten said "easier" (4 in the core group); only two (none in the core group) said residents see patients as "harder to manage" than nurses do.

23. When asked about the frequency of their social contact with one another, one nurse (not in the core group) said that she was with other nurses socially after hours "weekly"; six (4 in the core group) described seeing other nurses socially "monthly"; four (3 in the core group) said they saw other nurses socially "every two to three months"; eight (2 in the core group) reported that they got together with other nurses socially "less than that." The majority of nurses think they are "fairly close" to one another (13, 6 in the core group) rather than "very close" (1 core group member), "not close" (4, 1 in the core group), or as "going our separate ways" (2, 1 in the core group).

24. In response to the question, "To whom do you usually complain?," fourteen nurses (7 in the core group) said they complained to chief nurses; thirteen (7 in the core group) complained to the director of nursing. Eight (4 in the core group) said they complained to other nurses; five (2 in the core group) complained to residents; one member of the core group complained to the director, and another member of the core group said she complained to the chief resident.

in power. The status of the director of nursing, unlike that of her fellow nurses, is on a par with other members of the professional staff, including residents and social workers. Length of service on the hospital staff is an important basis for authority. Clique formation, particularly among old-timers, is an instrument for the indoctrination and control of other nurses.

The nurses want to be sure that senior doctors know and approve what they are doing. The camaraderie between old-timers and senior doctors was expressed in their patronizingly referring to residents with a collective, anonymous "they," just as nurses and doctors together referred to patients as "they." The reference implied that residents, like patients, required the knowing parental control that senior doctors and experienced nurses could offer them. During the pre-innovation period, chief residents and assistant directors gradually assumed more authority, and nurses had less direct contact with the director. They experienced this diminution of contact with him as a deprivation of respect, affection, and power.

The pre-innovation nurse strove to comply with standards established for her by those in authority. She was not encouraged to participate more actively in deciding hospital policy and did not appear discontented with this arrangement, so long as her seniors cared about her. Nurses would accept substantial deprivations in power so long as they felt indulged in respect and affection. The relative absence of discontent in the pre-innovation period also derived from the clarity with which the nurse's role was defined and her sense of being the master of the skills required in her work.

Decision-Making

The influence of the pre-innovation nurse in the hospital decision process stemmed directly from the link between her skills and the prevailing conception of treatment. The nurse helped maintain a social and physical situation which kept psychotherapy free from any possible interference. Because of her continuous association with patients and her familiarity with hospital precedents, she was an indispensable source of intelligence both about patients and about the rules upon which policy was predicated.

The pre-innovation nurse was content with the power she exerted in hospital affairs and had little ambition to play a more decisive role. Nurses were conscientious and informed appliers of policy; they knew when to invoke a hospital prescription in concrete circumstances; they realized the modest limits within which they were authorized to act without consulting a physician. They did not use their crucial asset (enlightenment about the hospital, including their secrets) as a power base with which to rival senior physicians in deciding significant questions, nor were they promoters of innovation or termination; the code as defined in the pre-innovation period prescribed limits within which they felt adapted to the hospital.

Nurses were asked to assess the relative influence of various members of the staff over the way things go at the YPI. The majority saw the influence of nurses as considerable, but relatively low compared with other staff members.[25] Nurses saw the director of nursing as exerting great influence (her importance exceeded only by the director and chief resident) and chief nurses as among the most influential members of the staff, and yet they looked upon themselves as having little influence.[26]

The pre-innovation nurses appear as a group to have felt gratified with their professional lives. Although there were complaints about strenuous work for insufficient pay, they seem to have experienced the YPI as sufficiently rewarding. They did not pursue comprehensive intellectual interests. They were content with the positive respect and rectitude evaluations accorded those whose social function contributes to the mental and physical well-being of others. Their spontaneous warmth—and conventionality—provided a foil for the detachment of their more highly trained colleagues.

The pre-innovation nurse exercised direct coercive control over patients. She operated as a subordinate to superiors who assumed

25. Five (one member of the core group) said that nurses exercise a "great deal" of influence; nine (5 in the core group) replied that the nurses' influence over the way things went was "considerable"; five (3 in the core group) said the nurses exerted "little" influence, and one core group member said nurses exerted "no" influence over the way things go. Nurses said the director clearly exerted greatest influence, and viewed the chief resident, director of nursing, residents, chief nurses, assistant director, social workers, and the business manager, in that order, all as having more influence than nurses. Only activities workers and aides were regarded as less influential.

26. Asked, "Do you think you have enough say about what goes on at the YPI or not enough say?," the majority stated they had "enough say" (14, including 8 members of the core group). Seven (3 in the core group) stated that they did not have enough say. The nurses' estimates of the extent of their power with patients were suggested by their response to the question, "Do you feel you have as much say as you should have" in deciding a series of management questions (for example, "whether or not a patient should be on the open ward"). The majority felt they had "enough say" on all these questions with one exception: "whether or not a patient should be taken off bedtime sedation." Ten nurses (5 in the core group) said they did not have enough say on this question; six (none in the core group) said they had "enough say"; two (1 in the core group) implied that this was a decision which doctors, not nurses, should make.

responsibility. The nurse, like the resident, absolved herself of any qualms about what went on in the hospital by acquiescing to a system in which she saw herself as relatively powerless; she was further absolved by her status as an employee. Sure of the respect and affection of the senior staff, the pre-innovation nurse functioned comfortably in her subordinate orbit within the power structure.

5. The Pre-Innovation Resident Physician

Predispositions And Perspectives[1]

The impact of the unusual, intensive hospital environment upon residents was particularly influenced by the professional self-image they had derived from their prior medical and psychiatric training. The age of professional commitment offers a partial index of the nature and degree of their involvement with psychiatry. The decision to become a psychiatrist was usually deferred until the twenties and the medical school years, a profile that differs from the choice of some older medical specialties.[2] Only four of the sixty-one YPI residents between 1950 and 1961 were women. In the United States, at least, the category of religious affiliation often combines the connotations of a relatively distinctive subculture with indications of theological, political, intellectual, and ethical perspective. In the group studied, twenty-six residents identified themselves as Jewish, twelve as Protestant, three as Catholic, two as of other denominations, and thirteen said that they professed no religion.

Only relatively routine inquiries were made about the socio-economic standing of the residents and their parents. Most described their own socio-economic status as "higher" than that of their parents.[3] This upward mobility has some significance for relationships with their largely upper-middle and upper-class YPI patients. It is also relevant to residents' attitudes toward democracy, emphasis upon opening opportunities, increasing the scope of individual responsibility, and power sharing.

When we examine residents' marital and family status the im-

1. Questionnaires were filled out and returned by sixty-one of the sixty-six psychiatrists who had worked as residents at the Yale Psychiatric Institute between July 1, 1950 and June 30, 1961 (92.4 per cent). Of these, thirty were pre-innovation residents and thirty-one worked at the hospital in the post-innovation period (after July 1, 1956).

2. Most residents decided to go into psychiatry prior to age 25 (9 prior to age 20; 28 between ages 20 and 25; 13 between 25 and 30; and 5 after age 30) and prior to completing medical school (3 in high school; 23 in college; 11 in medical school; and 18 after medical school).

3. Twenty-six so replied; twelve said their parents' status was "higher," and eighteen called it "the same."

pression is conformity to conventional norms.[4] Unexpected agreement was found among residents on political affiliation and orientation; the group differed in this respect from most other physicians and their professional organizations. The majority characterized themselves as "liberal Democrats" and favored programs of government-supported medical and psychiatric hospital and out-patient care.[5]

Among the considerations important in the resident's selection of Yale for his psychiatric training were the prestige enjoyed by the program as part of Yale University, its emphasis upon the preparation of researchers and teachers, its reputation for offering a very high caliber of training, which would qualify the trainee for positions of leadership in psychiatry, and its psychoanalytic orientation. The Yale resident had to endure some measure of economic deprivation. He had to be willing to accept a lower salary than available to him in state and other training programs.[6]

The typical program of a Yale resident includes a first year on the psychiatric service of the Veterans Administration Hospital, a second in the general hospital psychiatric out-patient clinic, and a third either at the YPI, the VA, the psychiatric section of the University Student Health Service, or training in child psychiatry at the Child Study Center. Between twelve and fourteen residents are usually involved in the first two years of training: only six of the third-year residents are assigned to the YPI.

During his year at the VA Hospital the resident first undertakes

4. Two-thirds (41) were already married during their YPI year; fourteen were single; one was widowed; no one was "separated"; and one was divorced. Eighteen had one child; twelve had two; three had three or more children; nine had no children.

5. "Liberal Democrats," 37; "conservative Democrats," 5; "liberal Republicans," 2; "conservative Republicans," 1; "liberal," 1; "Socialist," 1; and "uncommitted," 4. Twenty-two favored and seventeen opposed "a program of government supported medical care"; three replied "I don't know." Forty-one favored "a program of government supported hospital and outpatient psychiatric care"; eleven were opposed; one replied "I don't know."

6. Although the YPI resident is in a relatively disadvantaged wealth position, his expectations are rising. When this last residency year is over he will enjoy a high earning capacity. His protracted period of low earning not infrequently involves problems with parents because of his financial dependence on them, particularly if he is married and has children. The resident may become acutely aware of these problems because of the discrepancy between his economic position and that of patients or other staff members. He may be financially dependent upon his working wife. Financial problems have usually been compounded during the long training period, including college, medical school, internship, and residency, that now at last nears completion. The great cost of a personal psychoanalysis or of psychoanalytic training (which involves a training analysis) makes his financial problems still more difficult.

psychotherapeutic work with hospitalized schizophrenic and other severely disturbed psychotic patients. His year in the out-patient community clinic is very different from both his VA and YPI experience. He usually sees the patients he treats in the clinic in a single hour interview each week and has no contact with them between these weekly sessions. In the YPI he sees his patients in three to five psychotherapeutic interviews each week and has many other contacts with them. He is responsible not only for the way in which the psychotherapeutic interview is conducted, but also for the patient's hour-to-hour, day-to-day management throughout the entire year. Patients in the hospital are extraordinarily needful and demanding: the resident's predicament is the more difficult because his work with them is constantly scrutinized by his superiors with a thoroughness impossible in the larger VA Hospital or the outpatient clinic.

The out-patient experience affords the resident a greater opportunity to protect himself: he is the only person who sees his patients; his teachers and bosses are entirely dependent upon his reports for information about the character of his work and his competence as a psychotherapist; he is better able to present his work in a favorable light and to begin to feel some professional confidence. The subsequent scrutiny and criticism to which he is subjected in the YPI is the more distressing because it is experienced as tending to undermine the confidence which the resident had previously enjoyed, as a deprivation with regard to professional skill, enlightenment, and respect.

The resident brings an elaborate set of expectations to his YPI experience. He wants skill in assessing psychopathology, managing hospitalized patients, and in conducting psychotherapy with severely disturbed patients. The YPI year constitutes his prime opportunity to do intensive, psychoanalytically oriented psychotherapy with hospitalized patients, under careful and extensive supervision. This is his last year as student and apprentice, and in it he hopes to achieve some greater degree of mastery in the demanding role of psychotherapist. Regarding their expectations about professional training at the YPI, the great majority of residents throughout the period of this study underlined the central importance of this opportunity for intensive psychotherapeutic work in preparing them as psychiatrists. When they were asked both what they recalled of their estimates at the time they worked at the YPI, and about their present judgments, they saw psychotherapeutic training and work as the most rewarding aspect of their YPI year, the core of the hospital's philosophy and orientation, the most important aspect of the hospital's treatment program in determining whether or not patients get better, and the aspect of the resident's work most valued by him and his seniors.[7]

By this stage of his career, the resident is strongly committed not only to psychiatry but also to particular skills and doctrines he believes to be of basic relevance to psychiatry. Work with psychotic and other severely disturbed patients is considered to have crucial importance to psychiatry, and the resident is convinced of the therapeutic advantages of a psychoanalytically oriented psychiatry.[8] These perspectives were important in leading him to apply for training at the YPI, and these viewpoints tended to be confirmed by that training.

The YPI residents' predispositions included the expectation of certain deprivations as part of their training, including low income and deferred participation in family life, community activities, and relaxation. They were vigorously oriented toward the acquisition of professional skill and enlightenment. Although they correctly anticipated many of the deprivations of affection, wealth, wellbeing, and power, they failed to foresee many of the deprivations of

7. When asked to describe "the most rewarding aspect of your YPI training," the great majority (25 residents) emphasized their experience with intensive individual psychotherapy. In addition, twenty-three residents also regarded intensive psychotherapy as the most rewarding aspect of their YPI year, although they emphasized special aspects (19 referred to the high calibre of supervision; and 4 stressed the types of patients with whom they worked). Asked to characterize the "treatment philosophy and orientation of the YPI during your training year," thirty-nine emphasized intensive individual psychotherapy, and twenty-eight of these specifically characterized that treatment as "psychoanalytically oriented." The residents in the pre-innovation period experienced the hospital's orientation in this way without exception.

When asked to assess ten different aspects of the hospital's treatment program "in determining whether or not a patient gets better," the great majority (47, or 84 per cent) rated individual psychotherapy as of great importance; the rest (9, or 16 per cent) rated it of moderate importance; none rated it of little or no importance. In contrast, they tended to be dismissive of the use of drugs and physical therapies: the majority rated drug treatment and ECT and other physical therapies as of "little" or "no" importance in determining whether or not a patient gets better. When residents were asked which approach by a resident was most valued by the senior staff, a majority (27, or 50 per cent) replied that their seniors most valued "individual therapy." Asked about the approach they themselves most valued in a resident, an even larger majority (38, or 69 per cent) most valued "individual psychotherapy."

8. During their YPI experience the residents tended to be optimistic about "the effectiveness of psychotherapy in schizophrenia" (45, or 80 per cent) and about "the possibility of effecting something approximating a cure in schizophrenia" (38, or 70 per cent).

respect, well-being, and rectitude which they would be called upon to endure.

The YPI Experience

The resident's obligations entail an interlocking series of functions and role-designations. Patients, particularly the five to seven to whom he is assigned as therapist, regard him as their doctor. The director, chief resident, supervisors, and others in the senior staff view him as student and junior colleague. Work with the nurses and social workers involves both their orienting and guiding him on the basis of their greater experience, and at the same time their looking to him for direction as a staff member of greater authority. He is surrounded by social workers, nurses, and patients who have been in a psychiatric context much longer than he. The social workers, with long experience in teaching and research, are extraordinarily active intellectually and seriously engaged in psychotherapeutic work themselves; many patients have been in the hospital for months and in psychiatric treatment for years. To his peers, the other residents, he is competitor and colleague. Since the resident is often undertaking psychotherapy or a personal or training analysis himself, he is regarded as patient and to some degree trainee and junior colleague by his analyst. He is also a teacher, working with medical students, nurses, and nursing students, and sometimes lectures to lay groups in the community. He may also be involved in individual or group projects as a researcher.

Central to his experience as student, teacher, therapist, and patient are professional skill and enlightenment and the pursuit of his patients' and his own well-being. His respect position within the hospital and larger community is based on the skill and enlightenment he has achieved. Within the larger medical community his prestige derives in part from his undergoing training for a specialty in a university department, albeit in a discipline that remains confusing and controversial among nonpsychiatric physicians. Among psychiatrists, because of his student-resident status, he is on a respected but low rung of the ladder. This respect position within the hospital, the larger community, and the community of physicians and psychiatrists is undermined to some degree by the training predicament; he is constantly scrutinized by his seniors and is less well informed in many critical areas than nurses and patients.

In psychiatry the pursuit of skill and enlightenment is difficult; the vast areas of knowledge encompassed or relevant to the field include much of the social sciences, medicine (including neurology, physiology, and pharmacology), as well as the theory and technique of psychoanalysis. Much is not known, or remains closer to hunch, guess, and intuition than to the body of substantially clarified knowledge. An enthusiastic initiate, the resident tends to retain his curiosity and struggles to learn and understand. He finds that although some competence can be acquired in the classroom and by reading, more is attainable only through supervised experience in work.

Because the resident is involved in a complex of intense relationships, each of which demands a significant investment, he is in a most trying position with regard to intimacy and emotional warmth. His investments include those outside his work, with wife, children, parents, friends, and his therapist—with whom he struggles to clarify his own feelings and problems. He interacts with department and hospital seniors who boss and teach him, with fellow residents, particularly the five who work so closely with him in the hospital, with nurses and social workers whom he guides and by whom he is guided, and with his patients, each of whom looks to him to fulfill great unsatisfied needs for contact, emotional involvement, understanding, direction, and salvation. How can anyone sustain and endure such a multiplicity of intense involvements at the same time? Which relationship will suffer and to which will the resident commit himself wholeheartedly? Such choices, whether explicitly faced and decided or simply arrived at by chance, are inevitable. And during this trying year, with each commitment of a part of himself to a patient, his analyst, a fellow resident, and his teachers, he abstains from committing himself to some other relationship, potentially of importance and gratifying to him and to the other person (perhaps another patient, another friend, or his wife). No such choice can be satisfactory. Called upon to invest so much of himself in so many relationships, the resident feels depleted.

The hardships endured by the resident are compounded by the trying conditions of work in the hospital. He arrives early in the morning, reads the nurses' notes on his patients, and may chat informally about his patients with nurses or social workers and with the resident on duty the previous evening. He then joins with the other residents, social workers, nurses, and aides in a staff meeting conducted by the chief resident or hospital director. Issues regarding the management of his and others' patients are discussed, observations shared, and plans made.

He may then see three or four of his patients in individual hours of treatment, although the scheduling of psychotherapeutic hours during the morning may be limited by attendance at a clinical case conference, or meeting with a psychotherapy supervisor or with the director or assistant director for "administrative supervision." The lunch hour is often used for conferences with social workers or the chief resident and residents as a group. The afternoon includes hours of psychotherapy and at least brief contact with patients not scheduled for interviews on that day; it may include meeting with first- or second-year medical students as part of their introductory coursework or with advanced students assigned to the YPI to discuss patients they have been following. There may be a seminar on theory or technique, or a research conference, for his own instruction. His day includes informal discussions with nurses and social workers about his patients and their families, and on some days he confers with a patient's wife or parents. His organized program may be disrupted by particularly agitated and demanding patients who require his attention intermittently throughout the day. His duties at the hospital may be punctuated by a trip across town for an analytic hour of his own. He may, after a tiring stretch of thirty-six hours or more of work, be called away from a psychotherapeutic hour (in which his own conflicts with his parents may have been evoked) to help manage a combative patient whom he must restrain with the aid of other staff members. He alternates evenings and weekend duty with his colleagues, handling the general affairs of the hospital, seeing patients who require his attention. He may use some of this time to write required interview notes, progress reports, initial evaluation statements, and monthly summaries on his patients and to do the reading for his classes which he may not have completed during "free time." He must be available constantly throughout the workday and on evenings and weekends when he is on duty.

When residents were asked to "list the major complaints made by your residency group," they consistently reported vigorous complaints about the heavy work load, long hours, low salary, and great pressure, demands, and anxiety experienced in working at the YPI.[9]

Great emotional investments and extraordinary work demands

9. Such complaints account for thirty-eight of the 154 items in the replies; they were mentioned by members of every residency group. Asked about "the least satisfactory part of your YPI training," they mentioned "harrassment," "strain," "personal anxiety," "on duty too much," "not enough time for reading and thinking," "the work was too hard." Such difficulties were called "the least satisfactory part" of the year by eighteen residents. (The other major area of complaint, relations with the senior staff, will be discussed later.)

tended to absorb the resident totally through the year. The majority of residents characterized the amount of stress at the YPI as "great."[10] It was virtually impossible for the residents to pursue other interests or develop in other areas; they became increasingly dependent upon skill and enlightenment as a psychiatrist for self-esteem; previous bases of respect tended to become less substantial.

Despite these hardships and dissatisfactions, the great majority of residents describe the YPI experience "as their most rewarding year,"[11] and the other residents with whom they served during their YPI year as "contented."[12] In appraising the success of the hospital's treatment, training, and research programs, training was clearly rated most highly and research as the least successful.[13]

It is not uncommon for three or more of the six YPI residents serving in a given year to undertake a personal or training psychoanalysis at the time which, in addition to equipping them professionally, facilitates their emotional well-being. Most of those who do not undertake psychoanalysis during their residency are stimulated to do so subsequently by their experience at Yale, most particularly by their work in intensive psychotherapy with severely disturbed patients in the YPI.[14]

10. Forty-two so replied; thirteen described it as "moderate"; one said there was "some" stress in the YPI, and one that there was "little or no stress."

11. Thirty-five (or 61 per cent). Eighteen (or 32 per cent) viewed the year as "above average" in comparing it with their other residency years. Only four residents rated the YPI less well, as a "below average year"; none rated it their least rewarding year.

12. Only a few perceived their group as "enthusiastic" (5, or 9 per cent); most thought their group "contented" (29, or 62 per cent); but twelve (26 per cent) perceived the group as "discontented," and five said that feelings were "mixed." However, when the resident was asked how he "personally" felt about his YPI year, as distinguished from his group's feelings, the response was different: twenty-five (49 per cent) were "enthusiastic" about their YPI year, thirteen (25 per cent) "contented"; eleven (21 per cent) were "discontented"; two were "very dissatisfied"; and two "both enthusiastic and discontented."

13. The training program was regarded by the majority as "excellent" (28, or 50 per cent) or "good" (21, or 37 per cent), although six rated it as "fair," and one as "poor." When asked how successful the YPI was when they worked there in the *treatment* of patients, ten (18 per cent) felt that it was "excellent"; thirty-seven (66 per cent) replied, "good"; eight (14 per cent) "fair"; and one said, "poor." Asked to rate the success of the hospital in its *research* program, six (11 per cent) replied that when they worked there it was "excellent"; fourteen (26 per cent) said "good"; the largest group, seventeen (31 per cent) regarded it as "fair"; ten (19 per cent) said "poor." Seven (13 per cent) felt unable to make an evaluation, contending that they did not know what research was going on in the hospital or had not been involved in any; one of this group replied, "What research program?"

14. The majority of residents, as of 1961, had undertaken a personal psychoanalysis (41, or 73 per cent) and had been in psychoanalytic training (31,

In addition to its emphasis on psychoanalysis, the impact of Yale psychiatric training throughout the years studied was to stimulate a commitment to subsequent work with psychotic patients. An important component of this training, and a key factor in this impact, was the YPI experience, the major opportunity for residents to do supervised, intensive psychoanalytically oriented psychotherapy with psychotic patients. The majority of residents (41, or 79 per cent) reported that they "worked or taught in an inpatient setting" after completing their residency. This is a remarkably high figure for psychiatrists—particularly for those with an interest in psychoanalysis, most of whom devote their professional lives to the private practice of outpatient psychotherapy. This commitment derives from their sense of being useful in doing such work and from the attitude emphasized in the YPI that the psychoses constitute the major problem confronting the psychiatric clinician and researcher.

The Resident and the Patient

Residents spend more time with patients than with any other group in the hospital environment. When we examine the indulgences and deprivations available to the resident, we become aware of how potent a role patients play in his life. In exercising his responsibilities as a physician, the resident must manage himself as part of each patient's environment, estimating the impact of all that he does upon the immediate and long-range well-being of the patient.

The resident becomes a member of the hospital staff on July 1 and is promptly introduced to the patients assigned to him. He is the "new doctor," eagerly or perhaps skeptically awaited by the recently admitted patient and by the patient disappointed or dissatisfied with his "old doctor," who departed on the previous day. He is reluctantly met by the patients who struggle with their pain over the loss of their previous therapists, with whom they worked hard and well, to whom they remain loyal. In the course of the year some of the patients are discharged and new patients are admitted and assigned to the resident; some patients will work with him through all or most of the year and then continue with the "new doctor" who follows him.

---

or 56 per cent). These figures are more impressive when it is recognized that the majority of those not analyzed and not in psychoanalytic training were in the three groups which completed their residencies in the last years of this study, between 1959 and 1961. Many were in military service or for other reasons not yet able to arrange analysis or analytic training. Of the residents who completed their YPI work prior to 1959, 87 per cent had undertaken a personal analysis and 79 per cent had entered psychoanalytic training.

In the pre-innovation period, formal psychotherapeutic sessions provided the only structured opportunity for the resident and the patient to interact, and contact between resident and patient was limited to these scheduled hours. This arrangement retained the characteristics of a conventional medical relationship between the physician—the expert—and the dependent and physically ill patient. During the interview the resident wore a white coat and sat behind his desk. When we asked former residents what they wore when working at the hospital and how their interviews were conducted, those at the YPI prior to 1955 were nearly unanimous in reporting that they wore white coats. Between 1952 and 1955, however, a few described wearing street clothes, thus symbolically modifying the role of physician as traditionally defined and anticipating the shift toward less formal and closer relationships with patients that accompanied the innovations of 1956. During the early part of the study, residents "sat at their desks" during interviews with patients; with few exceptions residents who served at the hospital after 1953 report "sitting in a chair across from the patient." This shift from behind the desk coincided with the current director's appointment. It symbolized an important step preliminary to the innovations.

Contacts outside scheduled interviews tended to be experienced by the resident as awkward and difficult; he either tried to treat an encounter as though it were a psychotherapeutic session or, preferably, to avoid it altogether. When a patient was too agitated or disturbed to come to his office or refused to, the physician would reluctantly go to the patient's room and try to conduct a conventional psychotherapeutic hour there.

Inside the hospital, residents usually confined themselves to their offices or the nurses' station. When on evening or weekend duty, the resident typically remained in his office or in the quarters provided for him away from the wards. He sometimes talked with the nurses at their station or in a ward kitchen, but discouraged unsolicited contact with patients. When a patient sought him out directly as he walked through the ward or before he closed the door to his or the nurses' office or the kitchen, the exchange was minimal, unless there was a clear-cut indication that longer discussion was imperative; in that event, the two would go together to his office or the patient's room and proceed to have an interview which approximated the structure of a conventional, scheduled psychotherapeutic hour. When called by a nurse to see a patient who had asked to talk with the doctor on call, and who persisted in this request despite the nurse's efforts to discourage it, the resident in effect structured a conventional interview. The resident would report to the ward, talk briefly with the nurse, and then have the hopefully brief interview with the patient in his room. Such contact was regarded as somehow improper; the only sanctioned encounters were psychotherapeutic interviews with one's own patients and the necessary, formal inquiries and interviews with other patients when on duty.

This practice was not explicitly formulated; it was "just the way things went." Nurses, aides, and activities and group workers spent much of their time with patients on the wards. One of their functions seemed to be his "protection" from such contacts, preserving the patients' image of the resident as a therapist. This arrangement was interrupted when the resident participated in the administering of physical treatments. However, the nurses carried out most of the operations involved, setting up the procedure and remaining with the patient, enabling the resident to appear briefly, do what only he was sanctioned to do (press the electric shock machine button, oversee the patient's course during insulin coma), without too much direct contact with the patient being demanded of him. He could soon be on his way to follow his schedule of therapeutic hours and other obligations. In some ways this procedure was a happy one for the resident: it conformed with the conventional medical view of how physicians and patients should relate to one another; it coincided with his indoctrination in medical school and internship. The resident was predisposed to accept this arrangement without objection, indeed, to encourage it.

The group worker began to report at staff meetings in the early 1950s on how patients were relating to one another. Occasionally a resident, reporting on his periods of duty, included observations on groups of patients and their interactions with one another or with him. However, residents tended to perceive such reports as beyond their area of primary interest. Although informative or even stimulating, these reports were viewed as essentially irrelevant because they were based on the assumption that the hospital must be understood as a society in which perspectives and operations were both important; the conventional view was that intrapsychic events alone were worthy of record.

There was some feeling that residents should not see other residents' patients unless clearly necessary, and then spend as little time as possible. When meaningful relationships developed between a group worker or social worker and a patient, there was a similar tendency for his doctor to view this with disfavor; these feelings expressed the conviction that the important relationship must be the therapeutic tie between patient and individual therapist; this optimal arrangement seemed threatened when others became involved with or important to the patient.

The patients in the YPI are among the most difficult with whom to attempt psychotherapeutic work. Most entered the hospital either because they were too troubled to engage in out-patient psychotherapy or because treatment outside the walls of a hospital, usually with a competent and experienced psychiatrist, had failed. This fact, combined with the extraordinary scrutiny to which the resident's work is continually subjected, renders the YPI year one of his most stressful experiences as a psychiatrist. Yet the resident tends to demand of himself that he "cure" his patients, and that they be "cured" during this one year of his contact with them. His must be the telling therapeutic experience in the course of the patient's illness and hospitalization. Regardless of the patient's status when therapy begins, he must somehow undergo a thoroughgoing transformation as a clear-cut, direct consequence of the resident's work with him. To the experienced observer, or in retrospect, it is clear that the resident demands too much of himself and of his patients. He is bound to be dissatisfied with what limited success he may achieve. He doubts himself, questioning the validity of his calling, the adequacy of his training, and his suitability for psychiatry.

Many YPI patients are acutely troubled, agitated, at times destructive, combative, and unable to participate in a conventional interview. The patient's behavior may demand that the resident depart from his preferred mode of interaction. This may be a source of frustration and discomfort. His anxiety is often realistically heightened by fear of being physically assaulted by his patient.[15]

The resident is constantly challenged and tested by patients, most clearly and directly in the initial phase of therapy. Patients frequently exploit the fact that they know the hospital—"the way things are done here," the procedures, policies and personnel—better than the new therapist does. Experienced patients freely compare his work with that of his colleagues and their prior therapists, anticipate his every technique, criticize him, and at times patronize him as a neophyte. The resident feels vulnerable, unsure of who is orienting whom, and feels deprived in such crucial values in the therapeutic interaction as enlightenment, skill, and respect. And there may be disquieting evidences of his patients' superiority: discrepancies exist between the social and economic position of the

15. The large majority of residents report that they were at times physically afraid of patients in the YPI (47, or 82 per cent), and a smaller majority (31, or 54 per cent) describe being attacked by a patient.

resident and his patients; many adolescents and young adults in the hospital are unusually imaginative and gifted; other older patients achieved impressive positions of responsibility and authority prior to hospitalization.

Far outweighing these, however, are problems intrinsic to the work of psychotherapy with severely ill patients in any setting, including the great anxiety and troublesome feelings and thoughts aroused in the physician as he investigates and tries to understand the struggles within his patient. As he becomes closely involved with a psychotic patient and begins to appreciate his thoughts and feelings, he cannot evade similar disturbing conflicts and problems within himself. This central undertaking in the resident's work subjects him to great psychological stress, compounded by all the other stresses described as intrinsic to his position in the setting; these simultaneously contribute to his own emotional and professional development. Each gain by the patient at least potentially involves the doctor also achieving clarification, insight, and some greater understanding of himself. Hence the emotional transactions with patients involve the resident's value position in every dimension, with fluctuating degrees of indulgence and deprivation. We have commented explicitly upon the therapist in relation to respect, enlightenment, skill, wealth, affection, and well-being. Rectitude and power, also crucially affected in the process, will presently receive more exhaustive consideration.

The Resident and Other Staff

The life of a resident is deeply influenced by his relationships with other members of the staff, including nurses, social workers, aides, and fellow residents. Especially during the early years of this study, the great importance of his relationship with nurses through each working day must be emphasized. The nurses were with his patients through most of the twenty-three hours when the resident was not with them; their observations and assessments were important in his appraisal of patients' status.

The residents' high regard for the nurses' work is reflected in their judgment of nursing care as second only to individual psychotherapy in importance in the hospital's treatment program.[16] Further-

16. In their assessment of the treatment program, a majority of residents (35, or 63 per cent) regarded "nursing care" as "of great importance" in determining whether or not a patient gets better; one said "of little importance"; none viewed it as "of no importance."

more, in rating the overall performance of staff members in their main functions, the majority of residents characterized the nurses, including the chief nurse, as "good" or "excellent" in their work.

Most of the hospital's social workers had been on its staff for years and were capable of contributing much to the resident's understanding of his patients and their problems. The social worker saw members of patients' families regularly and discussed these contacts with residents individually and in staff meetings. The resident frequently experienced the social worker's comprehension of the patient's background, development, and continuing problems with the people important to him as undermining his self-imposed demand that he be the staff member most knowledgeable about his patients. Social workers also conferred directly with patients about visits by their families and plans about school and work, contacts which the resident sometimes also experienced as threatening the primacy of his relationship with the patient. The social worker's involvement with and appreciation of the concerns of the family, and the resident's alliance with his patient, and his often opposing needs and wishes, sometimes led to disagreements. Residents tended to experience social workers as more competitive and threatening to their position than nurses because of the greater similarity in professional status and work. Social workers are keenly sensitive to their role as members of a profession, hence they view themselves neither as working at a job nor as subservient to the doctor. Their activities with disturbed families are not easily distinguished from the resident's psychotherapy with patients; this overlapping is more threatening because of the social worker's greater experience. Whatever the tensions created by a threatened value position, however, they did not prevent the majority of residents from rating the performance of social workers as "good" or "excellent."

During the pre-innovation period, the hospital's treatment program consisted of three major elements: individual psychotherapy, nursing care, and activities. The last included social and recreational events in and outside the hospital and occupational therapy; this program was directed by a group worker and an occupational therapist. Aside from the patient's hours of psychotherapy and time on the wards under the supervision of nurses and aides, most of the rest of his waking hours were spent with them in the shops weaving at looms and making ashtrays, and on trips to beach or theater. The resident was informed in staff meetings of his patients' participation in these activities, but he was not directly involved or much interested in them aside from appreciating that they kept his patients occupied.[17]

The resident tended to have little contact with hospital aides. Since most are divinity students, they are the only group within the staff whose major work investment lies outside the hospital. They do not compete with the resident or question his greater authority. Since they are men, they offer the resident some refuge from the knowing women, the nurses and social workers, who surround him. And as graduate students, they share some of the residents' intellectual interests. They sometimes become involved with individual patients and may argue with some about theology, trying to impose reason upon their delusional systems; occasionally they get upset over the theological preoccupations of some patients. Residents may try to be helpful with such problems but otherwise, except for an occasional informal chat, see little of the aides. A resident looks to them for help when a patient becomes combative, and he is sometimes disappointed by their diffidence.

Relations among residents are characterized by cameraderie and competition. When asked about the way in which he and others within his YPI resident group tended to relate to one another at work and socially, most characterized their groups as "fairly close."[18] Two groups of YPI residents described themselves with impressive solidarity as "very close." These two groups were also distinguished by the unanimity with which they assessed their chief resident as "poor" or, at best, "fair" in the performance of his main functions and in their (perhaps consequent) lack of enthusiasm in recalling the YPI experience. This solidarity is characteristic of a group dissatisfied with and unified in opposition to their chief resident.

The residents were asked about the frequency of after-hours social contact with other members of the staff. Replies confirm that they enjoyed many social contacts with fellow residents. The residents' social life with other hospital personnel consisted of less con-

17. Activities were viewed by the residents as third in importance, after individual psychotherapy and nursing care, in the pre-innovation hospital's treatment program (12, or 22 per cent, said "of great importance"; 31, or 56 per cent, replied "of moderate importance"; 12, or 22 per cent, said "little"; none said "of no importance"); subsequent changes in the hospital drastically modified the importance of this program.

18. Thirty-four (61 per cent). Fourteen (25 per cent) said they were "very close"; only eight (14 per cent) said the residents in their group were "not close"; none recorded that "we went our separate ways."

tact with social workers and senior staff, and virtually none with nurses and aides.[19]

Contact with fellow YPI residents includes attending staff meetings and classes together, chatting about patients and seniors, often having lunch together, and covering for one another when off duty or away from the hospital. In addition to these intensive work associations and active social contact outside working hours, their wives and children are often close friends, and they often live near one another.

Although rarely acknowledged openly, competition among residents is stiff. They struggle for power, respect, and other values within the resident group, each seeking to be accepted as the most competent therapist, the most knowing theoretician, the most promising researcher, the most authoritative in matters of patient management, or all of these. The prestige position achieved among his colleagues may be used as an instrument of power in relations with patients, nurses, and other members of the staff. The prizes in this competition are appointments in the department faculty, including the YPI chief-residency, and other research and teaching opportunities. As the year proceeds, an assessment of the residents' relative competence evolves; ratings by patients, nurses, senior medical staff, and the residents themselves often show a high level of concordance.

The Resident and his Seniors

A resident is especially concerned with his seniors' assessment of his competence. He has most contact with the chief resident, and in the context of competition for the respect and appreciation of his seniors, the resident sees the chief resident in something of the position of an older brother. He chairs most staff meetings and oversees the daily management of patients; he questions and challenges orders written for each patient and must explain and justify them to the director, who holds him responsible. The residents experience his scrutiny of their work as irritating and intrusive, but they sometimes appreciate his having insisted that they reconsider

19. Thirty-three said they saw other residents socially every week, sixteen said monthly, five replied "every two to three months"; none saw other residents socially less frequently than that. In describing their social contacts with other staff members, the great majority wrote of associating with nurses (all but three residents) and aides (all but one) less than every three months. Social workers and senior staff were more frequently met by the resident. Four saw social workers socially "weekly," four "monthly," twenty-three "every two to three months," and seventeen "less than that"; three saw senior staff socially "weekly," three "monthly," nineteen "every two to three months," and twenty-nine less than that.

an imprudent move. As the senior most aware of their problems, he often runs interference and protects them when discord arises with nurses, social workers, outside doctors, families of patients, and especially with the director and supervisors. When residents were asked to whose attention they brought situations of which they were critical, they consistently replied, "to the chief resident." They complained much more frequently to him than to other members of the senior staff. They were resentful when he identified closely with the views and demands of other seniors; this was experienced as desertion. When residents were asked to "rate the overall performance of staff members in their main functions," the greatest variation in responses appeared in their estimates of chief residents.[20]

The director is the most important individual in the professional life of the YPI resident; his assessment of performance is clearly the most significant, his criticism the most painful, his approval the most gratifying. In the pre-innovation period the resident had relatively little contact with the director. He met with him individually in administrative supervision for half an hour each week; the director attended some staff meetings, and when present he usually took over as chairman from the chief resident. His opinions on hospital policies and patient management were often accepted as final, settling the issues under discussion. Occasionally he would appear on the wards and chat with residents about current problems. He attended departmental research and clinical conferences with them; his comments were carefully listened to, particularly when they concerned their treatment of YPI patients.

Asked to state any criticisms of the senior staff, thirty-eight residents were critical of the director during their year. They expressed some complaints about earlier directors,[21] but focused on the pres-

20. One group unanimously rated their chief "excellent"; three groups all rated their chief "poor"; one group rated their chief "poor," with one exception, who thought him "good." Other groups' assessments of their chief resident's performance vary more. For example, the members of one group rated their chief "excellent," "good," "fair," and "poor." Asked to assess their chief resident, twenty-five (58 per cent) were critical. Thirteen dismissed him as "not suited to the job," seven criticized their chief as "too passive" and "indecisive," two saw him as "too intrusive" and "dogmatic." Of the seventeen residents who offered suggestions, fourteen called for "improved selection" of chief residents.

21. The ten criticisms offered by residents at the YPI prior to the present director's term, and referring to earlier directors, were scattered: "He was not involved enough" (3), "not supportive enough of the residents" (2), "too emotionally involved with residents and patients" (1), and had "too mechanistic a view of the resident's job" (1). Two emphasized the disruptive effects of "the director's own discontent" and his "being under fire from the department administration."

ent director's "authoritarian," "dogmatic," and "vague" behavior.[22] Residents varied widely in how they experienced the director and in the degree of freedom they felt about complaining to him directly. They consistently report turning to the director when they were critical or dissatisfied. Next to fellow residents and the chief resident, they most frequently complained to the director; despite their criticisms, the channels of communication between residents and the director were kept open. However, when "critical of the director's treatment of a fellow resident," relatively few felt able to take the matter up with the director himself.[23]

These comments are put into perspective by responses obtained when residents were asked to "rate the overall performance of staff members in their main functions during your training year at the YPI." Despite their complaints about the director, they consistently rated his performance highest of all hospital staff members.[24] This striking discrepancy between residents' complaints about the director and their estimates of his performance will be discussed later.

Among the residents' opinions of how others in the hospital felt about their work in the YPI, a majority testified that other members of the staff and the patients were "enthusiastic" or "appreciative."[25]

22. Criticisms were offered by twenty-eight residents who worked at the YPI under the present director. Twenty criticized his behavior with residents: he was characterized as "too authoritarian and dogmatic," "too vague and unapproachable," "too critical," "too hostile," "too manipulative," "provocative," and "too defensive." Eight complained of insufficient personal contact and support. Twenty-three residents who worked under the present director made suggestions: their strongest recommendation was for "increased personal contact" between the director and themselves (13). Others suggested "better behavior" on his part (12), "support the residents more" (3), "explain why you do what you do" (2), "give up the father role" (1), "interfere with patients less" (1), "be clearer" (1), "tone down your criticism" (1), and "listen more" (1).

23. Such reticence contrasts with their freedom in bringing complaints about other staff members to the nurse, chief resident, or social worker concerned. When residents were asked "were there any complaints you did not feel free to bring up?," the majority (38, or 75 per cent) said "no"; thirteen (25 per cent) replied "yes." Thirty complaints they did not feel free to raise were listed: the director was the object of many of these unvoiced complaints (12, 10 by residents who worked under the present director). These again focused upon "the difficulty in communicating with him" (4), his being "authoritarian" (2), "dogmatic" (1), "insensitive" (1), "his personality" (2), and "the director's tendency to relate to residents as scapegoats and favorites" (1).

24. Nineteen (39 per cent) regarded him as "excellent," twenty-one (43 per cent) as "good," seven (14 per cent) as "fair," and two as "poor." Those who worked under the present director were the most emphatic in this high rating: sixteen (45 per cent) said "excellent," the same number said "good," two "fair," one "poor."

25. Residents so regarded the director (37), assistant director (33), their

The only exception was the chairman of the department of psychiatry.[26] The residents' feeling of distance from the chairman and the reality of his detachment from the affairs of the hospital is confirmed by the testimony that he was least often turned to by residents with criticisms or complaints. His gradual separation from direct participation in the day-to-day affairs of the hospital made it no longer appropriate to take such matters up with him, and the residents did not feel able to do so.

The chairman's central position in the affairs of the department makes his assessment of the resident very important, particularly if he seeks an academic or research position beyond his residency. The chairman's lack of participation in the YPI is therefore experienced as a sizeable deprivation; in judging a resident, he must depend on appraisals made by others, primarily the director, whose weight in affecting the future of residents is thus increased.

The supervisors advise the resident but do not discipline him; their responsibility is limited and of a different order than that of seniors on the full-time hospital staff. A supervisor rarely sees patients he discusses with the resident; he must depend entirely upon the reports. These meetings, the supervisor's only participation in the affairs of the hospital, give great prominence to the patient-therapist interview and exclude other aspects of the patient's experience in the YPI. The appraisals of residents' work by these experienced clinicians are important to the resident and the director. But conflict arises when a resident experiences his supervisor as taking a different position from members of the full-time staff on a therapeutic problem. The supervisor may, for example, question the extent to which a patient is restricted from participating in activities, a matter the resident may have accepted from the staff without understanding or agreeing. He may then perceive this questioning as opposing the rest of the staff and supporting his own disagreement and may present the patient's course to his supervisor in such a way as to invite this conflict. The supervisor tries to avoid a resident's exploiting any such disagreement by insisting that he think through his own position. A supervisor is in a freer position than others on the staff to encourage a resident to examine the nature of his involvement with patients. The supervisor's impres-

---

chief resident (36), other residents (46), nurses (44), social workers (42), and patients (47).

26. He alone was believed by the majority to be "indifferent" to (23), or "critical" of (3) their work. This view became progressively more emphatic with succeeding groups of residents; during the last five years of this study he was so viewed by seventeen of the twenty-six residents who commented.

sions about how the patient should be worked with are not derived from his own contacts and observations of the patient, and he cannot impose such impressions on the resident. His picture of what the patient requires develops out of what the resident reports to him, and therapeutic strategies evolve exclusively out of this exchange. He is then in an advantageous position to help the resident work out for himself how he will be therapeutically useful to his patient.

Dissatisfaction with insufficient supervision and with the caliber of supervisors and teachers was characteristic of residents through all the years of this study.[27] When residents were asked for criticisms of supervisors, they replied as they did about all members of the senior staff: they consistently complained about lack of involvement and recommended that the seniors participate more and invest more in the hospital. They saw their supervisors and other seniors as investing less than they, and wanted them to be more active and concerned with the day-to-day affairs of the hospital. This emphasis also expresses the residents' wish that their seniors have more personal contact with and invest more in them.

This longing with regard to teachers and bosses is understandable. His seniors teach him, but he must constantly demonstrate to them that he is learning, and they often seem indifferent to his needs. His bosses guide him, but he must demonstrate to them that he is thinking for himself and assuming responsibility for his own decisions and actions. His patients press him relentlessly to respond to their demands for affection and care. His analyst understands his predicament, but consistently insists that he nevertheless engage himself wholeheartedly in the demanding work of his own treatment. His family cannot understand what they at times experience as his indifference and cannot put aside their need for his concern and love. Although it may be gratifying to be sought, needed, and important, the conflicts evoked in the effort to respond to these depleting demands involve painful feelings of self-doubt, anger,

---

27. When residents were asked to list the major complaints of their residency groups, complaints about the instruction which they received as YPI residents, including the character, quality, and quantity of their teaching supervision were expressed in twenty-one of the 154 residency-group complaints.

When residents were invited to assess supervisors and suggest improvements, twenty-two offered criticisms. Their alleged remoteness from, and lack of familiarity with, the affairs and procedures of the hospital were criticized by eight residents; seven simply alleged that some supervisors were "not helpful." Of the fifteen residents offering suggestions, seven recommended greater involvement and participation by supervisors in the affairs of the hospital, and five called for "improved selection of supervisors."

and guilt. He looks to his seniors to reassure him, but they do not cooperate. They are stingy not only with praise but with any direct assessment of his performance, and this absence heightens the resident's uncertainty as to his competence.

Decision-Making and Power

The staff of the hospital, particularly its physicians, and most particularly the director, are in effect appointed by the larger society as expert custodians of members of the community judged incapable of assuming responsibilities to the community, their families, or themselves. In the service of their proper care and treatment, the doctors are authorized to exercise extraordinary powers over their patients, at times depriving them of rights and privileges regarded in a democratic society as the prerogative of every citizen. In the early years of our study this delegation of power was interpreted and exercised in ways traditional to psychiatric hospitals. In seeking to discharge this responsibility, the director delegated some of his extraordinary powers to members of the staff, including resident physicians in training; however, he alone retained full responsibility in the eyes of those from whom he derived his authority.

Asked to assess "how much influence" various staff members exerted "over the way things went at the YPI," only the director was seen by a majority (45, or 82 per cent) as having a "great deal" of influence; all other residents (10, or 18 per cent) described his influence as "considerable." Residents rated the chief resident, chief nurses, the residents as a group, and patients as the only others exerting substantial influence over the way things went.[28]

Although they saw the director as the primary influence in the affairs of the hospital, residents did not underestimate their own responsibility.[29] When asked whether they had "as much say as

28. The board of directors, department chairman, "outside doctors," business manager, supervisors, relatives of patients, chief social worker, director of nursing, and the assistant director were seen by a majority as having little or no influence.

29. Asked "how much responsibility you had in caring for patients," the majority (38, or 67 per cent) replied, "great"; nineteen (33 per cent) said, "moderate"; none said, "some" or "little." In rating the extent of their power in making decisions about patients at the YPI, the great majority of residents (41, or 73 per cent) replied that they had "enough" power in this regard; eleven (20 per cent) said "not enough"; four, all of whom worked in the hospital in the pre-innovation period, replied, "too much." When asked "who tended to make decisions about your patients that you felt you should have made?," pre-innovation residents most frequently singled out the chief resident (10 out of 33, or 30 per cent), and then the director and chief nurses.

they should have had in deciding" nine common, specific questions involved in patient management, the great majority (between 46 and 54, 90 to 98 per cent) felt that they did have "enough say" on eight of the nine issues.[30] One issue was responded to somewhat differently: "whether or not your patient was ready for discharge." Although a majority (35, or 65 per cent) felt they had enough say, this issue became increasingly controversial during the current director's service. These were not hypothetical questions; as the staff physician in sustained, direct contact with the patient, the resident was in large measure responsible for deciding each of them. All are of great concern to a patient, especially during the initial phases of hospitalization, when he tends to be acutely troubled, the staff is only beginning to know him, and his activity is likely to be severely restricted. The patient presses his therapist to give him more freedom, to let him leave the hospital, see family members and friends, and live on the open ward. The resident presses the patient to use their sessions together to investigate the problems which made it necessary for him to come to the hospital. The resident experiences the pressures exerted for greater freedom as irritating distractions from the more important job of psychotherapeutic exploration. The patient gradually appreciates the doctor's position and makes some effort to "work at therapy," and the resident begins to appreciate the patient's position and to regard some of his requests as "reasonable."

It was YPI procedure for the resident to present such requests in staff meeting, in a sense acting as his patient's advocate, stating the increased extent of freedom he now regarded as reasonable for the patient, and justifying the recommendation on the basis of the patient's "improved" behavior. The chief resident, other residents, social and activities workers, and nurses would then contribute their observations and impressions of the patient. The decision to accept, offer suggestions for modifying, or reject the recommendation was usually made by the physician of highest authority at the staff meeting, usually the chief resident, sometimes the director. Sometimes, however, the decision did reflect a consensus arrived at through discussion. Such decisions about changing a patient's or-

30. These included "whether or not your patient should be on the open ward," "whether or not your patient should be physically restrained," "taken off bedtime sedation," "should be given EST," "how late your patients could stay up at night on a given ward," "whether or not your patient might make phone calls at will," "whether or not patients' letters were censored," "whether or not patients might receive visitors," "whether or not patients had to remain in the hospital at all times or, if permitted to leave, how much they might go out into the larger community."

ders (a term expressing the quasi military, authoritarian character of the traditional hospital) hopefully were based on the staff's assessment of what would be useful to the patient and what he could handle at the time. But other considerations influenced these decisions, including the feelings of all who participated about the resident who presented his patient's request. Whatever the conscious or unconscious grounds for accepting or rejecting a resident's recommendation, the act indulged or deprived him, as well as the patient.

The extraordinary powers exercised by a resident over the conditions of life of his patients were, and continue to be, important in the prestigious role of the resident within the hospital community. This power, and the position of respect and fear in part derived from it, are values which the therapist may employ as constructive bases for psychotherapeutic work. He may reward patients who work hard at the investigatory work of treatment and impose deprivations upon those who evade the challenge. Such a manipulative view of the therapist's behavior with patients is experienced by the resident as offensive, and it is rarely stated explicitly. When patients complain about this cat-and-mouse game, the resident suppresses his doubts by regarding such characterizations as distortions expressive of the patient's illness. He may be unwilling to consider the possibility that they might sometimes describe what was actually happening.

The very power exercised by the therapist to facilitate therapeutic objectives also complicates the therapeutic process. The therapist is both trying to appreciate and understand the patient's feelings about his power deprivations and participating in the decision to impose those power deprivations. Because the restrictions are applied by the resident, it is more difficult for the patient to see and acknowledge his share of responsibility for them. The dilemma is not satisfactorily resolved by delegating these powers to someone else; only when the resident affirms the necessity of restriction because of the patient's problems and disturbed behavior can the issue be faced and worked out in treatment.

The resident's use or misuse of his power is in part determined by the quality and intensity of his involvement with patients. When he begins work with a patient, the bizarre character of the patient's behavior and his potential for self-destructiveness may be evident. As resident and patient get to know one another, the doctor enjoys less of that psychological distance which initially permitted him to see the extent to which his patient was troubled; he begins to feel guilty about confining him. His increasing involvement makes it more important to be a good friend to the patient, to indulge his wishes and needs. It may distort his assessment. When he feels that it makes sense for his patient to leave the hospital unaccompanied, he may bring it up in staff meeting, only to be reminded by nurses, social workers, and others who have had continuing contact with the patient that he remains disturbed and hence is not yet ready for this "privilege." The resident may then return to his patient and tell him that the staff decided against granting the request. Thus the doctor invokes "the staff" as a force outside the relationship between himself and his patient. Optimally, the resident will think through and consider carefully the assessments of the other staff members. If he then agrees with the decision, he will present it to the patient as his own and as a restriction he personally imposes. Such personal exercise of power is particularly difficult for the inexperienced therapist. The resident finds it trying to sustain his view that restriction serves the patient's interests in the face of a continuing barrage of complaints and reproaches. When told that he is restricted by "the staff," the patient tends to hear this as an arbitrary decision by the director. As long as the patient believes his therapist does not agree with the staff decision, he remains unconvinced that his interests have been considered and experiences the decision as arbitrary, uninformed, and irrational.

Such issues provide the patient with an indication of how his doctor feels about him. Supporting his getting more privileges may be experienced as an indulgence indicating that his doctor likes him; if his requests are unrealistic, however, the doctor's acquiescence may be experienced as indicating that the doctor has poor judgment and does not really care about his welfare.

The power of the resident is, then, an important basis for his high respect position. The extent to which his professional enlightenment and skill enable him to exercise this power judiciously influences strongly the effectiveness of his psychotherapeutic efforts. The resident's wish to receive or give affection modifies—at times disrupts—his use of power in the service of his patient's interests. The resident's exercise of power is also modified by rectitude considerations. He is apt to experience a moral conflict in the performance of tasks intrinsic to his work which detract from his preferred image of himself as a psychiatrist: when he physically restrains a patient, censors mail, confines a patient to the hospital, prohibits patients from working or attending school, or in other ways participates in usurping his patients' freedom. Is his assessment of the patient's status accurate? Do the aggressive acts which he undertakes, ostensibly in the service of his patient's protection and care, really serve the patient's interests? Can such interference with the rights of others be justified? To what extent are such actions contaminated by aggressive feelings toward the patient?

Although considerations of affection and rectitude may lead the resident to employ strategies which evade personal responsibility for restrictions imposed upon his patients and attribute responsibility for an arbitrary exercise of power to his seniors and other staff members, he strongly resents actual assumption of such power by anyone else, particularly by his seniors. When the chief resident or director opposes his view that a patient should be removed from isolation, or transferred from the closed to the open ward, or when he makes such a recommendation and it is rejected in staff meeting, the resident feels his judgment challenged, the position laboriously established with his patient undermined, and his psychotherapy rendered ineffective. His teachers and bosses are experienced as arbitrary and intrusive when they disagree with or overrule him, and he may then complain bitterly about their authoritarian, unreasonable, dogmatic, and dismissive behavior toward him. A resident may respond by surrendering and apathetically going through the motions, turning to his fellow residents for comfort and support in disappointed and resentful alliance against his oppressive seniors. He may even enter into a tacit compact with his patients in which they share feelings of being victimized, deprived, and uncared for, with the result that they isolate themselves from a fuller participation in the life of the hospital.

Upon the completion of his YPI year, the resident's formal psychiatric apprenticeship is ended; he is a trained psychiatrist prepared to undertake teaching, research, and practice. Any suggestion from teachers and bosses that he has not mastered his profession, is not a competent psychotherapist, is not skilled in patient management, or that his comprehension of the intellectual content of the field is inadequate is experienced as particularly threatening. The heightened sensitivity at this critical time makes it difficult for the resident to tolerate such expressions of power by his seniors.

Part II

The Innovations: A Contextual Analysis

6. Patient-Staff Meetings: Annotated Transcripts

This chapter consists of two verbatim transcripts of patient-staff meetings (two additional transcripts appear without annotation in the appendix). The meetings were inaugurated late in 1956; the analyzed transcripts are from the first full YPI year during which the meetings were convened regularly, 1957–58. It is hoped that the full reporting of the analyzed meetings will convey the dynamic interplay among the participants and offer vivid, individualized conceptions of the people who constituted the hospital. The transcripts are genuinely verbatim; only names (except that of the chairman, Doctor Fleck) and identifying phrases have been changed or omitted.

To facilitate their study, patient-staff meetings were tape recorded routinely from their inception. Transcripts of meetings for analysis were selected from the first full hospital year rather than later years in the expectation that the process of their formation and stabilization could be more clearly discerned in this early stage of development. Six meetings, distributed over the (July 1, 1957, to June 30, 1958) hospital year at roughly two-month intervals, were analyzed. An early July meeting, included because of the great impact of the annual change of residents and some other staff members occurring on July 1, is here presented. The other analyzed transcripts include a December meeting, chosen because of the strong emotional effects upon participants of the Christmas holidays, including concerns about separation from home and family. Feelings engendered by the imminent departure of residents are documented in a June transcript. The other analyzed transcripts (from September, October, and February) offer a portrait of the hospital between these times of predictable crisis: the September transcript is the second presented here.

The presentation of the meetings is preceded by brief descriptions of major participants. Samples and illustrations of the content analysis techniques used are provided primarily for researchers as a guide for the application of these procedures, which consisted of:

(1) A *value analysis*, assigning each statement (as divided into small units of arbitrary length) to the eight value-categories: power, enlightenment, well-being, skill, affection, respect, rectitude, and

wealth; delineating the extent to which these values were shaped and shared; analyzing the indulgences and deprivations imposed and experienced by the participants (indulgences and deprivations of the speaker and/or an object of reference) in each of these value categories.

(2) An analysis of the phases of the *decision process*, categorizing each statement according to its contribution to decision-making. The seven phases into which the decision process is arbitrarily divided are intelligence, recommendation or promotion, prescription, application, invocation, appraisal, and termination.

These procedures were first applied to the manifest content of the text (the ordinary meaning of the words, not reflecting any special knowledge of the context, the speaker, or the audience). An effort was subsequently made to examine other value impacts of each statement and interaction at progressively deeper levels (We refer to the manifest content procedure as classification from standpoint A. The more intensive procedure, that takes more of the context into consideration, is standpoint B.).

The results of the value and decision process analyses of the six transcripts are summarized in Chapter 7; the reader may choose to familiarize himself with that material before reading the verbatim transcripts.

The Participants

The following is a list of people in the order in which they appear, or are referred to, in the two patient-staff meeting transcripts which follow. Brief descriptions, as of July 1957, are offered of the most active participants. The length of stay included in patient descriptions refers to time in the hospital as of July 1957.

Patients

ADAM, 19, was acutely psychotic on admission to the hospital two and one-half years earlier. He is intellectually gifted, but incestuous fantasies constantly disrupt his efforts to study or work. He is admired by other patients for his boldness in questioning authority and for his assertiveness with women.

BETTY, 16, lived in an institution for the retarded for some years until her intelligence and capacity for learning, despite neurological handicaps, were recognized by a psychoanalyst consultant who undertook therapy with her and then recommended this effort at treatment in the YPI. Betty has been in the hospital for eight months, is very grateful, feels close to the director, and seeks all his attention.

CHARLES, 16, obese, has been in treatment since early childhood. On admission to the YPI two years earlier he informed the head-master that other students at his boarding school were planning to murder him. He attends high school in town while living in the hospital.

DEBRA, 15, obese, very bright, was severely troubled by her in-volvement in her parents' marital disputes when she entered the YPI three months ago. She arranges her hospital room as a club-house, hoping to be visited by other patients.

EDWARD, 28, single, tall and suavely dressed, was an executive in a family-controlled corporation. Acutely psychotic and suicidal on admission, he demonstratively complains about having no feelings.

FRED, 18, bright, muscular, had remained in his room at home alone reading and lifting weights for over a year before he entered the YPI two years ago. He was assaultive on admission; other pa-tients and staff fear his violent temper.

GREGOR, 18, European, was transferred to the YPI a year ago from another hospital, which regarded him as too violent for their facil-ities and staff to contain. He has never been violent at the YPI. Pre-occupied with fantasies about his depressed mother and discord be-tween parents, Gregor is cultivated and intellectually gifted, and active among patients in supporting hospital innovations.

HOWARD, 20, handsome, became acutely psychotic and was ad-mitted to YPI six months ago after a fight with his girlfriend. He had earlier left college after performing poorly, and then been dis-charged from the service on psychiatric grounds. He spends most of his day in the YPI writing poetry and is moderately talented.

MR. "IKE" IVES, 46, a university administrator. He entered YPI eight months ago when he became severely troubled after being promoted to a position of greater responsibility. He is referred to as "Mr." because he is old enough to be the father of many other pa-tients and because of the important position he attained.

KEITH, 17, admitted one month ago. He wears black leather jacket and boots, loves hillbilly music and "customized" cars. Keith was sent to the YPI rather than juvenile court and is described by his parents as having been beyond their control since birth.

MIKE, 26, short and stooped, was transferred to YPI three months ago from an open hospital. He left high school prior to graduation, has not worked, affects cultural and artistic interests, had begun and soon left out-patient treatment frequently.

NANCY, 22, has been mute, withdrawn, and hospitalized for ten years, entered YPI two years ago. Her father refuses to visit her; the mother is also psychotic.

OWEN, 21, an angry college student, was acutely psychotic when he entered YPI fourteen months ago. He is intensely competitive with his openly rejecting, highly successful father.

ROSE, 19, college student, was admitted four months ago. She was depressed and then became overly talkative and excited as final examinations approached. She experiences her parents as indifferent and as favoring her younger, more intellectual sister.

SANDRA, 17, attractive, an excellent student. She entered YPI one year ago after behaving bizarrely at boarding school and proving "uncontrollable" at home. She has cut her wrists many times and often refuses to eat. She is a very important patient in the sense that she is constantly discussed by staff and patients, regarded as unpredictable and dangerous.

TOM, 26, a lawyer, extraordinarily intelligent, admitted to the hospital five months ago when suicidal and acutely upset about discord in his marriage and difficulties in his performance at work. He tends to be silent and withdrawn and is experienced by other patients as rock-like.

VIC, 19, a talented college student, entered YPI five months ago when acutely psychotic. He is preoccupied with fantasies about his mother and sister and spends most of his day in the hospital writing plays.

ZEKE, 20, completed high school with the aid of intensive outpatient psychotherapy, despite having to carry out elaborate rituals in order to avoid killing God. He became acutely disturbed on entering college and leaving his parents and therapist; he has been in the YPI for two years.

MRS. FERRIS, 34, entered the hospital in September 1957, after a fight with her husband about her often being intoxicated; she remained for six weeks.

GLORIA, 21, entered the hospital two and one-half years ago, soon after her mother's death, acutely distressed about imagined changes in the contours of her face. She now attends college part time from the hospital.

DR. HASTINGS, 36, a woman clinical psychologist admitted to the hospital after becoming involved in disputes with her colleagues in a distant city, in September 1957; she remained for three weeks and then left against advice.

MRS. INGALLS, 58, entered YPI in August 1957 because she was severely depressed.

MRS. JONES, 41, became acutely distressed and attempted suicide when her husband threatened to leave her after an argument. She was admitted to the YPI four months ago.

KENT, 17, a very superior student, entered the hospital in August 1957, after cutting his face in a rage. There had been little evidence of his being troubled prior to this episode.

MARY, 16, admitted in August 1957, sucks her thumb and avoids contact with other patients. She bathes and changes her clothes only under pressure from nurses. She insists that she loves Frank Sinatra and hates her doctor.

NEAL, 27, long a graduate student in classics, has had intermittent catatonic episodes since adolescence. He was admitted to the YPI eighteen months ago. He is reserved, articulate, extremely polite, sometimes screams out an obscene word unexpectedly.

DR. ROGERS, 41, a physician admitted because he was severely depressed; he remained in the hospital for two months during the year prior to these meetings.

Staff Members

DR. FLECK, YPI Director.

DR. LONG, chief resident as of July 1957, spent his prior year as one of the YPI residents.

DOCTORS PRICE, BENNETT, LEARY, OLSON, QUINN, AND INGRAHAM, the 1957–58 YPI residents. All spent the two years prior to July 1957 as residents in training elsewhere in the Yale department of psychiatry, except Dr. Leary who received his medical training abroad and his prior psychiatric training elsewhere in the United States.

DR. WILLIAMS, a resident whose YPI year ended July 1, 1957.

DR. ROSENBERG, YPI assistant director.

DR. POWERS was a YPI resident two years earlier and YPI chief resident during the year which ended in June 1957.

MISS OAKLAND and MISS JACKSON, nurses.

MISS DIAMOND, a chief nurse on the closed ward.

MISS ALDEN, YPI business manager.

MISS NEWTON, YPI chief social worker.

Transcript I: YPI Patient-Staff Meeting of July 8, 1957

Prior to the entrance of the chairman (the medical director of the YPI), all other participants (all of the patients in the hospital, the assistant director, the chief resident, the residents, the director of nursing, the nurses and aides on duty, the business manager, social and activities workers) are seated in the large conference room.

Some sit quietly waiting. Others chat. One of the patients, Adam, walks to the blackboard at the front of the room and draws a cartoon of the medical director. He enters, sees the drawing, sits down at the head of the conference table around and in front of which the participants are seated, and begins the Patient-Staff Meeting, the third of the hospital year.

CHAIRMAN (Dr. Fleck) 1: *Did you want to speak, Betty?*

1. This first participation, essentially a routine recognition by the chair of a speaker, is classified as an exercising of the *intelligence* function in the decision process. He informs the group of the identity of an individual whom he authorizes to take the floor. Such routine participations are treated separately from other intelligence statements. This, in its manifest content, is an *indulgence* with regard to the value *respect* by the Chairman (staff member) of the patient, Betty. The notes of sarcasm and reproach in this participation, as the Chairman draws attention to Betty for continuing to chat privately after the meeting should have begun, and in effect challenges her to share her private conversation with the larger group, implies under this more intensive scrutiny, that Betty is being *deprived* with regard to the value *respect* in being focused upon as a target for ridicule by herself and by the group, and *deprived* with regard to *rectitude* in being reprimanded. At this level, the entire group is being *deprived* by the Chairman with regard to *rectitude* in that he uses Betty to express his disapproval of those in the larger group who remain inattentive and continue to chat. These deprivations extend to those who identify with Betty and her predicament. The Chairman at the same time *indulges* with regard to *respect* and *rectitude* those in the group who want the meeting to start. They have been annoyed and discomfited by Betty and others who have ignored their wishes, that is, they have been *deprived* by Betty with regard to well-being, and they are now *indulged* by the Chairman with regard to *well-being* as he reproaches Betty and gets the meeting under way. In reproaching Betty, the Chairman also *deprives* her with regard to *affection* in that she actively seeks all of his attention and desperately wants him to think well of her.

BETTY (patient) 2: *Well, I just announced that you were here, Fleck* (laughing), *Dr. Fleck. The people that I was pointing out, I've heard people call "nurse" when they want a "nurse"* (calls it out), *instead of—* (*One person laughs very loudly obscuring some of*

Betty's words on the recording.) *And I've heard people say, "O.K., Oakland" instead of Miss Oakland (a staff nurse, present in the meeting), and yet I don't know, but she doesn't—do you mind it, Miss Oakland? (short pause) Then I don't think Dr. Fleck should like it, if I called him "Fleck."*[1] (*There is general laughter in the group.*)

2. Again, in its manifest content, Betty's is a statement of information, an exercising of the *intelligence* function in the decision process and an indulgence of the chairman and the group with regard to the value *enlightenment*; she tells them what she has been saying privately. She imposes a *respect* deprivation upon the Chairman by omitting his title. Her laughter suggests that she is enjoying this exchange with him and the attention she receives; she is thus *indulged* with regard to *well-being* in her delight, indulged in *respect*, by being attended to, and perhaps indulged in *skill* in exercising her capacity to banter with him. In the self-justification implicit in her statement, Betty indulges herself with regard to *rectitude*. At a deeper level, Betty is expressing her fondness for the Chairman and inviting him to be fond of her, an *indulgence* of him in *affection*. In contrast with participation 1., the Chairman's opening question, a *non-committal* statement, Betty's statement is *committal* in setting forth the facts that she alleges.

Betty goes on to make a *deprivational respect* reference to "nurses" in general and to a particular nurse. She *deprives* other "patients" in *rectitude* in mocking their disrespectful behavior toward nurses. She implies that her contrasting behavior is *indulgent* of the nurses in *respect* and therefore *indulgent* of herself in *rectitude*.

Continuing, Betty discloses her assessment of what Dr. Fleck's attitude should be (thus *enlightening* Dr. Fleck), at the same time both repeating a disrespectful mode of address (*depriving* him in *respect*) and being coy with him (*indulging* him with regard to *affection*).

Betty's statement is punctuated by tension-relieving laughter, a *well-being indulgence* of the group by the group, and their response to Betty entertaining them with her *respect depriva-*

---

1. Modes of address within the hospital community retain hierarchical connotations. All physicians are addressed as "doctor." The patients are referred to and addressed by their first names. The chairman sometimes addresses other doctors in the meeting by their first names, but he is addressed by them as "doctor."

tions of the Director. Led by Betty, they laugh at him, and thus as a group *deprive* him with regard to *respect*. The jovial quality of this teasing suggests a simultaneous *indulgence* of the Director in *affection*.

ADAM (patient) 3: *If I may, you ought to call Dr. Fleck, "Steve."* (*pause*)

    3. Adam then carries this teasing further, flaunting and provoking the power of the Chairman-Director, testing how far he can go; he *deprives* him in *respect*, and at a deeper level, of *power*. Adam and Betty are learning how far they can go in depriving the Director, exploring the limits of toleration of the environment before counterdeprivations begin, in this sense *indulging* themselves in mastering an important *skill*. Adam takes the spotlight from Betty, *depriving* her and *indulging* himself in *respect* as the challenger of authority.

CHAIRMAN 4: *I don't suppose anybody could hear you, Adam.* (*short pause*) *I don't see how everybody could hear you.*

    4. The Chairman *indulges* Adam in *enlightenment* in giving him information. At the same time he *deprives* Adam in *skill* by criticizing his performance as a participant ("you did not speak loud enough"). He *indulges* the whole group by complaining in their behalf of their having been *deprived* by Adam (in not being able to hear) of *enlightenment* and *respect*. In then correcting his overstatement (shifting from "anyone" to "everyone") he *deprives* himself in *skill*. Perhaps the inner conflict expressed in this blunder was evoked by the *deprivation* imposed on the Director in *power, respect,* and *affection* by the group, and reflects his internal opposition to an impulse to impose a *counter-deprivation* upon the group. The extraordinarily polite overcompensatory character in this context of his statement tends to confirm this possibility.

ADAM 5: *That's okay.* (*There is general laughter, a pause, and then a loud noise is heard from repair work being done outside the conference room in the hallway.*)

    5. Adam carries the provocation further, *depriving* the Chairman in *respect* and *power* by patronizing him. The group laughter again echoes this *deprivation*.

CHARLES (patient) 6: *Lot of pipes around here. I was wondering whether there's any reason for them.* (*The repair noises obscure the beginning of Charles' next statement.*) . . . *and cigars, I was wondering whether there's any reason.* (*There is a pause while the doors are closed.*)

6. Charles' statement is an *indulgence* of the group in *enlightenment* and a bid for an *indulgence* of himself in *enlightenment* in asking for information. He turns to the Chairman as the source of information, indulging him in *enlightenment, respect,* and *power,* and also *depriving* himself in representing himself as *unenlightened.* In noting "lots of pipes around" he *indulges* himself in *skill* as an observer. Perhaps the reference to masculine pipes and there being lots of them is evoked by the preceding flaunting of the Chairman's power and the assertion of power by Charles' peers. The possible relationship between his statement about pipes and the external repair noises is apparently outside of Charles' awareness; these irritating, perhaps violent sounds may have momentarily frightened Charles and others (a *deprivation* of *well-being*), particularly when they have been made anxious by the challenges to which the Director has been subjected and their fear of retaliation by the Director-father. Charles' statement is manifestly an abrupt change of topic, *depriving* those who want to continue the discussion and *indulging* himself and others who are anxious and want it stopped. A shift from discussion in which the flaunting of *respect* and *power* have predominated to discussion in which *enlightenment* is emphasized is ostensibly invited, apparently in the service of the speaker's and the group's *well-being.* In making this shift, Charles *deprives* Adam of the *respect* position for which he has made a bid as a provocateur.

CHAIRMAN 7: *Recent stories.*[2]

7. An *indulgence* in *enlightenment,* but its cryptic form *deprives* many.

DEBRA (patient) 8: *Well, I think they're more masculine than cigarettes.*

8. Manifestly a coy *committal indulgence* of the group in *enlightenment,* informing them of her viewpoint. She asserts her preference for the mode of behavior which she characterizes as "masculine" displayed by those of her peers who challenge the Director; she invites his being flaunted and provoked further.

UNIDENTIFIED PARTICIPANT 9: *What's that, men?* (*General laughter. A pause. Someone begins to hum softly.*)

9. Nominally, a request to be indulged with information

2. Presumably a reference to publicity about cigarette smoking and cancer, and the subsequent increased popularity of pipes and cigars. The chairman chain smokes cigarettes during the meeting.

(*enlightenment*). A rallying cry for group assertiveness against the Director on the basis of an appeal to masculine strivings; it suggests a demand that the group mobilize and *indulge* itself with regard to *power*. The group laughter suggests conflict, excitement, and pleasure; the pause, "where do we carry it from here?;" the humming suggests an effort to control aggression, an invitation to group solidarity, and at the same time, a direct aggressive challenging of the director. Those who have taken the initiative in asserting themselves against the director, Betty and Adam particularly, are indulged in *respect, affection,* and *power* by those in the group who go along with them. In its responses the group also *indulges* itself, in its exhilaration and anticipation of challenge and conflict, in *well-being* (the subjective event of elation), *power,* and *affection* (the sentiment of solidarity in the group). A titilation is also expressed in these group responses, suggesting an overcoming of the fear of sexual excitement in the presence of the threatening father-director (an *indulgence* of the group in *well-being*); the humming also expresses a self-comforting *indulgence* of the group in *affection* in the presence of the feared director. By participating in these responses some members of the group are providing themselves and others with an opportunity to experience the advantages of "a social self;" that is, extend the boundaries of their individual egos to include the identity of the patient group as a whole, and to now include expectations of net indulgences as a consequence of sharing in group action.

EDWARD (patient) *10: Well, as long as, may I?—as long as no one's gonna say anything intelligent, I might as well say something silly . . . (more laughter) . . . It's about the telephone downstairs. I've asked Miss Alden* (YPI business manager) *about . . . I dunno how many times in the last month, if some type of arrangement could be made where there could be more privacy on that phone. Also, as of late, I have been making a lot of phone calls for business reasons, and I do tie up the phone a lot, which is in a way, unfair, although I can't help it. But the point is, both myself and many other people, they walk by, or they stand there impatiently. There's no privacy. And I really think that something should be provided where we can have a little booth, or maybe the telephone relocated in some way. Apparently Miss Alden just hears the story all the time, and she says there is no money available.* (pause)

10. Edward offers to *enlighten* the group, at the same time minimizing and ridiculing the contribution he is about to make.

His "may I," an indulgence of the chairman and the group in *respect*, seeks in advance their assurance that he will be exempted from any sanctions for what he says (that he will not be deprived in *power* and *respect*), and that they will share the responsibility for what he says with him (that the *rectitude* implications be borne by all, not by the speaker alone). The group responds with laughter, releasing some of the tension built up during the earlier challenging of the director, and, in laughing at Edward, directing their aggression at him. He outlines his complaint, emphasizing the deprivation of *respect* it entails, and implicitly questioning the explanation on economic grounds (*wealth*).

DEBRA *11: The second floor is even worse, your voice echoes over that whole cubicle that the phone is in, the whole circular . . . thing.*[3]

11. Debra echoes and endorses his complaint, thus making a bid for the attention Edward had usurped from her. She rides his bandwagon, a technique which requires little expenditure of energy; Debra does not initiate anything new.

CHAIRMAN *12: Pardon me, I couldn't catch the last . . .*

12. Every manifest reference will not be annotated here. However, all the references are counted and reported in Chapter 7.

DEBRA *13: Me? I say one's voice echoes in that little round corner . . . where the telephone is.*

CHAIRMAN *14: Fred.*

FRED (patient) *15: Ah, upstairs I can see where it would be quite difficult, but downstairs they have booths, ah, outside the ah . . . hospital, you just have to walk past the doctor's offices. You could call there, nobody would bother you. Costs you a dime extra.*

15. Fred introduces an explicit deprivation of Edward in *respect, rectitude,* and *skill*. Others then join in, expressing the group's feeling that Edward's complaint was trivial. In shifting the topic of discussion to his personal complaint about the lack of privacy when telephoning, Edward had made the group vulnerable to the implication that their reproaches of the director were groundless. He had also invited a displacement of the group's attention and aggression away from the director to him. He is now attacked because he has undermined the group's position, in effect at his invitation.

EDWARD *16: You—It's not even a matter of . . . it's not even a matter of that. It's many times that you get calls and not . . .*

3. The telephone used by patients on the second floor (locked) ward is located in the curved hallway which joins the men's and women's wards.

GREGOR (patient) *17: I understood that you could have the call transferred to the phone booth: when you get an incoming call, just ask the nurse to transfer it to the phone booth and take it out there.*
CHARLES *18: I don't know whether the nurse can do it. If it's an out of town call, ah, person-to-person, I think you can get it transferred out to the booth.* (pause)
EDWARD *19: Well, wouldn't anybody feel here that they'd like to talk in private, instead of passing the booth?* (*Some snickers. Pause. Someone mumbles.*)
CHAIRMAN *20: Howard?*
HOWARD (patient) *21: Aren't there um little plugs in the rooms for a telephone?* (*Edward laughs*)
CHAIRMAN *22: Not so far.*
HOWARD *23: Uh, the plugs are there; I don't know whether they're working or not. Right next to the little button that you push for the nurse.*
CHAIRMAN *24: To my knowledge they're not for phones.* (*An unidentified participant mumbles a question.*)
HOWARD *25: Well, I mean there's the call bell plug, and there's uh, right underneath it there's a grouping of holes.*
CHARLES *26: That's to plug the call-bell in there. It's nothing that they can use that runs out.*
HOWARD *27: Oh, I see.* (*An exchange between Adam and Charles that is not clear on the recording. Pause.*)
FRED *28: As long as there's nothing else to bring up, I might as well bring up something that isn't too important . . . As long as it . . . (clears throat), nobody's speaking, I might as well bring up something that isn't too important. Uh . . . the boys, the four-bed ward bathroom, on ah . . . or I should say, the bathtub in the four-bed ward ah . . . Davenport[4] side is busted again. And ah . . . used it the last time, the only thing that came out was cold water. Maybe when they fix the showers they ought to fix the bathtub.*

> 28. Fred now makes a bid to direct the flow of discussion, attempting to focus it upon his personal complaint; a quest for *power.*

CHAIRMAN *29: You told Miss Diamond* (*chief nurse on the locked ward*) *about it?* (*pause*)

---

4. "Davenport" refers to the male side of the hospital since the first floor open men's ward and the second floor locked men's ward are above one another on the Davenport Street side of the building; the women's wards are "Cedar One and Two" since they face Cedar Street. These designations are in general use in the medical center; they evade the use of the reference "psychiatric ward."

29. Fred is deprived by the Chairman's terse dismissal, by the failure of anyone else to respond to his complaint, and by the following introduction of a topic of substantial interest to the group.

CHARLES 30: *Is Mr. Ives [patient] here? I sort of think this is what the meeting is waiting for, at least one of the things the meeting is waiting for.*

30. Charles asks for information (seeks to be indulged in *enlightenment*) and shares information with the group (indulges them in *enlightenment*). His statement offers his assessment that an issue involving Mr. Ives (still unstated) will concern all present; he exercises the *intelligence* function in the decision process, projecting an estimate of what will be of interest in the meeting, as well as offering an explanation of the factors that conditioned the trivial character of the discussion so far, implying that it was simply a warm-up for the awaited issue he now introduces. He makes a (successful) bid for *power* in seeking once again to direct the flow of discussion: he was deprived of *power* when his earlier bids were not successful, and he therefore uses a more substantial and meaningful issue (he plays an ace) to achieve an indulgence in *power*. This act indulges those who wanted this issue discussed and deprived those who did not; the values thus indulged or deprived depend upon the predispositions of the participants.

MISS JACKSON (nurse) 31: *He's on Davenport two. I assume he's not coming.*

CHARLES 32: *Seems—seems to be one of the paragons of virtue around this place. And then all of sudden he takes off. This shook me up quite a bit. I mean aside from a personal relationship with him. This was something, here was a man who had stood pretty solidly for . . . responsibility . . . sort of what would be considered "correct" attitude around here, and he takes off. Somewhat parallel —or at least a little bit parallel to what Gregor did downstairs quite a while ago. (pause)*

32. Charles had earlier (in participation 30) referred to his fellow patient with unusual *respect* ("Mr. Ives"), but he now deprives him in *rectitude* (for running away) and *respect* (implying that he did not deserve the group's esteem). He presents himself as "shook" (deprived in *well-being*) by Ive's action, and in referring to his personal relationship with Ives, presents himself as deprived in *affection* (by the absence of his friend) but at the same time indulges himself in *affection* and *respect*

in referring to his closeness to a prestigious figure in the patient group. "Responsibility" is an important term in the hospital community; it is a key symbol appearing in the dominant ideology (*myth*) of the hospital at this time. "Responsibility" refers to the prevalent *doctrinal* prescription for therapy (*well-being*), for participation in the hospital community's decision processes (*power*), for proper conduct in all interactions with others (*rectitude*); the patient is encouraged to develop *skill* in assuming "responsibility," and is in effect promised *affection, respect,* and other value indulgences if he does. "Responsibility" also refers to the prescriptions constituting the *formula,* the sanctioned rules of the community. The term "responsibility" is also included in the *miranda* (folklore) of the hospital community: it is elaborated in the form of stories of heroes and villains, legends of the hospital's past and prophesies of its future, and jokes and serious slogans. The political impact of Charles' intervention is greatly enhanced by his linking a particular topic to an invocation of a fundamental symbol in the *myth* of the community.

ADAM 33: *Well, first of all, since he isn't here, I don't think we oughta be talking about it. And ah, unless you want to hold another clan meeting and decide . . . And second of all, I'd—in my, my own personal opinion, if Ike was at this meeting, then it would make him feel uncomfortable to talk about his leaving. I don't think it's our business to bring it up. I really don't see what . . . what constructiveness is brought up every time a person leaves to bring 'em up to a meeting like this and hit 'em with responsibility and functioning and all this other stuff. Now this is his problem. He's on the second floor, now, and he can talk to his own doctor about it, and work it out. And I don't think ah . . . ahm . . . I don't know of anything constructive ah I mean after hearing this for the nineteenth time in this meeting. Every time somebody breaks a rule, I don't think—think anything constructive can come out of bringing it up here, except people . . . ah learning the ah . . . ah . . . except people ah . . . having fun telling him ah . . . now this is responsibility, you broke it, and you stood for it, and this is his business, these things are.*

33. Adam joins the issue by a deprivational statement on an ideological level; he invokes an alleged prescription of the formula of patient-staff meetings ("since he isn't here, I don't think we oughta be talking."). He comes to Ives' defense, implying (in referring to him as "Ike") that they are close to one another, and asking that the group not "hold another clan meet-

ing" (deprive) "everytime somebody" (e.g. respected "Ike" or Adam) "breaks a rule." Adam uses this issue, leaning on respected Ives, to express his contempt for the hospital ideology and his wish to be free of it; he uses his asset (base value) of friendship with a respected figure as part of his strategy of seeking to influence the outcome and effects of the decision process to maximize his total value position in the hospital.

CHAIRMAN 34: *Gregor?*

GREGOR 35: *Well ah in answer to Charles, I'd like to say that for myself, I . . . I've been pushing a lot for this patient responsibility business, but as far as I'm personally concerned I don't feel a bit of responsibility for anybody. I feel if I want to take off, I'll take off. If I want to break things, I'll break things. It's only when I'm feeling well that I . . . I do—I consider it's actually good for the hospital and the other patients. But it doesn't—doesn't go in very deep to me. It's very possible that, that I'll break something again, and I can see why Mr. Ives might take off when he was feeling bad. I mean it's one thing when you're feeling good, you can take a . . . ah . . . well, abstract attitude and, and take some distance, and say that you're in favor of responsibility. When you're feeling bad, though, it's quite a different matter.*

35. Gregor joins (uncharacteristically for him) in the defiant expression of a counter-ideological position. He asserts that under various contingencies (e.g. "feeling bad") it is unrealistic to apply this "responsibility" prescription.

CHAIRMAN 36: *Edward.*

EDWARD 37: *Well, Adam, I don't think Charles was bringing it up in the way that he was gonna put Ike on the carpet. I think you didn't look at Charles' feelings. All he was saying was this thing really unnerved him, and he had a right to say it.*

37. Edward shifts the discussion away from the ideological level to vague particulars, indulges Charles in *power* (by backing him up), and in *rectitude* (in assuring the group that his motives were benign). He asks that the group indulge Charles in *respect*, appreciating his feelings and his right to express them. A coalitional situation begins to emerge: Edward defends Charles who has been attacked by Adam and Gregor for attacking Ike. Ives has enjoyed a highly prestigeful position in the hospital community, much envied by Edward, and has frequently used his *skill* as a persuasive speaker and his *respect* and *power* position in the service of making an ass of Edward. Charles has in effect acted as an agent for Edward and Edward

now pays him back and encourages him to continue his attack on Ike.

ADAM 38: *I didn't when I answered that, I did not ah . . . ah mean Charles specifically, but I . . . I had a feeling, this about Ike was going to come up, and I was just sick of it. Every time that a person skips out, or breaks a rule, or does something that—that isn't in . . . labelled—that is labelled irresponsibility is something they are put on the carpet, in my opinion. And I can't see anything constructive that—that comes out of it. In my own opinion, I think patient-responsibility, I'm . . . Is . . . a . . . I don't quite have Gregor's feelings for it, but ah . . . ah, I have ah . . . I do feel somewhat with—I dunno what Gregor meant. To me, to build up those two words, like patient responsibility into the . . . into a mountain, like it's done around here, is completely superficial to me. Because I don't think —I agree with Gregor—I don't think m-most of the patients, and many of them th-that talk about it so constantly and all this, really believe in complete patient responsibility and the whole thing seems somewhat superficial to me.*

38. Adam returns the discussion to the ideological level. He disclaims any intent to deprive Charles, explaining that he had intended rather to deprive the ideology. The ideological symbol "responsibility" is repeated and elaborated; it now becomes "patient responsibility," the specific form more commonly used in these meetings. The implicit allegation is offered that the hospital myth of "responsibility" is given a one-sided *application* by the staff, and a call for defiance is sounded.

CHAIRMAN 39: *Charles.*

ADAM 40: *Well, not completely, but somewhat.*

CHARLES 41: *I've found (clears throat) occasionally in the past when . . . somebody was, use quotes, "called upon the carpet," sometimes I got something from it which I would almost consider personal strength. I was able to experience somewhat what had gone on then. And therefore I can say that I can add this to my own list of feelings that I could control to a certain extent, and utilize, and helping me. Ah . . . in some ways . . . this was quite a surprise for me. In other ways I expected it. As . . . everybody around here's been going through a lotta tension. And I sorta had the feeling that he . . . was going to try and get out from underneath it. And I know I have been in the past couple of weeks, too. I think most of the people on the first floor have been . . . in some way or other. I know I've been doing it as . . . well, too consistently. And I—I think that we can all learn from each other some, I dunno how much. I know I*

can learn some from other people, by listening to . . . to them and
try to figure out what made them do it, and maybe getting a little
insight into myself. I mean this is the only reason I brought it up.
I—I like Mr. Ives an awful lot. I wouldn't want to put him on the
carpet.

41. Charles disclaims any intent to attack Ives personally, offers
an explanation of Ives' conduct (a flight from tension), and
accounts for his own behavior in the meeting as a well-meaning
quest for insight (indulging himself in *rectitude* as well-meaning, in *enlightenment* in seeking insight, in *well-being* in following the recommended therapeutic procedure, and in *skill*
in his demonstration of his facility in explaining the factors
that condition the conduct of all concerned). By emphasizing
his conformity to the ideology, he distracts the group from a
simple alignment for and against Ives, and confuses the image
of his role in the meeting. He thus wards off anticipated *power*
deprivations from those present who identify with Ives, and
invites further indulgences from the staff in *power, well-being,*
skill, affection, respect, rectitude, and *enlightenment* by asserting a position which they approve.

CHAIRMAN 42: *Fred.*

FRED 43: *Well, I'm just going to say that, in a sense, I agree with*
Adam. And ah . . . though Charles brings this problem of ah . . . Mr.
Ives up in a very gentle way, it's obvious that he isn't trying to put
Mr. Ives on the carpet, and maybe trying to learn something from
ah . . . or, try to learn something from what . . . it happened to Mr.
Ives, I would say that ah . . . if Mr. Ives were here, it's no doubt that
it would put him on the spot, no matter how you brought it up.
And a good example would be the many—not the many times—but
the several times that you have done something wrong, occasionally
escaping and so forth. And when it's been brought up here, you've
been put quite a bit on the spot. And you've been . . . y-you've tried
to get out of talking about it. And I could see where anybody put
on the spot in that sense, would not want to be—wouldn't want to
talk about it. And I think that ah . . . the best place to talk about such
a thing is . . . between the doctor and patient, and . . . therapist.

43. Fred accepts Charles' characterization of his position as not
wanting to deprive Ives and as seeking insight; he thus indulges Charles in *power* (by accepting his position) and *recti-*
tude (by seeing Charles' behavior as well-meaning). In agreeing with Adam he seeks to protect Ives from a deprivation in
respect, rectitude, power, and *well-being* by the group, stating

his preference for the handling of this matter in individual treatment rather than in the meeting. He joins Adam in flaunting the ideology and those who support it. Fred aligns himself with Adam and Gregor in defense of Ives, depriving Edward, Charles, and the ideology.

KEITH (patient) *44: Goin' along further on that, I spoke to Ike this mornin' about it, among other things, and talkin' for a good hour there. It strikes me that anybody who wants to know about somethin' like that, should ah go directly to Ike and ask him. I don't think it's ah . . . somethin' that oughta be hashed over behind his back . . . either hashed over at patient-staff meeting when he's there and everybody else is. I think it's ah . . . his business, so if you want to know about it, you oughta go up to him and ask him.*

44. Keith joins the pro-Ives, ideology-depriving bloc.

EDWARD *45: I don't think this conversation should be discontinued. I once read a joke in a Reader's Digest about a leopard that ran away from the Oklahoma City zoo. So they called out the Marines and gave 'em live ammunition, and the sergeant told those stupid privates, he said, "Now when you find the bugger, shoot 'im . . . on the spot." (Laughter from some members of the group.) So once . . . private from Jonesboro Arkansas finds the leopard, he takes aim, and then he stops, and runs back to his sergeant and he says, now, "Which spot?" So it's all a matter of conjecture in quality. No one here is putting Ike Ives on the spot.*

45. Edward reasserts the *rectitude* of the attack on Ives by disclaiming any wish to attack him, using the ideology (it is proper to discuss such events in patient-staff meetings). He invokes humor to release group tension (indulging the group in *well-being*) and to invite the warm attention of the group (indulging himself in *affection* and *respect* to the extent that this effort succeeds and the group laughs). This strategy seeks to deny any malignant intent and rallies the group to participate in an allegedly benign, *enlightenment* and *well-being* seeking "discussion" (attack). Edward again acts as spokesman for the anti-Ives group, responding to the pro-Ives arguments, and seeking to redress the balance in this conflict which he perceived as running against his side.

ADAM *46: Which spot?*

EDWARD *47: That's what I mean.*

CHAIRMAN *48: Debra.*

DEBRA *49: Well, it's rather disturbing to me to see a first floor patient who seemed quite well to me, suddenly on the second floor. I can't help but conjecture about that.*

49. Debra experiences the deprivation of a fellow patient with whom she identifies as a deprivation of herself in *well-being*. She implicitly *deprives* the staff in *skill*, questioning the effectiveness of their therapeutic efforts with Ives.

CHAIRMAN 50: *You mean you would conjecture about whether to talk about it here or not?*

50. The Chairman imputes a question—of interest to him—to a patient as a tactical device for steering the discussion without assuming responsibility for directing it. In form, he indulges the patient in *power* and *enlightenment*, but since he turns the discussion away from the issue actually raised by the patient, deprives her in *respect* and *well-being*. He invites discussion of the ideological issue of whether or not the Ives event should be discussed in the meeting, implies that it should be, and thus casts his weight with the anti-Ives bloc.

DEBRA 51: *Well, yes.*

CHAIRMAN 52: *Dr. Long.*

DR. LONG (chief resident) 53: *I'm just wondering what is so private about somebody escaping from the hospital, ah, we all talk about privacy here. We all knew about it. And at this meeting there are patients, nurses and doctors, staff members; they all knew about it. There is nothing very much private about somebody leaving this place.*

53. The first physician participant other than the Chairman does the Chairman's bidding and discusses the issue he wanted discussed (indulging the Chairman in *power* and *respect*, and joining in the deprivation of the pro-Ives bloc).

KEITH 54: *It wasn't.*

54. Perhaps Keith begins to waiver as a pro-Ives man under the impact of two anti-Ives staff interventions.

CHAIRMAN 55: *Charles.*

CHARLES 56: *I think this sort of denying that we're thinking about this kind of thing. I mean I know I've thought an awful lot about this, because I . . . again when I ran away last time, Mr. Ives asked me up here at the meeting whether it would've helped any if he'd come around and talked to me. Well, I feel like asking the question back at him. If he had—it seems that I am—it wouldn't of done any good, really. It might of a little bit, but . . . it's just a point where y-you just don't take other peoples' intentions very well, and you just wanna get out by yourself, and you have to.*

56. Charles invokes a component of the ideology (one must not deny) to indulge the now staff-supported anti-Ives position, stating it in a form which deprives himself and others ("we're

... denying"). He minimizes the malignant character of his attack on Ives by referring to his having run away himself. He indicates that his attack on Ives may be motivated by Ives having failed to keep informed about his (Charles') former state of inner distress and to be helpful to him at that time. Perhaps, however, he is gaining his revenge for Ives' participation in the "discussion" (attack) of his own running away.

CHAIRMAN 57: *Adam.*

ADAM 58: *Well, on ah coming back to what Fred said before, ahm ... I think that ah ... that you can ... ah ... skipping out, or whatever you do, is between you and your doctor, but ... ahm if a person comes up here, if Ike were up here, and he-he brought it up, or somebody brought it up, and he ... and ... y—Dr. Fleck said to him, if you have anything to say, and he said, "yes I would like to talk about why I did it," or if he brought it up, that he would like to talk about why he did it, then I could see where-where it could be okay. But ah ... I mean it's like ah ... I mean, if he doesn't wanna talk about why he did it, or if he—or if he isn't here to either not talk about why he did it, or talk about why he did it, I can't see any sense in talking about it. It seems like a gossip session to me. And what Dr. Long said about what is so private about somebody skipping out. Well ah ... th-there is ah ... a certain amount of ah ... of privacy in—in ah ... in a lot of things that are known about ah ... a person can skip out, everybody can know about it, but it doesn't mean that everybody should ah ... should ah bring it up in a big clan meeting and talk about it I ... the patient-staff meeting.*

58. Adam counters with a reassertion of the anti-ideology position.

KEITH 59: *Well spoken. (low voice)*

59. Mild support.

CHAIRMAN 60: *Well, how do you interpret ah Mr. Ives' not coming up here?*

60. The Chairman challenges the pro-Ives forces and at the same time initiates the specific discussion of the Ives event they have opposed.

ADAM 61: *He hasn't been out of his room for ah ... since he's been up today, once or twice.*

61. A defense of Ives; he has been deprived enough; it should not be demanded of him that he subject himself to further deprivations by discussion in the meeting.

CHAIRMAN 62: *I think it's he doesn't want to talk about it.*

62. The Chairman accuses Ives of a defiance of the hospital and

its ideology. By emphasizing this sustained deprivation by Ives of the entire hospital community, the Chairman implicitly deprives Ives in many value dimensions. He more openly assumes the role of spokesman for the anti-Ives bloc.

ADAM 63: *I don't know. I haven't discussed it with his doctor.* (*Some laughter in the group.*)

63. An implicit reproach of the Chairman, impugning his *skill* as a psychiatrist for wild speculation and for showing his hand. He mobilizes support from the pro-Ives faction and is personally indulged in *affection* and *respect*.

EDWARD 64: *Good for you, kid.*

64. Edward—the opposing faction—eggs him on by treating Adam with affectionate indulgence, perhaps reflecting his confidence in his faction's likelihood of success with the Chairman on its side.

CHAIRMAN 65: *Ahm . . . and you believe that one patient indicates through such action that something couldn't be talked about, this binds all of us.*

65. The Chairman articulates a *prescription* of the hospital, phrasing it negatively (all patient behavior can be discussed here), and challenges the anti-ideology group to openly oppose this prescription. He continues to lead the attack of the anti-Ives forces.

ADAM 66: *No, his doctor, I think, should ah . . . should be the one to talk with him. I don't think he should . . . he should be ah . . .*

66. Adam begins as if agreeing with the Chairman ("no") but goes on to again defend Ives against group discussion (attack). The disrupted character of his comment may reflect his conflict in openly opposing the Chairman; he deprives himself in *well-being* by enduring the anxiety which is perhaps evoked by his struggle against impulses to attack the leader more vigorously (deprive him in *power* and *respect*) or to escape (from possible counterdeprivations in *power, well-being,* and *respect*).

CHAIRMAN 67: *Well what . . . I'm asking you a specific question ahm . . . which I think we have to answer, and you can answer it, if some person indicates that something shouldn't be talked about, this should bind all of us. What we think, what we talk about. You understand that correctly?*

67. The Chairman behaves like a prosecuting attorney and tries to hold his opponent to a specific issue of his choosing. For the most powerful figure in the hospital to subject a patient to such

a demand involves his being threatened with deprivations in *power* and *respect*. In form, this is offered as instruction in logical thinking (a *skill* indulgence) and as an exercise in full disclosure and candid self-examination (a *well-being* and *enlightenment* indulgence.

ADAM 68: *Yeah. I'm not sayin'* . . . *I don't think it should or it shouldn't, just ah* . . . *what—what is the motive in talking about it up here, when he's not here.*

68. "Yeah" suggests agreement. He indulges the Chairman by appearing to move toward his position, is noncommittal, and then respects an argument defending Ives.

CHAIRMAN 69: *We still have to talk about it to find out.*

69. The Chairman continues to press for total capitulation to the ideology.

ADAM 70: *I'll grant you that.*

70. Adam capitulates.

FRED 71: *I've always gotten the impression when such a thing has been brought up, somebody has escaped or done something wrong, that it's an attempt upon, upon the part of the staff to bring a little bit of group pressure on patients, ah, in such a way that they do not break the rules any more. And yet I get the impression from all the escapes that have occurred, and things that have gone wrong, that talking about it doesn't seem to really stop it. In this particular meeting. And not only that, assuming that this statement that I— which I said was was true, ah, is true, then ah it would seem to really make a patient which is obviously feeling bad any way, feel worse.*

71. Fred steps in to reassert the pro-Ives position by *appraising* such discussions in the past as futile and contending that it will only impose a further *well-being* deprivation on Ives.

CHAIRMAN 72: *Mike.*

MIKE (patient) 73: *The only thing I wanted to mention was the first that time that I heard that Ike Ives had gone was through Adam. He came upstairs with the fantastic news report . . . a . . . blare of trumpets, Ike Ives had run away.*

73. Mike questions the basis for Ives' extraordinary *respect* position, thus depriving in *respect* all present who identify with Ives, especially Adam.

KEITH 74: *Some triumph!* (*in a low voice*)

74. Fickle Keith echoes this *respect* deprivation.

ADAM 75: *Now wait a minute, let me get—may I answer this?* (*to chairman*)

CHAIRMAN 76: *Edward.*

76. The Chairman gives the floor to an anti-Ives speaker, de-

priving Adam of *respect* and *power* (by denying him access to the attention of the group).

EDWARD 77: *Well, I want to caution the group to use the word escape. The past administrator of X University is not the kind of a man . . .*

NANCY (patient) 78: (*laughs*)

EDWARD 79: *. . . who is locked up in jail and escaped. 'Cause I have seen . . .*

UNIDENTIFIED PATIENT 80: *Now we get histories?*

EDWARD 81: *. . . many people run away, including myself. And I don't think that I'm the type of a fella, nor is Ike that escapes. The fact that he came back means he wasn't escaping from anything. But there are lots of times when you can just feel so scratched to the point that you're just gonna get. And that's what Mr. Ives did. He had a growing discontent in him. And I can't feel that everything has a psychiatric quotient in it, because a man has a growing discontent, that he's acting out. Because if that were the case then, there would be no human demonstration in the world that could stand free of accusation. Another thing is that on Adam bringing it up here, I agree with Adam in one particular area, that you don't get a damn thing out of pointing out to a man here. When I brought up with the last group of doctors here the big stink about cooking dinner, Owen (patient) was saying to me, it's so important that we don't drop dinner.[5] Everybody should get in their patient responsibility, etc., etc., etc. And last night when Owen was on duty, on the cook, he just went politely and played volleyball after dinner, and the hell with everybody else. So . . . when a person talks up here and says, I am the moral in the character, I think that's the thing that Adam is saying, let the guy himself figure it out.*

77, 79, 81: Edward has been indulged by the Chairman, and perceiving that he has won the Ives argument, now shifts his role from being a defender of the hospital ideology to attacking it. He obliquely introduces a reproach of the staff for the severe deprivation in *affection* and *well-being* experienced by patients with the change of resident therapists one week before (" . . . the last group of doctors"). By emphasizing the continuing anxiety and discontent experienced by patients he indirectly criticizes the ideology. His loose and disorganized

5. "Dinner" refers to Sunday evening meals prepared and served by the patients. This activity was inaugurated a few months before this meeting after lengthy discussion as an alternative to the usually drab Sunday evening fare offered by the hospital kitchen, and as a chance for the patients to carry something through together.

comments end in seeming agreement with those who oppose discussing Ives in the meeting (and thus defending Ives from attack), but his opposition to discussion emphasizes the deprivation this would inflict on Ives ("let the guy himself figure it out").

CHAIRMAN 82: *Charles.*

CHARLES 83: *I think one of the things around this place which is considered consideration, is really inconsideration. This business of paying no attention to somebody's eccentric—eccentricities and quirks and mild differences, or even strong differences. I think if these things can be brought up in a way that does not seem like you're trying to rip the person or . . . tryin' to hurt him, I think it can be a lot better to get it out in the open, and get it out where it can be beaten about and not definitely a conclusion come out, but—but at least be honest about it. And I know that I have talked with other patients about Mr. Ives' leaving, with some of the patients about Mr. ah . . . Doctor Price (a resident physician), who is a Negro. And this is something new here. It surprised me, shocked me. I'm somewhat prejudiced. I must admit I don't quite know what to do about it. But what I object to is this . . . what really is a clan meeting, it is not an organized or even semi-organized honest discussion. It's a bunch of people creeping around and gossiping. And I think this is one of the things that has to be dealt with, gotten rid of, I don't know what you can do with it. But I don't think we can keep on sneaking around in back of each other.*

83. The introduction of the topic of a Negro resident raises a number of issues including the feelings of all present about the recent change of doctors. In two earlier participations (Adam, 33, and Adam, 58) the "clan meeting" reference had been used, suggesting a latent preoccupation with the issue now explicitly raised. Charles and Edward had been the only anti-Ives patient speakers; Charles now shifts his position as did Edward, vying with Edward for leadership in initiating new discussion. Charles seeks to retain his *power* position as a major directing influence in the discussion; he had first introduced the Ives topic.

CHAIRMAN 84: *Rose.*

ROSE (patient) 85: *Well, I . . . I agree with, with Charles about this gossiping, because I can remember when Sandra (patient) and I took off, ah, it was the same to me, everybody talking about everything else. And then someone brought it up, and everyone wanted to know what happened. And the point was that everybody wanted to know the gossip. Well, Edward touched on the point, he used*

*the word discontent. Well I don't know about Ike Ives, but I know
for myself, that it wasn't just plain discontent with myself. I think
it had to do with the system here. And it seems to me that people
are breaking the rules, and are doing things like this. I mean you
can't just say, well, they're a mental patient. Because ah . . . even if—
if you're a patient in here, you've got feelings just like anybody else.
I think that maybe you oughta look into—into the, the hospital system and what it is that's brooding this discontent. (pause)*

85. Rose avoids the hot topic of Negro Dr. Price and attacks
"the hospital system" which includes not only the *ideology*
(*myth*) but also the whole *technique* of operation of the hospital. She reasserts the reproach of the doctors for the discontent experienced by patients.

CHAIRMAN 86: *Gregor.*

GREGOR 87: *I think it's interesting that two people that oppose an
examination of a person's running away or breaking the rules are
Fred and Adam, both of whom oppose the meal preparation and
both of whom seem not to feel that, that what they do in the hospital affects the other people very much, and therefore subject to
discussion by the other people—Charles . . .*

87. Gregor also stays clear of discussing Dr. Price. He shifts
from his earlier pro-Ives, anti-discussion, anti-ideology position
to a defense of discussion and an attack on its opponents, Fred
and Adam.

ADAM 88: (*interrupting*) *What about yourself?*

GREGOR 89: *. . . Wait a minute. Charles has been discussed up here.
And I don't think he, he objects to it. I was dis- after I broke the win-
dow, it was discussed up here, and I didn't, I thought it was an appropriate topic. . .*

ADAM 90: *Well, you break another one, and then you won't.*

CHAIRMAN 91: *Ah, you don't have the floor Adam.*

ADAM 92: *No, I haven't.*

CHAIRMAN 93: *You through?* (*to Gregor*)

GREGOR 94: *Yeah, I . . . I . . .*

CHAIRMAN 95: *Tom.*

TOM (patient) 96: *Charles, you said you'd like to get the subject of
Mr. Ives out in the open and talk about it. Ah . . .*

CHARLES 97: *I'd prefer that, that he were here.*

TOM 98: *. . . Well, since he isn't—there's no reason to go on talking
about it, because he's not here.*

CHARLES 99: (*peeved*) *I'm talking about it because I think it has to
be brought out whether he's here or not.*

TOM 100: *Well if you're actually talking about the subject in talking about Mr. Ives, you haven't said much about him. Is there something you'd like to say about him?*

CHARLES *101: I don't know anything . . . any intimate material, any more really worth anything.*

EDWARD *102: I think the most important thing that was said ever in this room was the statement that Charles just said about Dr. Price being a Negro. I don't wanna thing like that hangin' over this room. And the reason I don't, is I wanna point out to Charles, an analogy that may be his feelings on it. In nature, (pause). . . . well, Adam, when you get finished havin' yourself a good guffaw . . . .*

102. After others make lame efforts to keep the Ives discussion alive, Edward returns to the topic of Dr. Price.

ADAM *103: (querulous) Can't I laugh?—and fight afterwards an impregnated impulse. Go ahead, I can't stop. Cripes, you even get pinned down for laughing now, every . . . (mumbling about Russia).*

103. Adam has been sat on by the leader (Chairman, 91) and now by Edward for laughing; he feels severely deprived in *power,* and *affection* and *respect.*

EDWARD *104: In nature, in the whole physical world of nature and the whole emotional world of nature, everything turns toward light to survive. This is probably one of the suspicious reasons that has kept Negroes and whites apart. And it might be a thought you never thought of before. But you're tryin' yourself, Charles, to come out of blackness. And you don't like it. You don't like your blackness because you don't know anything about it. A flower turns to the light to live, a . . . an atomic cube of metal turns to a field of light radiation to gather strength [sic], and everything orientates itself on the axis towards light. And Dr. Price may be dark, but that is all the darkness that there is. (pause)*

CHAIRMAN *105: Vic? Fred?*

105. A note of desperation.

FRED *106: Well, I don't wish to leave ah Gregor's little statement unsaid, or un . . . ah . . . how shall I say it, I don't want to leave his statement ah . . . just leaving in the air, leaving . . . let it just hang in the air. Ah, I have been discussed here quite a bit, I assure you. I need only ah . . . ah . . . bring up the one time when I spoke about Dr. Williams [a former resident, no longer on the hospital staff]. I spoke quite a bit then. As for the ah responsibility committee,[6] I was on the responsibility committee, even though I admit I didn't particular*

---

6. "Responsibility committee" refers to the patient committee which organized the preparation and serving of Sunday evening suppers.

wish to be. And I did help make out quite a few of the things, and now when most of the patients don't wish to work on figuring out the list, list of who is supposed to ah . . . work, at what time, I usually have helped. So I would just like to . . . say that. And as for one thing the thing that Edward said, ah . . . in . . . with—with regard to what Charles said, ah, . . . I think that everybody here, whether they know it or they don't, has a little prejudice. And I don't think Charles is bringing this up in such a way, as to deprecate Dr. Price, but rather to state his feelings, which have been ingrained in him as they have been in me and most everybody here, by society. And ah . . . I have nothing against Dr. Price as a doctor, I think he's an excellent doctor, and he happens to be my doctor. And ah . . . and somebody would say to me that he was a no-good such-and-such, well I would say to them, well ah . . . it's very unwise to do such a thing, because he's a very good doctor. Nevertheless, occasionally the feelings are there, and it can't be helped. (pause)

106. The discussion of Dr. Price is directly connected with the issue of the change of doctors in this comment. Fred defends Dr. Price.

CHAIRMAN *107: Keith.*

KEITH *108: This business, Edward brought up about ah . . . creatures . . . (Adam giggles) . . . I'm gettin' to you, this business Edward brought up about creatures ah . . . strainin' towards the light and so on, ah, he brought it up sorta on the dramatic side. I think he made sense. And I don't feature this laughin' goin' on in the background about it, for the simple reason that, like Fred . . . like Fred said ah . . . Dr. Price bein' my doctor, I know the guy. He's a good doctor, and I hold nothin' against him. And as far as what ahm . . . somebody else said, Fred I think it was, ah prejudice is not ingrained in ya unless you let it be ingrained in ya. If you fight off ah what you hear, and sort it out as fact instead of blind prejudice, you come to the same conclusion Fred came to. And ah . . . I don't feature this laughin' goin' on about ah what Edward's saying, 'cause I think it ah . . . that he was makin' sense at the time.*

108. Keith now echoes Edward's attack on Adam for laughing and Fred's defense of Dr. Price.

CHAIRMAN *109: Mike.*

MIKE *110: It seems what we're doing here is . . . something we always . . . as Charles says, we somehow deny . . . ah . . . or overlook the eccentricities of various patients. I think Adam owes not only to Edward, but to the entire group, an apology. I think he's terribly rude.*

110. Mike carries the attack on Adam further: the coalitions

which emerged earlier during the discussion of Ives are sustained in the new discussion.

KEITH *111: Right.*

MIKE *112: I think that everybody has a right to say what he thinks.*

KEITH *113: Right.*

111, 113: Keith echoes again.

CHAIRMAN *114: Zeke.*

ZEKE (patient) *115: If Adam owes you an apology, I do also. The reason I couldn't help laughin' is I, I wouldn't possible see any connection with ah Ike Ives ah leaving here and Dr. Price being a Negro. It just . . . it just, it just didn't fit together. (General laughter in the group). I couldn't . . . I could not—I couldn't help it.*

115. A demonstration of Zeke's *skill* in making an incongruity explicit, offered as a gratuitous self-deprivation in *rectitude*. The group shares his perception and expresses their appreciation of his *skill*.

CHAIRMAN *116: Charles.*

CHARLES *117: I don't agree with you, Edward. I think if I'd been born bright yellow and grown up with people all around me who were bright yellow and I met somebody who was blue, I would immediately react in a sort of surprised and somewhat frightened sense. I think it . . . I've been conditioned to being with people who were white, and people who . . . the people I've become intimate with have been white, and this is the first time I've ever run across a Negro, and encountered as a superior, really, or somebody who's gonna decide about me, instead of me deciding about them, or having nothing to do with them at all. And this is, I can't see this business of turning the light. I think if I'd grown up in a Negro environment and stayed in a Negro environment, and all of a sudden was presented with somebody who was white, who was gonna be in this situation, I would be just as impolite.*

117. Using much the same strategy he employed in introducing the Ives discussion, Charles now invites the group to attack Dr. Price without seeming to do so. He invokes elements in the hospital ideology (offensive feelings and prejudices are derived from earlier life experiences; the good patient is obliged to acknowledge and express them).

CHAIRMAN *118: Adam.*

ADAM *119: I'd just like to say something. Ah . . . about this ah . . . apology that I owe. I . . . I don't know if laughing is being rude. I think laughing is being rude. And I'd like to explain a few things, though. Ah . . . now first of all I have the same feeling that Zeke did, and when something strikes me as being very funny, I laugh. And I can't help it. And I don't think anybody else could either. And anyway I do apologize to the group for being rude, laughing and being rude. But there's another thing I'd like to get . . . get ah . . . across, is what I was laughing about. And it wasn't in ah . . . in ah . . . putting Dr. Price down the scale or anything like . . . the su—the subject, and the thing that I was laughing about is the way that Edward brought it up, which struck me as being very funny. And the way he said in ah . . . in nature and ah . . . in a dramatic way. And it struck me as being funny, and I thought it was funny. Now another thing, Dr. Price (someone coughs) is my doctor also. And today in the se—an I think the second day I saw him, we spent the forty-five minutes discussing about his being a Negro, which ah . . . which did not ah present itself as being any great problem. But ah . . . I would just like to say the whole session today with Dr. Price, or many parts of it, I was laughing at things which he was saying. And I was in a very laughing mood today. And this might've carried over to this meeting. And ah . . . And ah . . . I don't know wha-how Mike gets over here to tell people when they owe other people apologies. And all of this which ah I just don't get at all.*

119. Adam says that he was depriving Edward, not Dr. Price. He defends himself by explaining (*enlightenment*) that he could not control his predispositions (to laugh) under the environmental conditions (Edward's ridiculous and provocative behavior) to which he was exposed. He thus denies responsibility for his behavior, employing strategy similar to that of Charles, who also invoked explanations in the service of such evasions.

CHAIRMAN 120: *Keith.*

KEITH 121: *Ah . . . (clears throat) I'm that far am with Adam, I don't necessarily say that ah he owes the group ah . . . or even Dr. Price, or Edward an apology. I'm just sayin' that ah . . . for the record, I didn't feature this ah . . . business of laughin', I don't think it belonged there, 'cause I think it could've tended to obliterate a good point that Edward was makin'. Ah . . . I don't think ah necessarily that Adam or Zeke, either, owes anybody an apology. But ah . . . I don't think that laughing anybody any good [sic] was understanding what Edward was tryin' to say.*

121. Adrift in a sea of compromises Keith tries to indulge everyone.

CHAIRMAN 122: *Miss Newton.*

MISS NEWTON (chief social worker) 123: *I was just wondering whether there might be some connection between Mr. Ives and Dr.*

Price. Ah . . . someone said that—that ahm . . . Mr. Ives was discontented the past two weeks which may have something to do with the change of staff. And Dr. Price at the moment is epitomized in the newness and the shock of their doctors too.

123. *Enlightenment* in the interest of *well-being.*

CHAIRMAN 124: *Edward.*

EDWARD 125: *Well, if I were Dr. Price, I'd walk out of the room now. Because, no matter what your undertone is here, none of you, goddammit, are makin' him feel as though you're doin' him a favor. And if you say not, I'll call you liars. I wanna tell you why. I know a fella by the name of Arthur A——— in Colorado. He is the head of a riding club. And they're a very bunch of bigoted bastards. They don't like Jews. They don't like Italians, they don't like Spics. If you write 'em a letter, their secretary sends you a "dear John" back. So I went to Art in 1949. And I said, Art I love to ride and I want to get associated with a ranch workin' on a weekend. So he asked me my name, at that time my name was Ekstein. Now he just stopped and looked at me. And then he turned around and in so many nice words he said, "Well, you're a white Jew, it's okay." So I just wanna point out to you, that when I walked outta his office, you know what I was sayin' to him inside myself. And I don't care how much psychiatry he has, how much control of his emotions he has, how much intellect he has, that Dr. Price came from the same idea of creation as anybody else here. And I think that if anybody doesn't treat him that way, they're really slobs! (pause) Even in general discussion don't give 'im the feelin' that you're doing anybody a favor.*

> 125. While ostensibly protecting Dr. Price from aspersion, a whole series of deprivational slanders about low status groups is rehearsed. In gratuitously defending Dr. Price, Edward assumes an unctuous, self-righteous position.

CHAIRMAN 126: *Fred.*

FRED 127: *Well, I'd just like to say that, that ah . . . Charles brought up the idea of being very open, and so forth, yet, one of the few people around here who I found who was completely closed in to himself, practically, is Charles. And ah . . . it seems that ah . . . Mike back there, ah . . . (half laughs) seems to be ah . . . the ah . . . big brother of everybody, and ah . . . he got the name of "Nasty" ah . . . with good cause. And ah . . . I think that if we're gonna talk about things and let them be open, I think we oughta talk maybe about Mike's nastiness and his sarcasm, and maybe Charles' ah . . . fact that— . . . (Mike mumbles a reply which is not clear on the recording. There is some laughter). . . . ah, a—and maybe we ought to talk about Charles' ah . . . Charles' problems out here. He's never spoken about them once that I can remember. And ah . . . I'm very interested, I'd like to hear them. You might as well start.*

127. Fred responds by attacking the other two members of Edward's anti-Ives, pro-ideology coalition, Charles and Mike. These comments depart sharply from the ideological level and again serve to divert discussion from the Dr. Price–doctor change issue.

KEITH *128: Well, what . . .*

FRED *129: . . . Mike want to do such a thing.*

KEITH *130: . . . if they don't want to do it?*

CHAIRMAN *131: Maybe Mike is asking for, is asking, or feels that he's owed, too, an apology about it. I think he made it in some other direction. Dr. Bennett.*

131. The Chairman counters Fred's attack on Mike (a deprivation in *respect* and *rectitude*) with a *respect* indulgence of Mike, appreciating his wish to also be apologized to (see Mike *110* and Adam *119*).

DR. BENNETT (resident physician) *132: Well, what Fred says, I think relates to what I thought was the connection between Mr. Ives being brought up and Dr. Price, in a sense, I think much of the discussion I've listened to centered around the question of what is discussed at this meeting. Ah, what sort of things can be brought out? And it seems to me that the feeling is that if you discuss another patient here, in other than the kind of way that Fred is doing now there's some disloyalty involved in bringing it up here. I was wondering why that is . . . you're being disloyal to your own group in it discussing it here.*

132. Dr. Bennett returns the discussion to the ideological and prescriptive level (all patient behavior may be discussed in these meetings), depriving those who have sought to evade this issue.

CHAIRMAN *133: Zeke?*

ZEKE *134: Well . . . I think what could be brought up is the reason . . . what he said is the reason why I laughed. Ah . . . this meeting seems to be used for some way of being indignant about all sorts of things and other patients. That's all I ever hear at this meeting. And, and it just struck me that everybody is trying to get in their blow a— at the other guy. Like Edward is saying that ahm . . . a Negro is as good as a white or, or this or that, and I'm getting tired of that. And it . . . the whole thing struck me as kinda ridiculous.*

134. Zeke expresses his opposition to the use of the meeting for

the expression of intense destructive power demands. This reflects his core problem with aggression: he constantly fears that he has inadvertantly killed someone or God, retraces his steps to reassure himself, and tries to undo such acts with elaborate rituals (self-deprivation in *rectitude*). In the course of condemning aggression in the meeting, he partially loses control and his destructive impulses break through ("saying that a Negro is as good as a white").

CHAIRMAN 135: *Well, I admit you aren't the only one who remembers, but ah . . . every other week it seems to start out with everybody being indignant at me, at least somebody. Charles. (Laughter.)*

135. A bid for *affection* and for a general release of tension. He may also be trying to identify himself as the target of anger which has been displaced onto Dr. Price. He employs the strategy of reminding the group of their common experience together and of placing the present discussion in an historical perspective ("every other week"). He thus makes a contribution to the development of an enlarged, common, shared self for all members of the hospital community, and thus facilitates the development of group loyalty (*affection*). The responsive laughter of the group does indulge him in affection but is probably also determined by the Chairman having presented himself in an incongruously pathetic role.

CHARLES 136: *I think a closer parallel could be drawn between Dr. Price and Mr. Ives ah . . . I just sorta had the feeling that I sorta think I brought both of 'em up. The similarity I see is Mr. Ives' departure surprised me and so did Dr. Price being a Negro surprise me no end. These two things sorta run concurrently along the same line of, I think, of things that surprised me quite completely.*

136. He reminds the group that he initiated the major topics of discussion in the meeting (Charles indulges Charles in *respect* for the *power* and *skill* he has displayed) and describes the meeting as focusing upon his subjective concerns.

NANCY 137: *(laughs)*

137. Perhaps hebephrenic Nancy perceives Charles' message.

CHARLES 138: *I also wish to—I don't know whether it's necessary to answer Fred or not—but I don't think this is the place to drag your personal therapy out and trot it around. It's not what I'm saying, I don't think, if I am, I wish to withdraw this. What I do think should be discussed, so that perhaps other people can get profit out of it, is other people's acting out in an obvious way. This is what I think we*

*can get profit from each other on. And I think, in a sense, that you
. . . No, I haven't disclosed my private affairs with my doctor. And I
don't think it would be helpful to anybody else, that's entirely to
do with me. But I have brought up, continually, my feelings and
pretty well lay 'em out on the table and let anybody look at 'em that
wanted to. And this is something that you haven't done. And I think
it would be . . . to be ah close about this, you oughta take a look at
yourself first.*

138. Charles again uses his *skill* in affecting a self-revealing pose,
actually revealing nothing of himself, and serving neither therapy (*well-being*) nor self-examination (*enlightenment*).

CHAIRMAN 139: *Rose?*

ROSE 140: *I don't know, Zeke said something about everybody,
y'know, ah one patient against another and this discontent. And I'd
like to repeat what I said before, that with all this discontent, not
only at . . . at patient-staff meetings and sometimes at patient-government, I . . . I still think that the place to start examining it i—is right
here in the hospital system, ah, is there something about the hospital
system, or—let's put it this way, what things about the hospital system ah . . . are causing discontent, and whether it's people against
people, for the sake of being one person against another person for
the sake of being against another person, or ah is it that way because
one is—is in a way, y'know, very discontent with the situation he's in
in the hospital and just what he is or is not getting out of therapy or
. . . and out of the group.*

140. Rose asks, is the ideology deprived because it is intrinsically
at fault, or do people who feel deprived for more personal reasons displace these feelings onto the ideology? She offers both
as possibilities. In so doing, Rose appears to indulge an important prescription in the ideology (examination and explanation
of one's behavior). She had introduced the term "hospital system" earlier (see Rose 85), expressing in this way her sense of
estrangement from the common self which includes the entire
therapeutic community.

CHAIRMAN 141: *Howard.*

HOWARD 142: *(clears throat) I was ah . . . ah . . . stimulated by what
Charles said, everybody's bringing out personal therapy. I think
there's quite a bit of this going on today. I don't know why everybody's bringing out a little ah . . . ah . . . interesting facts about themselves. And I think back to the connection between the reference of
Ike Ives and the reference of Dr. Price. I think, in a sense, this is one
way, seeing that this is ah . . . more or less new, this meeting since*

the new resident staff's come, this is a way for the patients who really ah . . . miss their other doctor, the ones that left, getting to know, and letting the other doctors—the new doctors know that they . . . with the others.

> 142. A more explicit restatement of an earlier, by now obscured, clarification (see Miss Newton *123*): a belated indulgence of those who have sought to pursue the doctor-change issue.

CHAIRMAN *143: Keith.*

KEITH *144: About nine or ten minutes ago ah, Dr. Bennett brought up a point. It's still in my mind, I raised my hand and wasn't called on. And I wanna go back to it for just a minute. Ah . . . he said that he thought in a way that Fred might be being disloyal to a fellow patient, meanin' Mike ah . . . over there, by sayin' what he did about his sarcasm and some of those other . . . I think . . .*

NANCY *145: (high-pitched, short laugh)*

KEITH *146: (mutters something) I think ah . . . ah that ah . . . what he said was ah . . . less ah . . . thinkin' about loyalty or disloyalty, and more a reaction to this ah . . . business of apology that ah Mike brought up before. Ah, I think myself that that was unnecessary, ah . . . I saw kind of a gleam of triumph on his face as he closed in for the kill on that business of the apology action. I don't think that ah . . . I think what I said covered the business . . . enough. And, as I said before, I don't think that ah . . . an apology was ah really necessary. However, ah, I don't ahm think Fred was bein' deliberately disloyal to Mike as a patient. I think it was just disagreein' with him as a person.*

> 144, 146. More compromises. Keith sees the character of his participations in this meeting unrealistically as assertive and authoritative ("I think what I said covered the business . . . enough"): a self-indulgence in *power*.

CHAIRMAN *147: Fred. (pause) Fred.*

FRED *148: Well ah . . . I thought a little bit about what ah . . . Dr. Bennett said and ah have come to the conclusion that ah I don't think it's really ah . . . disloyalty to the group. I don't think that I'm really that way. It's rather that ah . . . It's more that I feel almost a disloyalty to myself bringing up things which are very personal. And now when Charles says before that he's laying his feelings ah . . . on the table so that everybody can see them. Now I know I've rarely seen his feelings, and I wondered how many other people really have. And when he talks about he's feeling like he was a chicken with his head lopped off and so forth, I ah . . . (Adam laughs and others begin to laugh.) . . . I don't see . . .*

> 148. Fred attacks Charles for his evasiveness: he deprives him

in *rectitude* for defying important prescriptions in the ideology (self-examination and discussion: *enlightenment* in the service of *well-being*). Adam is mobilized by Fred's imagery to respond negatively to Charles: others join in.

UNIDENTIFIED PARTICIPANT *149: When did he do that?*

149. A reality-testing confrontation challenging a purported *enlightenment* statement.

FRED *150: Well . . . he talks that way sometimes. I mean I . . . I don't see what good it really does. And I'd like to know, really, ah . . . but if he wishes—well, let's put it this way, ah, you bring up the question of Mr. Ives, you're going to be getting personal questions, no matter whether you want to or you don't want to, because the fact that Mr. Ives stands up for righteousness and then runs away obviously means that something in him deep made him do that. I mean it just seems to be that way. And I don't think this is the place to talk about really personal things. You want it that ah . . . well . . .*

150. Fred resumes the Ives controversy, accusing Charles of hypocrisy (deprivation in *rectitude*) for demanding public discussion of Ives' conduct but evading such discussion of himself.

EDWARD *151: Just a minute . . . Fleck?*

151. A chummy addressing of the chairman-director. Perhaps Edward feels able to take the risk of depriving the chairman in *respect* without fear of retaliation and to permit himself such an indulgence in *power, respect,* and *affection* because he has fought on the same team with the chairman in the Ives controversy.

CHAIRMAN *152: Edward.*

152. Edward is not subjected to a counter-deprivation, vindicating his expectation.

EDWARD *153: I'd like to point out to Fred that I think what Charles has said is extremely true. He is one of the few people up here who has consistently—and I have always remembered this of him—who has consistently expressed the feeling of the one thing he yearns for is control. And to see a reflection of somebody who has some kind of virtue that he can turn to and use.*

153. Edward indulges Charles, his teammate in the Ives controversy, in *rectitude, well-being,* and *enlightenment.* At the same time, however, he implies that Charles seeks *power.* He refers to Charles alleged disillusionment with Ives, thus again taking an opportunity to deprive Ives in *respect* and *rectitude.*

CHAIRMAN *154: Adam.*

ADAM *155: I'd like to just get one thing straight, what Fred said, was that ah Ike stands up f-for righteousness and law and order, what-*

ever it was, but that ah he skipped out, and ah . . . it was something deep in him that made him do it. From what I got you're implying that skipping out isn't very righteous, it's a bad thing. Now to me skipping out is not a bad thing, it's not an unrighteous thing, it is not a disloyal thing to the hospital. And not only that, I don't think Ike felt it was—it was many months ago when he was chairman of the refreshment committee, or whatever it was. And I, I never think Ike ever said anything about skipping out being irresponsible or anything. And I remember the night when, when you and Charles skipped out and went to New York or something and went to the movies, or . . . some night, and said-said to Ike ahm oh, Chester was there and ah, and Ike said "Where is Charles?" or something. We said, ah, "He and Fred took off," and he said, ah, "Oh, yeah?" And we said to him, "Well, do you think that he'll be okay?" He said, "Sure, they can handle themselves, they'll be back in a day or two." And he didn't think skipping out was unrighteous and, or bad, and I don't think it is myself. And I don't see how we can classify Ike as an irresponsible person because he skipped out. All right.

155. Adam chastises Fred who had earlier assumed a more clearly pro-Ives position with Adam for conceding too much to the opposition in depriving Ives in *rectitude;* he reminds him that Ives did not deprive him in *rectitude* when he (Fred) ran away. He invokes a prescription from a counter-ideology (loyalty among patients) as against the therapeutic community ideology (which includes patients *and* staff).

CHAIRMAN 156: *Mrs. ? (Neither her name nor her voice are identifiable on the recording.)*

MRS. ? 157: *(very soft, small voice) All I have to about Mr. Ives. I don't feel that he's trying to escape to his home. Because in the first place that's where he should be. I mean as each one of us has our rightful place in our homes. We're in this place presumably to get help, but it's not a matter of escaping, when you go to something that you is yours. (pause)*

157. An interpolation of a private theme; an effort to indulge Ives in *rectitude.*

CHAIRMAN 158: *Fred. Charles.*

CHARLES 159: *I . . . maybe I'm trying to push myself up a little in the world, but I consider myself one of the preachers of responsibility and being a good boy in general. Well, I . . . have acted out, I've gone out of here in the past and gotten a little bit drunk and I've . . . I've done a whole series of things which I don't think are good. (pause) I . . . think I can control these things, otherwise I wouldn't be on the first floor, I'd end up upstairs. But I feel the only way that this hospital can get into a patient's world so we can help each other is to bring out the things that are—the way we're acting out, and not deep inner motives or our little secrets that are boring here, that's not what I mean. What I mean is . . . I went out and . . . and had a beer because I was uncomfortable, extremely uncomfortable and I didn't want to take this. And I think this is the same reason that Mr. Ives went home. And I know this is the reason why I run away the times I have. You get tense, you get frightened. This place makes you concentrate inward, you can't look anywhere but in yourself and your own tension, and you . . . all you see is the res—the reflection of a bubbling pot of molten feelings. And after a while you can't take this anymore. And when you, you can't take it anymore, you do something. And I guess I've used about every method there is. And I know they don't work. And I think . . . I can help other people find out other, these other methods won't work if they can help me to find out these methods. I mean the only thing you can do is sit there and look at them. It's no fun. But you gotta.*

159. Charles indulges the ideology, refutes the charge that he has evaded disclosing his personal conflicts to the group (without actually doing so), wards off counter-deprivations from Ives and his supporters by now assuming a pro-Ives position, explaining and "understanding" his behavior, and in the course of his comments indulges himself in *power, respect, rectitude, skill, and enlightenment.* He closes with a deprivation of the staff in *skill* and of the ideology, presenting himself as one of its victims, deprived in *well-being.*

CHAIRMAN 160: *Well, Charles, we've got to stop. As I see it, the real question is can people here be helpful to each other or can they not, and therefore sort of a question, is it wrong to discuss them whether they're here or not. I think along with it I . . . I have to, in my own mind, ah, ask the question, can somebody by his absence, so to speak, dictate what we're going to talk about or not talk about. That's all, see you Thursday.*

160. The chairman joins Charles in indulging Charles in *power, respect,* and *affection* in addressing him to the exclusion of others present and in refraining from responding to him critically. He then reasserts the importance of the ideological issue of which he has unsuccessfully sought general discussion.

Transcript II: Patient-Staff Meeting of September 23, 1957

CHAIRMAN (Dr. Fleck) 1: *Is the door closed here? Will you close that door, please?* (*As latecomers are seated there is whispering in the group. The door is closed. A whistle is heard. Silence.*) *I'm sure there must be some people who have not met Dr. Dunn,[7] at least.*

EDWARD 2: *Dr. who?*

CHAIRMAN 3: *Dr. Dunn.*

EDWARD 4: *John?* (*Laughter in the group obscures the chairman's next remark.*)

MIKE 5: (*Laughing—mumbles something*) *Really?*

UNIDENTIFIED PARTICIPANT 6: *Can you smoke in here?*

DR. DUNN 7 : (*whispering*) *What is he saying?*

CHAIRMAN 8: *Generally. The lady next to Dr. Rosenberg. I guess interest in who is here and who isn't is very low.* (*pause*) *Is that right?* (*pause*)

    8. Making a statement in factual form, the Chairman expresses his feeling deprived in *respect, power,* and *affection* by the group's indifference to his efforts to arouse their interest in Dr. Dunn. His comment chastises those who have not given their attention to this topic: he sarcastically implies that they are defying prescriptions in the ideology (pursue *enlightenment* in the service of *well-being;* indulge others in the community in *respect* and *well-being*), and thus deprives them in *rectitude.*

EDWARD 9: *It's not that the interest is low: it's just that anybody here who's a stranger is invariably a psychologist.* (*pause*)

    9. Edward refuses to respond responsibly; he deprives the Chairman in *power* and *respect* by not talking about Dr. Dunn and by introducing a new topic which has the flavor of depriving the professional staff in *respect* ("every ambiguous figure present is a psychologist.")

CHAIRMAN 10: *You see, the rule's been broken.*

    10. A whimsical deprivation of Edward in *enlightenment* ("Your forecast is mistaken"), which also indulges him in *affection* and *respect* by responding directly to him.

EDWARD 11: *No, I mean most—you get a lot of people from the department of psychology coming here. Dr. Everett has, 'course he left.* (*Laughter and talking in the group. Pause. More laughter and talking.*)

UNIDENTIFIED WOMAN PATIENT 12: *I believe it would be fairest to repeat it for the benefit of all, with Mrs. Ferris'* (*patient*) *permission.*

CHAIRMAN 13: *Mrs. Ferris?*

---

7. Dr. Dunn will be identified later; she is not included in the list of participants at the beginning of the transcripts. She has a heavy European accent.

MRS. FERRIS (patient) *14: No!* (*laughter*)

UNIDENTIFIED WOMAN PATIENT *15: We do not have permission.*

MRS. FERRIS *16: I just asked the doctor if it were a Quaker.* (*laughter*) *No disrespect intended.*

EDWARD *17: You're three meetings too late.*[8] (*laughter; pause*)

CHAIRMAN *18: Well, I can report this about the Quakers: I've heard that the difference between the Quakers and the Unitarians is that the Quakers keep their thoughts to themselves and the Unitarians can't. But it also implies that the Quakers are comfortable in doing so.*

> 18. The Chairman is apparently in a jolly mood. He good-naturedly refers to his identification, depriving it and thus himself in *skill*, in self-control ("Unitarians can't keep their thoughts to themselves"), but at the same time indulges himself in rectitude in following an ideological prescription (full disclosure in these hospital meetings.)

UNIDENTIFIED WOMAN PARTICIPANT *19: Yes. I don't know very much about them except in public they don't talk too much.*

DR. ROSENBERG *20: Is that healthy?* (*Pause*)

> 20. The next ranking power figure takes this opportunity to support the Chairman's behavior ("it is healthier to disclose your thoughts as the Chairman does"), echoing the Chairman's earlier challenging of the group on an ideological level.

EDWARD *21: Since Gloria is studying sociology now, I think we ought to hear a few words.* (*laughter*)

GLORIA (patient) *22: It's wild, daddy-o. I think I'll start by analyzing you.*

HOWARD *23: Sociologically speaking.* (*Pause*)

DR. DUNN *24:* (*whispers*) *May I ask a question?* (*speaks*) *May I ask a question? Since first I ah am new here, ah I don't understand what is the meaning of this meeting.* (*laughter*) *When you laugh, I laugh with you because it looks for me very funny. I don't know exactly what is the meaning—meaning of this meeting. Excuse me because I have difficulty to be understand, but try to explain me. I don't know which is the people who is responsible of this meeting.* (*loud laughter*)

> 24. Dr. Dunn asks basic questions in good faith, requesting fundamental *enlightenment* about what is going on and who is in power here. The group's laughter is a non-verbal expression of

---

8. A reference to a discussion of religion, including the fact that Dr. Fleck is a Unitarian.

their latent anger with the authoritative regime of the hospital and their own confusion regarding what these meetings are about.

DR. ROSENBERG 25: *We laugh because we're not sure.* (*loud laughter*)
25. An effort to exploit the therapeutic potential of the situation through *enlightenment* and indulging the ideology by seeking to make feelings explicit.

CHAIRMAN 26: *Well, I don't know whether it's so funny and whether really it's so helpful to Dr. Dunn to beget laughter as response to it. It is really a very serious question for her personally, and I think obviously, as the sounds indicate, for all of us. Dr. Hastings?*
26. A self-indulgence and a deprivation of the group in *rectitude*.

DR. HASTINGS (patient) 27: *Perhaps one way of answering Dr. Dunn's question, I think you refer to the ancient ouija board. (pause) Are you aware of what a ouija board is, Dr. Dunn?*

DR. DUNN 28: *This, I don't understand English . . .*

DR. HASTINGS 29: *A ouija board was an old American superstition, I think it may have come from the other side of the water at one time. But people who believed in this used to sit around the table and the person who was supposed to be able to see more than other people would put her hand on the board too and they would wait for the board to move. And whichever way the board moved, they would learn.*
27, 29: A deprivation of the Chairman and the hospital regime in *respect* offered in the form of an indulgence of Dr. Dunn in *enlightenment*.

CHAIRMAN 30: *Gregor?*

GREGOR 31: *I'd say, Dr. Dunn, that usually at these meetings, these meetings, a lot of people talk about problems that come up in the hospital. This is one of the meetings where nobody has had anything to say. That's why there's been silence. It's not usual to have a-a silence at the beginning of the meeting. There are a lot of problems that come up in the hospital. Different kinds of changes in the way the hospital is run that—that we all talk through. These things haven't been brought up yet.*
31. A serious effort at *enlightenment* which indulges Dr. Dunn in *respect* and implicitly deprives the group in *rectitude* for not fulfilling their ideological obligation (responsible participation in these meetings.)

DR. DUNN 32: *I see. So this meeting, this meeting is not stupid?*

CHAIRMAN 33: *Vic?*

VIC 34: *I think one reason why ah some of us are rather silent is there are three or four new faces there and we've been sort of able to ease in, ah-ah, ease into problems because we know each, ah, other . . . ah, and we know people fairly well, and we're sort of on test now with ah three or four new people and we come to ask ourselves well, again through your eyes, well what are we here for, instead of ah . . . sort of making it more natural. There—there's ah, ah—ah, an awful lot done here. But it doesn't sound like really enough, now.*

34. Vic offers enlightenment in defense of the group in the face of the charge that they have not lived up to their *rectitude* obligations, explaining that they have been silent in the service of *well-being* because they have been deprived in *enlightenment* regarding the people unknown to them in the meeting.

CHAIRMAN 35: *Fred.*

FRED 36: *I was just going to say that, carrying the idea of the ouija board a little further, that, ah the ouija board was a rather dubious way of answering question, and I gather that the meeting is something like this. (laughter; pause)*

36. Fred makes the ouija board analogy a more explicit deprivation of the hospital authorities in *respect* and *skill.*

CHAIRMAN 37: *Keith.*

KEITH 38: *Well, along with what Fred said, ah, I'd like to answer the doctor by say—her first question of what does this meeting mean by telling her that been here for three and a half months and I don't know yet what this meeting means, so you're not alone.*

38. Keith again echoes the discontent of the moment: the group is deprived in *enlightenment* and in *power* ("we can't get them to tell us what these meetings mean.")

MRS. INGALLS (patient) 39: *Doctor, may I say . . . ?*

CHAIRMAN 40: *Mrs. Ingalls?*

MRS. INGALLS 41: *I s'pose I'm the oldest person here. And I've lived in a lonesome country house which is very quiet. And the first two nights I came here the hub-bub nearly drove me crazy. It seemed to me that everybody within listening distance was playing the radio, or a banjo, or singing . . . (laughter) . . . I was just frantic. I have come to feel, though, that those amusements and those entertainments, and the radio, and the television, and the singing, and the getting together and the meetings are a perfectly splendid factor, and they take planning and they take thinking, and they make these young people who are all children to me, grea—make them much happier and now they can bang away all they want to, and I'm glad to hear them . . . it's entirely . . . all right.*

41. A revival meeting testimonial: "I thought I was deprived but now I know that all that noise indulged me in *well-being.*"

KEITH 42: *I'm with you.*

CHAIRMAN 43: *Edward.*

EDWARD 44: *Dr. Dunn, I'd like to answer your question by telling you a joke.*

HOWARD 45: *Oh, oh.*

EDWARD 46: *A lighthouse keeper worked on the lighthouse for thirty years, and every hour on the hour for thirty consecutive years a bell went "boom" and sounded off. So the night before he retired, at 3 o'clock in the morning for the first time the bell didn't go off. He was fast asleep, so he jumped up and he said, "My God! What's that noise?" (laughter)*

MRS. INGALLS 47: *Which means?*

EDWARD 48: *So the definition of quiet can be a very disturbing noise as well as something that sounds noisy and is also defined too. As far as this being a comic opera, this meeting here is quite the contrary because I have found it, and many other patients have found it to be a place that's pretty serious in its implication. Many times we start out this way; there's a lot of levity and a lot of lightness and then somebody'll say something. And it'll start heating the place up. So if you just stick around, you'll see how heated up it can be. But what we do talk about here is what he said, it's primarily the way we look at the doctors, the way the doctors look at us, the administration of the hospital, individual cases . . .*

> 46, 48. Another of the testimonials indulging the ideology offered in response to the Chairman's earlier deprivation of the group in *rectitude* for depriving the ideology.

DR. DUNN 49: *May I ask you a question?*

EDWARD 50: *Yes, Ma'am.*

DR. DUNN 51: *Are you a patient here or ah . . . your face, it's ah . . . (laughter)*

EDWARD 52: *I am a patient.*

DR. DUNN 53: *A patient. Just what people here, I know one one people is not a patient. I am sure of that, it is Dr. Long . . . (some laughter) . . . That I know, and is . . .*

> 53. Dr. Dunn knows a European doctor when she sees one: she indulges Dr. Long in *skill, respect, affection,* and *power.*

EDWARD 54: *I'd like to answer that.*

DR. LONG 55: *I don't think this is really fair though. Because . . . Dr. Dunn came to the hospital the day before yesterday and was so tired and exhausted, she slept most of the time. She couldn't get oriented at all around here. I think in consequence we really should stop joking and somebody, if not now, but later on, should explain, it appears, how this thing operates.*

55. He indulges her in return in *respect* and in *well-being* (protecting her from provocation by the group), indulging the group in *enlightenment* and depriving them in *rectitude*.

EDWARD 56: *Evidently.*

DR. HASTINGS 57: *All right. I started the joking, but obviously the doctor is . . .*

57. An inaccurate self-indulgence in *power*.

DR. DUNN 58: *I don't try to help people. It's—it's only an explication I ah—I ask because I have been—the first time I have been ah . . . inside a hospital psychiatric and unfirm with the key. I was not a patient. And I arrived at this place in my country with some people I was knowing and we meet a man and we look together. And we has —we have—we—it's difficult—for me to explain in English, but we were not patient. And we look a man, and together we ask is a patient or is not a patient, and this man was not a patient. It was a psychiatric doctor. And after this man was a very good friend for us. But if this man was a psychiatric doctor, perhaps one can in his life and certainly he gets some problem to resolve and chooses his career, and chooses his orientation. But I remember and when I talk about that I think it was funny to look around and don't be sure if this man was a doctor or not. And here I am in this (chair? jail?) by another way, I have—I don't know exactly what I am, if I am a doctor or patient. But it's terrific because when I look for you, I look at you, I am not sure . . . of what you are, just this man because I-I have known him before. And I know he's a doctor, but for you, I don't know. I don't say that to hurt you. It is the truth, in my sincerity.*

58. I sincerely seek enlightenment; I do not want to deprive you in *respect* or *well-being*.

EDWARD 59: *Doctor, you, you yourself have not only just started this meeting, but you have answered what the nature of this meeting is . . .*

DR. DUNN 60: *Yes.*

EDWARD 61: *. . . because just the way you talk, and just the way you try to make yourself understood, in our own ways here, is exactly the same thing that we try to do. So that is the fundamental structure of this organization here, of this group meeting . . .*

DR. DUNN 62: *And these . . . ?*

EDWARD 63: *. . . And most of the people sitting around the table are patients. . . .*

DR. DUNN 64: *Yes.*

EDWARD 65: *. . . The nurses are in blue[9] . . . and white . . .*

9. Student nurses present all wear blue uniforms. Some staff nurses wear

DR. DUNN 66: *Yes.*

EDWARD 67: *. . . And the doctors invariably wear a tie,*[10] *except a few of the old patients. (laughter)*

> 59, 61, 63, 65, 67: Edward orients Dr. Dunn, indulging her in enlightenment and respect, but in his tutorial condescension and in his childlike instruction in how to distinguish between doctors, nurses, and patients deprives her in *respect.*

GLORIA 68: *Getting back to what Vic said about silence in the meeting at the beginning. Well I, I came in a few minutes late, but rather than ahm . . . the pa—the new faces being, being something that stops us, I think it gives us a new orientation, and a new way of looking at things. And I've never seen the meeting like this before and I think it's quite in—not only is it interesting but it—it's very . . . it's very helpful in many way, I think too.*

> 68. Gloria had been indulged in *respect, skill,* and *enlightenment* earlier (Edward 21). She now joins in Edward's playacting in which the patients instruct and deprive the childlike doctors.

EDWARD 69: *Dr. Dunn, I'd just like to remind you that at no time since this meeting started today was there any ridicule or slander or any kind of ah . . . type of ah base humor pointed at you by us. Knowing—we all knowing each other here, that we therefore, well, say, have fun with one another before the meeting starts. But it has nothing personal, vraiment, that means truly in French.*

> 69. Edward uses the same strategy he employed in transcript I, vigorously denying his aggression, pompously insisting that there has been no slander or ridicule, indulging himself in *rectitude.*

CHAIRMAN 70: *Mrs. Jones.*

MRS. JONES (patient) 71: *I just wanted . . . (trails off into inaudible whisper)*

CHAIRMAN 72: *Well, to me, it points out the question or the problem why was Dr. Dunn not better oriented prior to the meeting ah . . . by somebody.*

> 72. The Chairman tries to steer the discussion (thus indulging himself in *power*) to a topic he regards as important. It con-

---

white uniforms; other nurses, including the director of nursing and some chief nurses wear street clothes.

10. Not so. Some doctors wear ties and dress as carefully as Edward. Other doctors sometimes appear in open necked sport shirts and without coats. Doctors rarely wear whites except for Dr. Fleck, who always wears a long white coat. Most patients, especially the adolescents, wear blue jeans, sport shirts, bermuda shorts, and informal dresses.

cerns an ideological prescription ("all in the community are to
be helpful to one another").

KENT (patient) 73: *Didn't Dr. Long answer that? He said ah, she
was ah, asleep and she'd been here for these two days in rather ah . . .*

DR. LEARY (resident physician) 74: *Wasn't she up this morning?
She was up fairly early this morning.*

SANDRA 75: *Well I told her that there was going to be a meeting and
she could go, about twenty past two, I guess, explaining to her that
there was a meeting of patients and staff. Guess that's why she . . .*
(*pause*)

DR. HASTINGS 76: *Well, I think that after her rest this morning we
were more interested in answering whatever questions she was willing to ask us, rather than to volunteer information, and bother her
with a lot of unnecessary detail.* (*pause*)

> 73, 75, 76: Patients defend themselves against the Chairman's
> implicit accusation which deprived them in *rectitude*, and also
> against Dr. Leary's amplification of the Chairman's charge (74:
> "she was up and there was time to orient her").

CHAIRMAN 77: *Vic.*

VIC 78: *Ah, I think, again, this brings up the problem of whether the
best process of treating a new patient is to say, "This is the schedule
and this is what you will be doing," or to just impress her or him first
with a friendship to try to understand each other and sort of work
out things as they come along. I know when I first came here, I was
terribly confused for the first week. And ah . . . for even longer, about
the schedule, about who I should look to as a doctor and patient.
Ah, and we had ah, a group of patients serve as a committee to welcome them once or twice; but that didn't really work out, because it
was sort of an official function. And there's nothing so odious as an
official function at times. Ah . . . but ah it is a big question which is
better, to make it—to make sure that the new patient is informed
on everything ah, or just sort of have a schedule, work upon ah her
and just see how it comes out. I have certainly had no knowledge
of the two or three new patients who have come in and this would
be, from what I can see, add a great deal of life and character to the
. . . hospital already. Ah . . . I think there's no doubt about that.*
(*pause*)

> 78. Vic offers policy alternatives for dealing with new patients
> (*intelligence* planning, not yet *promoting* particular alterna-
> tives, in the decision process); at the same time, he deprives the
> hospital in *skill* for the way in which new patients have in the
> past been oriented.

CHAIRMAN 79: *Sandra obviously tried. Anybody else try?*

DR. LONG *80: I-I have to say this all the time, I expect I myself dropped in several times to see ah Dr. Dunn over the weekend and I didn't consider it . . . since she came . . . ah that she had not had rest for several days before she came here, and that she was so exhausted that she preferred to rest. And I think ah patients like Mary (patient), who is in the same room—also respected this and left her alone and to rest up and sleep off her tiredness and this had very little to do with the patients or meeting them or to introduce her. She was up in the air . . . I'm sure about that. Also the other thing is that over the weekend, I wasn't sure that at this point the meeting might make it even more difficult. (Pause)*

80. The Chief Resident, like some of the patients (73, 75, 76), feels called upon to defend himself in response to the Chairman's accusation, a self-indulgence in *rectitude* and *skill*.

EDWARD *81: If I can say so, Dr. Fleck, this is the first time I've ever seen on your face the thought that . . . well it seems that everybody has let the matter down, or let me down. I know I . . . I may be masking it, but I think you think and feel that somehow a kind of a laxity both on the staff and patients' part at the beginning of this meeting probably just because . . . it might reflect, or you might feel it in some way reflects upon you, being the head of the hospital, that a new patient should be introduced to a lot of kidding around like this. I don't know.*

81. Edward again uses a strategy he employed in Transcript I, depriving the Chairman in *power* and *skill*, presenting himself as sympathetically understanding of the Chairman's position, ostensibly indulging him in *affection* and *respect*.

CHAIRMAN *82: I don't know how this makes it for me, I do think we can only confirm what Dr. Long says that we saw Dr. Dunn together this morning, and obviously Dr. Dunn doesn't feel . . . and was feeling quite sleepy and groggy. Of course under the circumstances it might have been helpful to Dr. Dunn not to come to the meeting right today. Because it is very confusing. Would you. . . .*

82. The Chairman now feels called upon to defend himself against the accusations which he had initiated regarding the unskillful handling of Dr. Dunn, probably because Edward has emphasized his responsibility (81: "it reflects on you . . . being head of the hospital").

DR. DUNN *83: May I ask something ah . . .*

CHAIRMAN *84: Surely.*

DR. DUNN *85: . . . this does not concern me and I am very tired about the problem of the other. You, you are interesting, people who*

*are doctor here are interesting about their patient. But here I am not
a doctor, and I am not interesting about . . . them. And I need my
rest and I ask you may I go by my room and take some rest. Yes.
(Dr. Dunn leaves the room.)*

DR. HASTINGS 86: *For what it might be worth, I would like to tell
you about what I have observed, in confirmation of what Dr. Long
said, I visited Dr. Dunn when she was first awake on the ward to
my knowledge and she expressed the desire to rest further, where-
upon I visited a few minutes and left. She was not available, to my
knowledge, until this morning when she was sitting out in the living
room and we were ironing, a group of us. One of the nurses was on
hand and we all engaged her in some desultory conversation. She
asked me who her doctor was. And I said that whoever it was had
spent considerable time with her over the weekend was probably her
doctor. At this point she seemed somewhat relieved and said that oh,
then, she knew who it was, presumably Dr. Long. She had a few
other questions which we answered as best we could. She still
seemed somewhat tired, so we didn't press information upon her.
She came to lunch and had a pleasant time as far as I could see. She
didn't sit at my table, but the others seemed to be getting along with
her all right. (Pause)*

86. More defensive reports (*enlightenment*) indulging both patients, including the speaker, and staff in *rectitude* and *skill*. Her
double identity (clinical psychologist and patient) is reflected.

CHAIRMAN 87: *Mr. Ives.*

MR. IVES 88: *I'm wondering whether I'm the only one who failed to
discern that she was a patient until she so declared herself. I thought
she was a visiting medico.*[11]

88. *Enlightenment.*

CHAIRMAN 89: *Well . . . I ah . . . (pause) . . . did want her introduced
in one sense, and I think this is what Edward picked up right away,
that if she were a visiting fireman of some sort, a psychologist or
otherwise, why can't ah . . . other people in the room be curious
about and would be wanting to know or wondering who it is. Neal.*

89. Although it seems relatively clear that the staff has assumed
major responsibility for handling new and disturbed patients,
the Chairman is attempting to enlarge the scope of the patients' sense of responsibility for orienting new patients; a deprivation of the patients in *rectitude* (arousing their guilt).

11. Dr. Dunn, 28, "schizophrenic," entered the hospital as a patient, confused and disoriented, three days prior to this meeting. She had come to the
United States to participate in a medical research project one month before.

NEAL (patient) 90: *Well, i-it seems to me that ah often in the past that ah there's naturally interest, but I think people's manners ah on the whole are such that they feel that the move ah comes from the chair and that to be overly inquisitive is not polite. Now ah, sometimes it hasn't worked this way. But I, I was puzzled by the same question that Mr. Ives was, that I, when you said, ah, isn't anybody curious about new faces and Dr. Dunn, that I didn't know what her status was here and I thought I'd be embarrassing to ask that question, "Are you a doctor ah on the staff here or are you a patient?"*

90. Further *enlightenment* in extenuation.

CHAIRMAN 91: *Ah, at the expense of Dr. Dunn, unfortunately, to some extent, doesn't point up ah the situation as it should be, in a way, because it doesn't make so much difference whether it's a patient or a psychologist . . . on the staff. Tom?*

91. The Chairman *invokes* prescriptions in the hospital ideology ("we're not doctors or patients here, we are all citizens of the community here," and "in avoiding an issue for fear of embarrassing someone, we may deprive others, particularly the very person we do not want to embarrass, of needed attention and help, *respect, affection,* and *enlightenment* in the service of *well-being*"). He keeps the ideological issue in the focus of attention (trying to transmit *skill*), and continues his deprivation of the patients in *rectitude*.

TOM 92: *Well ah when you introduced her was there any reason why you didn't introduce her as a new patient? I never saw her before, and she came out of Dr. Olson's (resident physician) office just as I went in, but I never saw her before that . . .*

92. A counter-accusation, depriving the Chairman in *rectitude* and *skill*.

MR. IVES 93: *She's not the only new patient who is here for the first time.*

TOM 94: *I didn't know there was a new patient when I was upstairs some time ago.*

MR. IVES 95: *She's not the only new patient who's here for the first time.*

95. Insistent *enlightenment*.

CHAIRMAN 96: *No, but I wasn't aware that she was asleep most of the weekend. This is the first opportunity, certainly, I assume for the most of the first-floor people to meet up with her. Half the patients don't show up until just before the meeting. Dr. Leary.*

96. The Chairman pleads ignorance: "I was deprived in *enlightenment*."

DR. LEARY 97: *I'm wondering what sort of a group spirit prevails*

*that this situation could ah happen. And it strikes me that in a small
forty bed unit, if there was communication, if there was very good
group spirit that everybody would be aware of who is coming, what
they were, etc., etc. And it strikes me that this indicates ah certain
disharmony or disinterest. I don't know whether this is correct or not
and I was wondering whether there aren't three or four patients that
were admitted, what way they felt about the first four hours.*

97. A resident counterattacks, echoing the Chairman's deprivation of the patients in *rectitude*.

CHAIRMAN 98: *Mike.*

MIKE 99: *I gather when I came here that Dr. Powers [chief resident
until July, 1957] announced to the patients, all of them on both floors,
I believe, that I was going to arrive. And since Dr. Long has taken
over his position this has never been done to my knowledge, that the
new patient has been announced or he will come. And I-I don't know
whether it's really a question of patient responsibility whether they
should know or not, or whether it's Dr. Long's responsibility to let
us know that this is happening.*

99. "It isn't the patients' responsibility, it's the staff's—especially
the Chief Resident's—responsibility": a counterattack depriving
the staff in *skill, respect,* and *rectitude*.

CHAIRMAN 100: *Well, this could not be announced in advance because nobody knew about it in advance. Neal.*

100. The Chairman continues his self-serving declaration indulging the staff in *rectitude*: "they were deprived in *enlightenment* and could not therefore effectively apply their skill."

NEAL 101: *Ah, this in reply to Dr. Leary; this is a subject we've di-
gested here in the past year very thoroughly that ah . . . as Dr. Fleck
just pointed out it's a rare occasion, as Dr. Powers said on so many
occasions, when you can tell ah in advance that somebody is coming.
He did in the case of Betty and in the case of Mike. Ah, but it's a rare
thing around here. And I think that ah, as has been pointed out, ah
how ah Dr. Dunn has spent the last forty-eight hours and people respecting her privacy, that ah it's ah . . . things ah happened the way
they did out of people's kindness and consideration.*

101. Neal defends the staff against an attack upon their *skill*
allegedly made by Dr. Leary (97) in which Dr. Leary had actually made no reference to staff and had deprived the patients
in *rectitude*. Neal offers his comment as a condescending *enlightenment* of Dr. Leary (thus depriving him in *respect*).

CHAIRMAN 102: *Fred.*

FRED 103: *Well, I think maybe one of the reasons why ah people ah
more or less ah were sarcastic in a sense in laughing at Dr. Dunn was*

because she was new here. But I don't think that was the only reason. I think ah it had really nothing to do with Dr. Dunn as far as I, I felt, because I don't know Dr. Dunn and I know—I do know several of the other new patients that came here and I think they are all very nice. But I—I felt the general feeling of annoyance at this meeting and having to come up here because we come here and we talk about the same thing over and over again. Maybe one, one week we talk about one thing, the next week we talk about another thing. But it gets all-it-it goes over and over and over again, just like a record playing over and it gets rather boring after a while.

103. A rebellious deprivation of the ideology.

CHAIRMAN *104: Gloria.*

GLORIA *105: The one thing I was thinking about in connection with Dr. Dunn was ah if I were to end up in a foreign mental institution with foreign psychiatrists and foreign nurses I'd be even more confused than going to an American one. And one of the main points of communication here and ways in which you get help is through talking, and this met—could possibly make things twice as difficult and make it more, twice as important for the patients to take a stand and, and help her around in the ward, because of ah just having to communicate and having difficulty is a problem in itself anywhere, and then also to be in a place so suddenly and without really knowing, so far as I could see, that she was going to land here must make it doubly tough.*

105. An indulgence of Dr. Dunn in *respect*. Gloria compensates for having joined with Edward in attacking Dr. Dunn (Gloria, 68) and also displays the professional know-how ascribed to her earlier (Edward, *21*), indulging herself in *skill* and *rectitude*.

CHAIRMAN *106: Vic.*

VIC *107: Ah, I'd like to quickly ah say that I don't think anybody was laughing at her, and it was more of a sharing and-and a pleasant surprise that somebody could be so completely sincere about asking questions that most of us have been sort of ah . . . (half-laughs) well, I think she did a marvelous job, and I think all of us were very impressed by it, and I don't think anybody laughed at her, Fred.*

107. An indulgence of Dr. Dunn, and a deprivation of all others present, in *rectitude*. He laughs instead of completing the statement in which he began to criticize the group, in conflict about the risks to his own value position of subjecting them to such a deprivation and inviting counter-deprivations. He ends with an indulgence of the group in *rectitude*.

EDWARD *108: Nor was anybody sarcastic I think.*

108. Edward echoes this indulgence, again demonstrating his capacity for denial (Edward, 69).

VIC *109: Yes.*

CHAIRMAN *110: Mary.*

MARY *111: I was just going to say that she didn't land here without knowing she has to come here herself. At least that's what she told me when I was speaking of the meetings. It will was. . . .*

111. A comment which appears to be addressed to something going on inside of Mary rather than to the discussion.

CHAIRMAN *112: Dr. Hastings.*

DR. HASTINGS *113: Regarding the question of her language difficulty, she did ask me this morning whether I was able to understand her adequately, and I replied that I was and that if I shouldn't be able to I would tell her so. I think that her English is probably much better than we could speak her language under the same circumstances. And I've had no difficulty in communicating with her in English and I don't believe the other patients have either.*

113. Indulgence of Dr. Dunn in *respect.*

CHAIRMAN *114: Gregor.*

GREGOR *115: Well, I wonder whether there's really enough material for two meetings of this sort or whether we ought to go back to one meeting,[12] because I think this isn't the only meeting where there's been silence, and I notice in ah patient-government there've been a lot of meetings where there hasn't been too much taken up, whether a fuller meeting of patient-government and just one meeting on Thursday mightn't be better than two meetings a week.*

115. Gregor joins Fred in depriving the ideology, but the form of his comment is more that of a constructive *appraisal.* Gregor has been a vigorous proponent of the ideology, although he appears disgruntled at the moment.

CHAIRMAN *116: Edward.*

EDWARD *117: Well, I think if we drop this meeting, we would be doin' a fatal error, I mean drop one of the meetings, because Fred said that it's the same theme. I have been in therapy goin' on three years plus and I guess I've just said about the same God-damned thing to the psychiatrist in different shades for three years. Now how many people here in this room say something new to their psychiatrist? Ah, now you may be able to express a new idea, but it's on the*

12. Patient-staff meeting had initially been held once weekly; they began meeting twice each week in the spring of the year of this meeting.

same central theme. How many people here have a theme that they say to their psychiatrist over a six months' period? (laughter)

> 117. Edward indulges a psychotherapeutic prescription ("talk is useful"), reducing it to an absurd form which burlesques it ("it doesn't matter if you don't really say anything or say the same thing over and over again for years without gaining understanding"), depriving its participants in *respect*. The laughter of the group constitutes their indulging themselves in a deprivation of the powers that be in *respect* and *skill*.

CHAIRMAN *118: Mrs. Ferris, Mrs. Ferris.*

MRS. FERRIS *119: I would like to say, if it doesn't seem presumptuous, that this lady, Dr. Dunn is it, does speak French, and I've been in France a good deal and studied it. If the time ever comes when it would be a convenience to her or her doctor to have somebody to translate, I'd be very glad to offer my services.*

> 119. A self-indulgence in *skill* and *rectitude*.

EDWARD *120: Dr. Fleck I wasn't finished with my . . . with having the floor.*

CHAIRMAN *121: Well, I'm awfully sorry. (laughter)*

> 121. The Chairman uses this opportunity to permit the group to release tension (indulges them in *well-being*). Edward participates with him in a court jester-like role; the Chairman indulges him in *affection*.

EDWARD *122: No, I mean, I mean I, I never wanted back the floor, but I mean I . . . it, my speech was just started. (Pause. Laughter. Talking in the group.)*

CHAIRMAN *123: Mike, I wasn't sure whether you had your hand up, Mike, or not.*

MIKE *124: It seems to me that we are still faced with the fact that we have a lot of difficulty welcoming or getting to know new patients. Dr. Fleck has said well, we didn't know that she was coming before hand, but he also didn't say that there was-hasn't been absolutely no opportunities since she has come for Dr. Long or one of her, or her own doctor, whoever it is, to make some effort to help us and . . . get to know each other a little better.*

> 124. A deprivation of the staff in *skill* and *rectitude*.

CHAIRMAN *125: Vic.*

VIC *126: Ah, it seems to me the hospital will ah never find an easy way to greet a new patient. Ah, I think one of the best ways is to have some doctor recognize the fact aloud to the new patient that it must be terribly hard for them ah over here. And it is, and nobody ever recognizes that fact. You, when you first started, you said, you gave the impression, well something must be wrong, it really should be terribly easy, or if we plan things right you wouldn't feel this way. Well, I don't think that's right, I think she'd feel, feel this way anyway. And I ah . . . I don't understand the function of ah . . . having her ah the focal point ah . . . at first anyway. But I really do think that if some doctor in-in this meeting could acknowledge to a new patient that it must be terribly hard for her or him and that if he had to try, to try, well granted to try to make it easier. This is never done, there's always an . . . ah some sort of implication that it really would be easier if things were, if the wheels were oiled or . . . or something. I don't think that's helpful.*

126. Vic offers a policy alternative for the group's consideration about how new patients should be oriented, referring to alleged failures to date, supporting Mike's deprivation of the staff in *skill* and *rectitude*.

CHAIRMAN *127: I find I fail to follow the point you're talking about.*

127. A defense of the staff which deprives Vic in *skill* as a speaker, alleging obscurity. His comment is offered in the form of a self-deprivation in *enlightenment*.

DR. HASTINGS *128: I would like to go back to Dr. Leary's question about how some of the other new patients feel about the way they were welcomed here, differ with the last speaker on this point. I know that with my own entrance to the hospital, and as soon as was convenient for the other patients so that it would not disturb their rest, I was welcomed to the room that I now have, and the nurse was available to talk to me and answer my questions, ah, apparently with limitless time on her hands, with nothing to do but talk to me. My doctor made it clear to me that I must have many feelings about being admitted here as a patient and that he was willing to listen and to understand these. When it came to my first meal in the dining room, a nurse escorted me to the dining room and indicated some of the patients that she thought I would enjoy having lunch with. I was introduced to them and I had a rather pleasant lunch except for a little kidding about being a doctor. This I tried to take in good part, and thereupon was fairly well accepted by the group, I felt, and went on my ahm well, scarcely merry way, accepting the fact that I was a patient.*

128. All are indulged, especially the speaker.

CHAIRMAN *129: Fred.*

FRED *130: I think it's rather strange that ah . . . I think it's ra—I think it's rather strange that ah . . . when Dr. Dunn asked the question of what this meeting is for, nobody could really give a decent answer, including the doctors . . . who made this meeting. And I think perhaps if ah they were to give this meeting some definite purpose, and if the purpose isn't broad enough, then they might broaden it. At least they might have . . . it would be easier to re—easier to explain it, if nothing else. And as for ah . . . ah . . . the trouble that Dunn had, I think that perhaps if one of the doctors was—when a new patient came in—was to ah introduce the new patient to all the other patients and to the other doctors, then the problem which Dr. Dunn had would be eliminated.*

130. An impatient and blunt confrontation which is calculated to both *enlighten* and discomfit. He makes explicit the reaction expressed earlier in laughter by the group in response to Dr. Dunn's questions about the meaning of these meetings, and addresses himself to the further consideration of policy questions.

CHAIRMAN *131: Edward.*

EDWARD *132: While Fred is talking today I think this is a good theme that we should get on, talking about definiteness versus vaguery. Ah what I said before about . . . how many people here actually said something new to their physician once they've gotten the story out or started to get the basis of the story out. It all goes around one theme . . . (Someone is tapping his fingers on the conference table throughout Edward's statement.)*

132. Edward purports to support Fred's effort to face issues squarely, but then returns to the topic of repetitively saying nothing in psychotherapy.

MIKE *133: How would you define it?*

EDWARD *134: It all goes around one theme. I myself from my own experience have found this: at first I thought this theme was a waste of time because mental sickness absorbs yourself, but then I found out, Fred, that it wasn't, 'cause like in group therapy I told Dr. Quinn [resident physician]—Quinn in the group that I have fallen down probably four and a half million times since I've been in this hospital, both literally and figuratively, and each time I've come back because I've said the same thing over again. So I want to know what disqualifies you from defining yourself and being able to define yourself that we should have to cut down on something which is definition.*

CHAIRMAN *135: Neal.*

NEAL *136: Ah, Fred, I think this is a very interesting point and I think that ah her raising what the meeting is for ah set us about questioning again and then we didn't have it down pat enough, but it seems to me that-that ah, I don't know if everybody agrees with this, I feel*

*it strongly, that the most precious things in life are very very hard
to define. I mean two examples that came to my mind, "strong character," "good government." I mean you can give definitions but you
can't get the whole thing because it's such a comprehensive thing,
and ah . . . I think this ah is something that maybe we should accept
more. I mean ah I think most people would agree, I know I feel that
this is a meeting what ah is very meaningful to everybody's life here:
I mean sometimes they're good, sometimes they're bad but over a
period of weeks I think it's a great asset.*

136. A comprehensive indulgence of the proceedings.

CHAIRMAN 137: *Dr. Long.*

DR. LONG 138: *I was ah just wanted to make one comment on what
Mike said. I think he was right. I goofed on introducing Dr. Dunn in
a way. However, ahm on her admission I felt—and this is my feeling
many times—that it is perhaps better to leave a patient alone for a
couple of days: I particularly want to mention despite the fact that
Sandra was very upset over the weekend, she volunteered to talk ah
to Dr. Dunn when she seemed to be available. She complained on
her admission that it is more difficult for her to speak English. I am
sure this was an immense difficulty, she has been . . . knowledge for
only three months or so; Sandra volunteered to be able to breach
this gap for us for the present time . . . probably forgotten ahm and
it would be best when she feels better or at least to find out whether
she would have been better off, you know, us rushing and meeting
her, or whether in this instance this has been a bad ordeal for her,
I'm not sure, you may be right.*

138. The Chief Resident concedes a partial deprivation in *skill.*

CHAIRMAN 139: *Well, ah I'm going to point out the way I see it. I
wonder whether it was advisable to ask or allow ah Dr. Dunn to
come up to this meeting, when somebody in ah questioning it before,
because when a patient does come to the meeting ah, while I could
make an effort to find out in detail, the assumption is the patient
knows, is oriented about the meeting and has at least met the patients on a particular floor. And ah I could have figured for myself
that this was hardly possible in this case, and the fact she was here.
So I think that we did err in ah letting her come without preparing
her for it. Gloria.*

139. The Chairman joins in the concession. By conforming to an
ideological prescription ("full disclosure, however painful"),
he indulges himself in *rectitude.*

GLORIA 140: *Isn't there some ah happy medium be-between rushing
up to a patient and overwhelming them and ah staying completely
aloof? Even when a patient is feeling very bad or seems to be feeling*

terrible or seems to want—want to be left alone or, or rest, I'm sure that five minutes of—of casual introduction of someone she's seen in the hall, and nurse to be with her and explain that this is a patient and this is the dining room and, and things that are necessary to any-one who lives on the second floor, that this could be something which doesn't have to be overwhelming nor false, but could be rather natural and casual which is, is very important, as far as I can see from the way Dr. Dunn reacted it is. It was terribly important to her to find out exactly the function of the different people and, and to explain, perhaps before she went to patient-staff, I don't see any reason why a patient shouldn't go to patient-staff but perhaps she could be explained the, the function of patient-staff to a certain de-gree that we air problems here and that we bring things out into the open, anything we feel like bringing out, we may do so. And ah ahm ther-there are certain d—there are doctors, nurses and patients here and social workers and psychologists, and that when she gets to the meeting if ah, the doc—who-whoever is her doctor can help intro-duce her to the various, to the various doctors and patients. And I don't think it should take so much time, nor could it take so much effort from Dr. Dunn and that she'd be so exhausted from this.

140. A careful, relatively comprehensive enunciation of the complicated considerations involved in orienting a new patient.

CHAIRMAN *141: Well, ah there's something you can't know, Gloria, in this instance that the reason it's so difficult and ah while it doesn't take much time, Dr. Dunn has had a lot of medication and it proba-bly still might be hard to think, in view of it, from one minute to the next right now, assuming . . . must realize that. Ah, Mike?*

141. The Chairman treats Gloria with *respect*, and contributes an *enlightening* point.

MIKE *142: I was only going to say that I . . . was in something of the same situation with Mr. Ives. He and I didn't know until . . . I'm still not terribly sure she is a patient. And I, and I, and upstairs I was here most of the weekend and I never knew that there was another person there that I hadn't known before. And it just seems sort of strange, and that no one knew of the fact, did you know?*

142. Mike discloses his persisting uncertainty about whether Dr. Dunn is really a patient (*enlightenment*). He thus empha-sizes his need for assistance from the staff in comprehending reality.

HOWARD *143: Why should I?*

CHAIRMAN *144: Fred.*

FRED *145: Well, ah, I would agree with you Neal, when you say that*

ah, that some things are very difficult to define, but ah . . . neverthe-
less when a patient comes in here, they have absolutely nothing to
which to hold on to, and ah . . . I sometimes think that poor definition
is better than none at all, especially for a new patient that comes
here. And ah, I think that more than a poor definition could be made
of ah patient-staff, ah, certainly with the help of the doctors.
CHAIRMAN *146: I wonder if you would mind repeating what you had*
said, Howard. I think it's very cogent. You didn't know that she was
here either, did you?

146. The Chairman singles Howard out for attack, drawing the
group's attention to his comment (Howard, *143*) in which he
deprived an ideological prescription ("we are meant to inform
ourselves about one another as part of assuming responsibility
for one another"). Howard's brusque disclaimer of responsibility had apparently irritated him.

HOWARD *147: I don't know.*
CHAIRMAN *148: What you said to Mike just now?*
HOWARD *149: I said no, why should I?*
KEITH *150: I was gonna say that ah in view of the fact you said that*
ah she was on medication sleepin' most of the weekend, or so, ah I
think just about everything that ah, could be done by people who
were gonna do it, I think, was done. I mean ah I don't see how she
coulda been ah, you know, ah told any more than she was ah, con-
siderin' the fact that she was ah sleeping for the past coupla days that
she's been here.
CHAIRMAN *151: Neal.*
NEAL *152: I think ah another point ah in reply to Dr. Leary's ques-*
tion that ah this happened about a year ago this time. A man was ad-
mitted, Dr. Rogers [former patient], ah as a patient and ah, while
ah there is such a reservoir among the patients of kindness and good-
will and consideration for one another, ah at this particular time,
I don't think ah the patient-body has acted worse in my experience,
that they were ah put on edge and were ah made very nervous by ah
the introduction of the new patient; and I think particularly the fact
that he was a medical man. And there was a really terrible ah display
in the dining room. I, we discussed this at length, and I think peo-
ple since that time may have taken a, a different attitude that ah to
be ah . . . less obtrusive, less noisy, ah . . . when a new patient is first
admitted. I—I think certainly the, the improvement in regard to new
patients has been tremendous the last few months.

150, 152: Keith and Neal offer favorable appraisals of the hospital's treatment of new patients.

CHAIRMAN *153: Well, we have to close, I—I do want to pick up*

Howard's remark, because I think it indicates the kind of feeling apparently that made for the silence at the beginning of the meeting. Why should I, why should I bother about anybody here. I think it's . . .

HOWARD 154: *But I said that?*

CHAIRMAN 155: *Ah . . . ah . . . it's this attitude that makes for discomfort and ah silence at the beginning of this meeting and in many other situations apparently, that it's easier not to be involved and ahm . . .*

HOWARD 156: *I w-was misquoted.*

CHAIRMAN 157: *. . . stay kind of settled within one's own preoccupations. Ahm . . . you have not been misquoted because everybody heard what you said. (laughing) That's why I asked you to repeat it so that would . . .*

> 153, 155, 157: The Chairman elaborates on his attack on Howard.

HOWARD 158: *Well, maybe it was geared to the question you asked me. You said, "Did you know she'd been here," and I said, "Why should I?" and the "why should I" was, "nobody had told me." I had no idea at all that there was a new patient here. That is the answer to "Why should I?"*

> 156, 158: Efforts at defense. Howard denies any intent to deprive the ideology.

CHAIRMAN 159: *Well that's a . . .*

DR. HASTINGS 160: *I would like to bring up the possibility . . .*

CHAIRMAN 161: *Let's go on on Thursday.*

7. Value-Institution Analysis of the Meetings[1]

A cursory inspection of the patient-staff meeting transcripts is enough to dissipate illusory expectations revealed when laymen, at least, are told of an attempt to engage psychiatric patients and staff together in regular discussions in a mental hospital. Frightening images persist from the days when witches flew abroad, and when an addled mind was the sure sign of a compact with Satan. It is not astonishing that every step toward living and working together without special concessions to craziness is taken fearfully: innovation challenges that degree of complacency arduously achieved by relatively stabilized patients and requires the staff to meet new and exacting demands.

The patient-staff meeting transcripts read remarkably like the verbatim records of large committee meetings or small conferences any-

1. The procedures of content analysis used in the present study were applied by Mrs. Peggy Vranesh, who has had much experience as a coder of psychiatric interview protocols, including work under Professor John Dollard, which required the application of techniques of this kind. Note that two separate sets of reference, the one quantitative, the other qualitative, are made to the verbatim records. The quantitative summaries result from Mrs. Vranesh's coding, validated by test runs with Rubenstein and Lasswell, conducted to make sure that the value and decision process definitions (which are contained in the text of Chapter 7) were being interpreted in the same way. The qualitative notes, which characterize the changing tactics of the participants in the meetings, were prepared by Rubenstein and Lasswell. They are not restricted to the "manifest content" of the record, but draw upon all sources of inference available to the interpreters. If the volume of recorded material analyzed were greater, it would be practicable to adopt a formal scheme of coding which would permit the interplay at the meetings to be described quantitatively. This would constitute a much more "intensive" standpoint of observation than the relatively "extensive" (surface) standpoint utilized in the coding procedure adopted in this study. The coding method used permits a wider comparability of the more evident characteristics of the patient-staff meetings with other meetings of a deliberative character in American or other than American societies.

Content analysis requires the choice of "reading units" and "recording units." The coder was authorized to read sentences in the verbatim text and to record any relevant reference that occurred in a sentence, noting the number of lines (lines of transcript of standard length as typed on specially prepared forms) of the whole sentence in which the reference appeared. In this way, duplicated references, if found in the same statement, were avoided. The coder's self-consistency was high, approximating 95 in 100 in test runs. This is the usual result in such procedures since, after a brief learning period, coders stabilize their perspectives in interpreting rules. In check runs (with the coder and the authors), we were content to fluctuate near 90 in 100.

On the many considerations that enter into judgments of this kind see Harold

where. If there were initial doubts about whether any patient would raise his voice and speak out, fears that "mad men's raving" would disrupt the public dialogue, or supposed dangers to life and limb involved in bringing "crazy people" into the same room, such apprehensions have been dispelled.

However, courage was required to initiate such a new set of social practices. The whole posture of the hospital community was altered, and, as we shall see in later chapters, coercive instrumentalities and stratagems from the recent and remote past were modified.

To what extent is it justifiable to assert that the meetings constituted steps toward genuine democratic participation, that patients were given an effective voice in decisions? Political scientists and jurists are professionally involved in making appraisals of this kind when they refer to the conventionally recognized institutions of politics and law. Only recently have the rewards of stepping outside traditional boundaries and scrutinizing the decision process of unofficial institutions anywhere in society been recognized. It is especially worthwhile to confront the research problems presented by such highly circumscribed situations as the patient-staff meetings. Technical innovations are necessary to bring out the subtler interplay of power and other values in the context.

Among the devices now at the disposal of political and social scientists are the quantitative description of communications (content analysis). The fundamental idea is quite simple. Words can be recognized by speakers and readers of a language. Hence it is possible to count the frequency with which words or groups of words are used by individual communicators or by groups. Innumerable complications can be introduced into the description of what people write or

D. Lasswell, Nathan Leites, and associates, *The Language of Politics: Studies in Quantitative Semantics* (New York, George W. Stewart, 1949, republished 1966 by the M.I.T. Press, Cambridge, Mass.). See also Bernard Berelson, "Content Analysis," in Gardner Lindzey, ed., *Handbook of Social Psychology* (Cambridge, Mass., Addison-Wesley, 1954), pp. 488–522, and Ithiel de Sola Pool, ed., *Trends in Content Analysis* (Urbana, University of Illinois Press, 1959). Concerning the study of clinically derived materials, consult John Dollard, Frederick Auld, Jr., and Alice M. White, *Steps in Psychotherapy* (New York, Macmillan, 1953); E. J. Murphy, "A Content Analysis Method for Studying Psychotherapy," *Psychological Monographs, 70,* (1956) (Whole No. 420). It will eventually be helpful to compare the results obtained by various modes of subjecting verbatim reports to quantitative summary. Note especially Phillip J. Stone, Robert F. Bales, J. Zvi Namenwirth, and Daniel M. Ogilvie, "The General Inquirer: A Computer System for Content Analysis and Retrieval Based on the Sentence as a Unit of Information," *Behavioral Science, 7* (1962), 484–94. A volume by Philip Stone and associates on the general inquirer procedure is announced by the M.I.T. Press for 1966. We plan in subsequent studies to deal in more detail with problems of content analysis.

say to one another, and it is important to pursue such complications so long as they contribute helpful answers. It is no less important to adopt a *methodical sequence* as investigation moves from a relatively simple, matter-of-fact position of observation to standpoints of increasing scope and sophistication.

For present purposes it is convenient to begin by relying on uncomplicated methods. We do this in part because some of the most interesting questions about a decision process can receive a sound, through provisional, answer if we deal directly with the *manifest content* of what is said. By examining "who says what to whom," we may reach a working conclusion about the degree to which power is genuinely shared.

When words in a verbatim text are classified according to manifest content, the classifier reads the text solely to identify usages for a reader who, let us say, commands high-school English. Many localisms and vocational words will be overlooked by this method. (If more detail seems worth obtaining, it can be recorded by classifiers who operate under more specialized instructions.)

The six transcripts are studied from several perspectives to disclose the finer structure of the decision process of the meetings. Some features will be emphasized for the sake of stimulating a wider and deeper study of decision processes than has been usual up to the present. Only when decisions are studied microscopically can we become aware of problems that are overlooked when they are examined by wholly conventional and approximate methods. It is more usual to assume that institutional arrangements survive "because people get something out of them" than to try to demonstrate whereof the "something" consists.

In preparation for recognizing the significance of the findings, imagine the most extreme limit of nonparticipation on the part of the patients. The summary would then read: No statements are made about events in the hospital; no changes in hospital practice are recommended or promoted; no rules are voted; no provisional stand is taken on or applied to particular problems; no appraisals are made of hospital aims and performances; no established practices are terminated.

The Setting of the Meetings

That the physical setting in which meetings occur is of some importance for the process of decision is part of the lore of political scientists, even though it is easier to demonstrate that political differences originally affected internal architecture more than architectural constraints influenced political alignment. Proceedings are modified by structural factors that over- or underemphasize the role of particular participants. When small galleries are built for spectators, it is usually evident that the occupants are to keep their distance and also to keep the peace. The dignity of presiding officers may be inflated by elevating them above the floor and leaving both a gap and a physical barrier between them and the floor. Respected emblems of power (flag, gavel, mace, or uniform) can suggest that deliberations proceed decorously.

The physical arrangements of patient-staff meetings at the YPI were conducive to informality. The room appeared full when the sixty people who usually attend were present. The chairman sat at the head of a long table. Other participants chose chairs distributed randomly around the table or along the walls. The chairman was on the same physical level as the group. His dignity was enhanced by a white medical coat which only he wore. It was difficult to distinguish patients from staff unless they were previously identified. Visitors were often present; they were sometimes introduced to the group by the chairman. Parliamentary procedures were at a bare minimum: the chair was addressed to obtain the floor. In 1957–58 there was no agenda of topics or speakers, although subjects discussed were often anticipated in hospital gossip.

Attendance

The extent and basis for attendance are of obvious importance in characterizing a decision body. More than ninety per cent of patients and staff members on duty usually attended patient-staff meetings (thirty-five or more patients, about twenty-five staff members, the director, assistant director, and chief resident, the six residents, three to five social workers, one or two psychologists, three group and activities workers, five or more nurses, the business manager, and an occasional aide). Others who were not part of the hospital community also attended (three to eight student nurses rotating through the hospital for brief periods of training, and visitors, usually physicians from other hospitals or departments of psychiatry). Attendance was required of patients unless it was impossible because of an acute psychotic crisis or because conflicting obligations at work or school were judged to be more pressing by staff or, after 1957–58, by the patient-staff advisory committee.

Talk and Silence

Persons unacquainted with patient-staff meetings are curious to learn whether patients were willing and able to speak up. The record is

TABLE 1   Participation in Patient-Staff Meetings:
Amount of Talking and Silence (Minutes)

Meeting	1	2	3	4	5	6	Average
Patients	47′	30′	36′	38′	32′	33′	36 min.
Talked	35″	59″	0″	22″	37″	2″	26 sec.
Staff	3′	15′	16′	7′	6′	13′	10 min.
Talked	0″	16″	16″	14″	50″	23″	20 sec.
Silence	6′	6′	7′	5′	10′	11′	7 min.
	21″	25″	34″	2″	48″	19″	55 sec.
Total	56′	52′	59′	50′	50′	57′	54 min.
Meeting	56″	40″	50″	38″	15″	44″	41 sec.
Time							

unequivocal: patients did most of the talking. In the first transcript, for example, patients spoke for over forty-seven minutes, the staff for three minutes. The other meetings followed this same pattern: patients did about eighty per cent of the talking, the staff about twenty per cent (Table 1). Of patients and staff present, between one-third and one-half participated actively (Table 2). In all but one of the meetings analyzed, the percentage of patients (of patients present) who spoke was higher than the percentage of staff members (of staff present) who actively participated (Table 2).

The extent to which silence was tolerated was impressive: from ten to twenty per cent of meeting time (Table 1). Conferences often began with periods of silence, which were sometimes explicitly deplored by patient participants. The silence pattern is in striking contrast to practices that usually prevail in other decision bodies. Silence is a rarity in the Senate and House of Representatives, and in arguments before the Supreme Court. There may be occasional pauses in committees and courts while someone pores over a document, but silences are rarely tolerated, and a recess is usually taken when no one asks for the floor. At the YPI, silence may derive in part from the participants' familiarity with the toleration of silence as an accepted practice in psychotherapy. Such silence patterns are also characteristic of some institutions which encourage religious and ethical meditation (as a Quaker meeting), groups engaged in operations which demand individual concentration (such as a game of bridge), and groups seeking to avoid detection (an underground party meeting).

In considering patterns of silence and verbal participation in

TABLE 2   Participation in Patient-Staff Meetings:
Number of Speakers[a]

Meeting	1	2	3	4	5	6	Average
Patients							
Male	10	11	7	15	13	13	11.5
Female	5	8	1	4	3	6	4.5
Unidentified	1	1	1	1	1	1	1
Total	16	20	9	20	17	20	17
Staff							
Director[b]							
Asst. Dir.			1	1	1		
Chf. Res.	1	1	1	1			
Residents	1	1	3	3	1	1	1.6
Nurses	1		1		1	4	1.1
Soc. Wkrs.	1		1		1	1	.6
Other Staff						1	
Total	5	4	7	5	4	8	5.5
Total Number of Speakers	21	24	16	25	21	28	22.5

a. There are usually about 35 patients and 25 staff members present at patient-staff meetings.

b. The director was absent from Meetings 3 and 4; they were chaired by the assistant director.

deliberative bodies, it is important to examine the conscious perspectives of each of the participants and to analyze their efforts to employ strategies that will culminate in the greatest net value indulgences to them. Such efforts are not always available to conscious control; a patient may remain mute despite his wish to communicate, frustrated by factors within himself that block speech. Other variables, including the demands, expectations, and identity systems of participants—to be understood only by detailed familiarity with the given social context—influence active participation and silence patterns. An example is the seasonal flow of activity in the hospital.

July marks the beginning of the YPI year with the arrival of new residents. Patients realistically expect to obtain advantages by participating at that time. They want their therapist and other residents to get to know them as soon as possible. It is frightening and lonely if the resident on duty at night or weekends does not know the patient and cannot anticipate difficulties that may arise; it is only when the therapist is familiar with the patient that he is likely to approve an extension of his privileges. At this time of shift in staff,

TABLE 3 Frequency of Participation in Patient-Staff Meetings
(Number of participations by each category of speaker)

Meeting	1	2	3	4	5	6	Average
Patients							
Maximum[1]	18	26	13	25	15	23	20
Total	103	106	47	131	90	111	98
Staff							
Director	17	30			26	47	
Asst. Dir.		2	9	9			
Chf. Res.	1	3	3	7			
Residents	1	2	13	7	4	5	6.5
Nurses	1		1		1	8	1.8
Soc. Wkrs.	1		2		1	1	.8
Other Staff						6	
Total	21	37	28	23	32	67	34.6
Total Number of Participations[2]	124	143	75	154	122	178	132.6
Chairman Acknowledgements[3]	35	26	13	21	13	25	22.1

1. Maximum number of participations by a single patient speaker.
2. Does not include chairman acknowledgements.
3. Acknowledgements by the chairman of participants who raise their hand to gain the floor.

patients are better informed than new residents about YPI procedures and institutions. By participating actively, they help assure the continuation of power sharing in the hospital. New residents are cautious as they face teachers, bosses, colleagues, and patients. The taciturnity of the staff and the relative talkativeness of patients at the beginning of the hospital year is illustrated in the July meeting: patients spoke 103 times, often very briefly, some repeatedly (one patient spoke eighteen times, others fifteen, thirteen, and eleven times); five staff members participated a total of twenty-one times, but seventeen occasions must be attributed to the director (these participations do not include routine acknowledgements by the director-chairman). One nurse, one social worker, and two physicians, in addition to the chairman, each spoke once: the July meeting consisted in a dialogue between patients and the chairman (Table 3). Although the staff becomes more voluble as the year proceeds, the chairman and patients are consistently most active.

Participation in the Phases of Decision

The transcripts were analyzed to discover whether YPI patients do in fact participate in detail in policy making and execution. We have analyzed a decision process into seven phases: intelligence, promoting or recommending, prescribing, invoking, applying, appraising, and terminating. The manifest content of statements were classified according to the contribution they made to the phases of decision; hence the relative prominence of these phases of the decision process in patient-staff meeting deliberations was determined (Table 4).

Intelligence

The intelligence phase of the decision process includes exchanges of information and planning (short of promotional activity or the adoption of programs). For example: "But what we do talk about here is . . . primarily the way we look at the doctors, the way the doctors look at us, the administration of the hospital, individual cases" (2, 48).

"Well, uh, there's something you can't know, Gloria, in this instance that the reason it's so difficult . . . Dr. Dunn has had a lot of medication and it probably still might be hard to think, in view of it, from one minute to the next right now" (2, 141).

"The fact that Mr. Ives stands up for righteousness and then runs away obviously means that something in him deep made him do that" (1, 150).

"May I ask a question? Since first I, ah, am new here, ah, I don't understand what is the meaning of this meeting" (2, 24).

The following provides a relatively detailed guide for the classification of *intelligence statements:* what did happen; what will happen; is happening; planning; matter-of-fact assertions, statements given in "fact form," as though they were true designations of events (however, there is no implication that the coder regards the assertions as true or false); specifications of goal without expression of preference or determination in regard to it: the specification of operational indices relating to individual or collective events whether subjective, behavioral, physiological, or part of the surroundings; assertions about past trends of events when unaccompanied by evaluation; explanations given as statements that identify determining (causal) factors, formulate the pattern of determinative impact, purportedly verify (or fail to verify) an explanation; estimates of the future in "fact form" statements, unaccompanied by appraisal; prediction of probable consequences under stated contingencies (unaccompanied by evaluation); formulation of probable consequences of policy

TABLE 4   Phases of the Decision Process in Patient-Staff
Meetings (Percentages of units[a] in each phase)

Meeting	1	2	3	4	5	6	Average (%)
INTELLIGENCE							
Patients	45	38	21	61	56	47	44+
Staff	6	20	3	11	12	21	12+
Total	51	58	24	72	68	68	56+
APPRAISAL							
Patients	38	22	36	17	16	14	23+
Staff	2	5	20	0	4	2	5+
Total	40	27	56	17	20	16	29+
PROMOTION							
Patients	5	2	2	<1	0	6	2+
Staff	0	0	5	0	0	2	1+
Total	0	2	7	<1	0	8	3+
INVOCATION							
Patients	<1	1	1	1	1	1	1
Staff	0	1	8	<1	<1	0	1+
Total	<1	2	9	1+	1+	1	2+
APPLICATION							
Patients	<1	5	2	5	8	1	3+
Staff	0	3	0	2	1	3	1+
Total	<1	8	2	7	9	4	5+
PRESCRIPTION							
Patients	0	0	<1	<1	0	0	<1
Staff	0	0	0	<1	0	0	<1
Total	0	0	<1	<1	0	0	<1
TERMINATION							
Patients	0	0	0	0	0	0	0
Staff	0	0	0	0	0	0	0
Total	0	0	0	0	0	0	0

a. A unit is one line of transcript of standard length as typed on special forms.

alternatives (similarly free from expressions of preference or volition); mention of policy alternatives (without commitment by statement maker).

Analysis of the six transcripts clearly delineates the great importance of intelligence in these meetings: fifty-six per cent of all meaningful statements by patients and staff combined were in the intelligence category (see Table 4).

Promotion

The promoting phase of the decision process adds a demand for action to the simple statement of a possible option. For example: "Why don't you just plan on starting the meeting five minutes early?" (6, *21*)

"I don't see why we can't have a-a, a movie group go outside to the movies on either Saturday or Sunday night, I guess Sunday night would be better" (6, *150*).

"Ah, it seems to me that the hospital will, ah, never find an easy way to greet a new patient. Ah, I think one of the best ways is to have some doctor recognize the fact aloud to the new patient that it must be terribly hard for them, ah, over here" (2, *126*).

The instructions for *promotional or recommending statements:* pressure for a general policy innovation or against proposed change (going beyond mere mention of an alternative to expressions of preference or volition); advocacy of new hospital rules or changes in the rules of society; alterations of structures, not particular applications.

Less than four per cent of all meaningful statements in the analyzed transcripts belong in the promotion category (see Table 4).

Prescription

Because no formal votes are taken at patient-staff meetings, almost no statements constitute explicit prescriptions. Although many intelligence, promotional, and appraising statements refer to prescriptions alleged to be part of the authoritative code of the hospital or of the meetings, they do not affect calculations for the prescription phase.

The authoritative position of the chairman renders his every formulation of a possible norm important. Such statements are often phrased as interrogations. For example:

CHAIRMAN: "And you believe that one patient indicates through such action that something couldn't be talked about, this binds all of us" (1, *65*).

PATIENT: "No" (1, *66*).

Instructions for identifying *prescriptive statements:* instituting a general hospital rule: formal declaration of a "hospital law" or affirmation that such a law exists.

Prescriptive statements are negligible in these meetings, much less than one per cent (see Table 4).

Invocation

Invocations apply alleged prescriptions to concrete situations. In patient-staff meetings, invocations tend to precipitate discussion of the legitimacy of a particular act by a patient or staff member or call attention to a problem situation within the jurisdiction of the hospital community. For example:

CHAIRMAN: "We're talking about why people are late, Abner, and what we can do about it" (6, 7).

"Well, first of all, since he isn't here I don't think we ought to be talking about it" (2, 33).

"The staff . . . didn't want this at this time [to allow me to go to a party]. Ah, I'd like to know, ah, at this time if the staff has any ideas about why this was" (4, 53).

"Is Mr. Ives here? . . . Seems . . . seems to be one of the paragons of virtue around this place. And then all of a sudden he takes off" (1, 30,32).

"We're gonna start? Well, ah (pause), well, has anything then happened about freeing the second floor at all?" (3, 4)

Guides for *invocation statements:* demands to apply general prescriptions to concrete circumstances; a proposed provisional finding of conformity or nonconformity. The prescriptions invoked include the alleged rules of the hospital or general standards of another group, or even of an individual "who makes his own rules." They typically appear in the form of adverse criticism of specific individuals or acts: invocation of any procedure is equivalent to arrest and indictment (not of final judgment or punishment).

Only two per cent of the meaningful assertions made in the analyzed transcripts were in this category (see Table 4).

Application

Application, unlike invocation, is perceived by the participants as final, rather than provisional. Since patient-staff meetings do not adopt different procedures to delimit a preliminary and a final problem under consideration, the line between invocation and application is indistinct, unless the classifier regards as "application" all further discussion of a concrete normative issue after it has been introduced.

CHAIRMAN: "So I think that we did err in, ah, letting her come without preparing her for it" (2, 139).

DR. LONG: "I goofed on introducing Dr. Dunn in a way" (2, 138).

PATIENT: "And I need my rest and I ask you may I go to my room and take some rest" (2, 85).

The instructions for *application:* final, rather than provisional or preliminary, characterization of concrete circumstances as conforming to, or deviating from, a prescription. A person or an act may be formally referred to, and the judgment is expected to be made effective. Application involves the expected use of sanctions, that is, of value indulgences or deprivations allegedly justified by the judgment of conformity or deviation; many alleged objectives may be asserted to guide or justify the sanction (for example, *deterrence* of future deviation; *withdrawal,* that is, bringing the current deviation to a stop; *restoration,* or reestablishing the situation as far as possible as it was at the start; *prevention,* or reforms intended to reduce provocations to nonconformity; *reconstruction,* or revolution rather than reform of institutions; *correction,* or the reconstruction of individuals to overcome lack of capability or opportunity to conform); many justifications may be alleged on behalf of, or against, these objectives (such as rectitude, "punishment" and "Divine will"); procedures of application may include arbitration as well as administrative "hearing and judgment."

Patient-staff meetings devote very little time to application. Few explicit decisions are made that are expected to be put into effect. At times the chairman or some other staff member exercises his judgment, or characterizes a judgment, in ways that lie clearly within his jurisdiction in the hospital, as in the examples cited. But applications constitute only five per cent of the meaningful statements made in the analyzed meetings (see Table 4).

Appraisal

Appraisals refer to an aggregate flow of events that are characterized according to the goal values (or specified objectives) of the community. All participants, patients and staff, made many appraisal statements. For example: "I, we discussed this at length . . . I think certainly the, the improvement in regard to new patients has been tremendous the last few months" (2, *152*).

"It seems to me that in the last couple of weeks there has been quite a let-down in the amount of organized activity that's going on around here" (6, *129*).

UNIDENTIFIED PARTICIPANT: "Nothing was planned" (6, *139*).

CHAIRMAN: "Maybe this has something to do with the members of the committee, they're not very . . ." (laughter) (6, *140*).

"I think the basic reason . . . is that, that for a long time, not so much now, ah everything had to be planned around this place, ah, and if you didn't plan on something, you got hell for it" (6, *193*).

Instructions for *appraisal statements:* characterizations of the aggregate flow of events in terms of the policy goals alleged to be sought; assertions that the hospital is succeeding or failing to accomplish its overriding objectives, or that particular objectives are attained or not. Theoretically an appraisal statement can be free (or nearly free) of commitment by the statement-maker to any other value goal than discovering "the facts" about the degree to which generally recognized objectives have been achieved. But statements are often accompanied by commitments for or against the policies in terms of which the appraisal is made. Hence appraisals purport to proceed within the frame of hospital policy or of some other set of policies. Appraisals refer to past events; future references are part of the intelligence function. Assessments of particular cases are part of invocation and application. Appraisals also include attribution of responsibility to persons or impersonal factors.

The appraisal function plays a prominent part in patient-staff meeting deliberations. Over twenty-nine per cent of statements in the transcripts were in this category (see Table 4).

Termination

The seventh decision phase, termination, plays no role in these meetings because of the absence of explicit prescriptions. The instructions for the categorizing of *termination statements:* explicit formal declaration that prescriptions are no longer authoritative; an allegation that prescriptions are, in fact, obsolete. Demands may sometimes be justified by saying that the termination of a prescription has had disadvantageous consequences for which the group is accountable, that is, the prescription permitted various expectations of advantage to become stabilized as grounds of behavior. Termination includes whatever arrangements are made to compensate an individual for reasonable expectations regarding "rights" that have been permitted to grow up while the prescription was in effect.

General Characterization

Two phases of the decision process emerge as especially important in patient-staff meeting deliberations: intelligence and appraisal. Promotion, invocation, and application are underemphasized; prescription and termination are not important in the meetings.

These findings contrast with results obtained in examining other decision bodies, e.g. an appellate court, where lawyers for the plaintiff or defendant promote the cause of their clients within the framework of authoritative prescription as effectively applied by the judge. In the context of the decision process of the larger community, the court is specialized to the application phase of decision; there is little of the ambiguity of outcome apparently characteristic of patient-staff meetings.

The impression of ambiguity of outcome is confirmed in comparing patient-staff meetings with a municipal council or a board of trustees. Such councils and boards vote; they leave a record of easily identified prescription, termination, and application. Of all the various structures of government, the patient-staff meeting seems most like an advisory council that refrains from pressing its advice to the point of formal resolutions. Deliberations in patient-staff meetings culminated in no legislative statutes, executive regulations, or judicial decisions. The record suggests that these meetings share very modestly in the YPI power process.

If this initial impression is accurate, patient-staff meetings might presently be dismissed by patients in a manner similar to their rejection of ineffective patient government. The meetings could also become a substantial instrument of power sharing in the hospital. A serious estimate of their future requires the systematic exploration of the value indulgences and deprivations obtained by patients and staff from the meetings.

Value Indulgences And Deprivations

In any human situation, "tone" comes in large part from the pattern of indulgent or deprivational communications. For example, contrast with a bitter, hostile, quarrelsome, backbiting debate the tone of a meeting in which everybody acclaims everybody else. If participants make disparaging remarks about one another, it is reasonable to ask what net value advantage keeps the discussion going.

In capturing the tone of a meeting, we can classify the symbols that identify the participants according to the positive (indulgent) or negative (deprivational) references made to them. The following excerpts, far from exhaustive of the many combinations that occur, indicate how these categories are used.

Power

"I mean y—in a sense you're [the chairman] reacting the same way, you're getting irritated with us just as we're being (laughing) irritated with you. You're threatening us just as we sorta threaten the hospital" (6, 84: deprivations of chairman and staff).

"Well, I'm quite aware that this hospital attempts to take responsibility for the patients, and in doing so, they place on me rules that are designed to protect six-year-olds, and I'm not a six-year-old . . . I hate these rules!" (*4, 146:* deprivation of hospital prescriptions)

Enlightenment

"As long as no one's gonna say anything intelligent, I might as well say something silly" (1, *10:* deprivation of all present and the speaker himself).

"We may live with the patients, but I must be the exception, I even . . . I was thinking that we have no way, really, of knowing how a person feels, or whether he's tense or not" (3, *62:* deprivation of self).

Wealth

"It's now six days since we learned that Vic's father would have to withdraw him" [The patient had been informed that the family could no longer afford his remaining in a private hospital] (5, *77:* deprivation of patient).

"And if Vic wants to come on over he's welcome to stay there for a week or so, if he has to leave the hospital . . . He can get started that way and find his own place" (5, *92:* indulgence of patient).

Well-being

"The people that are tensest are the ones that on the weekend are left by themselves" (6, *177:* deprivation of patients).

"I said yesterday when I went upstairs on the second floor I was impressed with the idea . . . the way the hospital allows the patient to sit away and sit away and sit away. And I often wonder what is the wisdom . . . in allowing and letting people just sit there in the same environment" (4, *24:* deprivation of staff).

Affection

"I-I like Mr. Ives an awful lot" (1, *41:* indulgence of patient).

"I was merely going to say that I found Vic a much more sympathetic individual since he's been under pressure the last few days" (5, *62:* indulgence of patient).

Respect

"Dr. Price is a Negro . . . and this is quite new here. It surprised me, shocked me. I'm somewhat prejudiced" (1, *83:* deprivation of staff).

"I think he's terribly rude" (1, *110:* deprivation of patient).

TABLE 5   Percentages of Value Indulgence and Deprivation
Statements by Patients and Staff Combined[a]

Meeting	1	2	3	4	5	6	Average
INDULGENCES	14	33	33	6.5	34	10	21.7%
DEPRIVATIONS	31	25	41	21	41	31	31.7

a. Calculated as per cent of units which could be categorized under a value.

Rectitude

"It's not your fault and it's not the patients' fault" (6, *159:* indulgent of staff and patients).

"Well, I . . . have acted out, I've gone out of here in the past and gotten a little bit drunk and I've . . . I've done a whole series of things which I don't think are good" (1, *159:* deprivation of self).

The Overall Balance

Deprivational statements by staff and patients are more frequent in the six transcripts, taken as a whole, than indulgences (see Table 5). The ratio is about three deprivational references to two indulgences (31.7 per cent to 21.7 per cent). Only one meeting (the second) contained more indulgences than deprivations (33 per cent to 25 per cent). The fourth and sixth transcripts show the most marked excess of deprivations (ratios of about one indulgence to three deprivational statements). All statements not included in these calculations involved no clear-cut positive or negative reference.

These results reflect hospital events already described. The deprivational balance was greater in the July meeting, when patients had just been separated from their resident therapists of the previous year, in December, with increased concern about family problems at Christmas, and in June when separation from current residents was imminent.

The flow of value indulgences and deprivations is only incompletely indicated by examining manifest content: words are only part of the interactions among patient-staff meeting participants. The analysis may be refined by employing other techniques. For example, if the speaker who makes a deprivational statement is presumed to obtain some gratification from doing so, it is not implausible to adjust the gross picture by adding the number of deprivational statements to the explicitly indulgent statements. If the number of deprivations is added to the indulgences, the balance of indulgence exceeds the negative references by five to three (53.4 per cent to 31.7 per cent).

TABLE 6   Ratio of Value Indulgences and Deprivations in
Statements of Patients and Staff

Meeting	1	2	3	4	5	6	Average
Indulgences							
by Patients	13	22	19	4	28	8	15.6%
by Staff	<1	10	14	2.5	6	2	5.8
Deprivations							
by Patients	29	16	28	17	35	24	24.8
by Staff	2	9	13	4	6	7	6.8

The transcripts do not reveal when others indulged a speaker by
giving him their attention instead of conducting private conversations or reading, nor the number whose eyes were on the speaker but
whose fantasies and thoughts were far away. Nor can we report how
many emulated the college professor of tradition who dreamed that
he was lecturing and woke up to discover that he was.

The Balance of Staff and Patient References

What, specifically, did various categories of participants derive from
the meetings as individuals, group members, and members of the
hospital community? Value analysis of what was said by and about
patients is pertinent to this question. To begin with perhaps the
weakest available index of indulgence, an average of about twenty-
five per cent of staff members present participated actively: the very
fact of their attendance and participation may be viewed as a value
indulgence of patients, demonstrating an investment made in them
by the hospital decision elite.

Comparing the balance of indulgence and deprivational statements of patients and staff (Table 6), patients make three deprivational statement to every two indulgent utterances; staff about
fifty-fifty. The overbalance on the negative side is especially heavy
by patients in the fourth (a ratio of four to one) and sixth meetings
(three to one). In the second transcript only, indulgent exceed deprivational statements (three to two). Although staff statements are
usually more equally distributed, they are also strongly depriving
in the sixth meeting (three to one). However, the total number of
staff evaluative statements was small.

As a preliminary means of summarizing interactions during
patient-staff meetings, the balance of favorable and unfavorable references made by participants were analyzed. For comparative purposes any statement can be described as a message *by* a communica-

tor in a given medium of communication *to* an audience. Explicit terms may be used in the message to refer to the communicator himself or to someone else; such expressions are classified as symbols of "identity." The terms may be singular or plural in the number of persons referred to. A patient may begin with a pronoun ("I") or a noun that designates the one addressed ("Dr. Fleck"). Symbols of identity may be plural ("We patients," "you members of the staff"). The singular terms refer to an "ego"; the plural terms of reference to more than one ego designate a "self" or "other." The self of a communicator can be taken to include singular symbols ("I," "John") and plural symbols ("we patients," "my family," "my hometown"). The communicator's self includes other egos, but all other egos are not part of the self of the communicator. As a "patient," John includes other patients as part of the self, but staff members are excluded from the patient component of John's self-system. These distinctions make it feasible to summarize "who" among participants refers how often to "whom," and permits us to distinguish speakers who are ego preoccupied ("I," "me") from those who are alert to other participants. The balance of ego and self as against other (not-self other) may be weighted in either direction.

An important therapeutic aspect of patient-staff meetings is the enlarging of the "we" within the patient's self-system, facilitated by (1) increased awareness of belonging to a faction within the patient group, in the community of patients, and in the total hospital community, including staff, and (2) active participation in coalitions that form at the meetings. The enlarging of the "we" in the process of coalition occurs not only with active membership in a coalition, but also by becoming silently identified with positions that are actively supported by others.

An important component of the value interplay at patient-staff meetings is the number of favorable references that patients make to themselves. At the first and sixth meetings twenty-one per cent of all evaluative statements of any kind made by all participants (including patients and staff) were indulgent references by patients to the self (to individual egos or the patient group). Staff speakers occupied much less meeting time and made few favorable references to themselves (.75 per cent).

The flow of explicitly favorable self-reference to patients was augmented by positive allusions to patients by staff speakers (1.5 per cent); when added to "pro self by self" patient references the total is 22.5 per cent. The staff was favorably mentioned by some patients (3 per cent of total evaluations); if added to the few staff "pro self by self" references, the total flow of indulgent references to staff is less than four per cent (3.75 per cent).

The inflow of indulgences to the patient group may be regarded as including gratification from the opportunity to express themselves adversely about staff. If the 6.5 per cent of staff deprivations by patients is added to the combined indulgence figure (22.5 per cent), the resulting total is twenty-nine per cent. Correspondingly, the total indulgence of the staff group would be 3.75 per cent; if deprivational references to patients (7.5 per cent) are added, the total for staff indulgence reaches 11.25 per cent.

Another possible adjustment consists in augmenting the positive side of the staff's indulgence-deprivation balance by a factor that expresses the percentage of meeting time occupied by patient speakers. This may be justified by the fact that staff members who identified with the demand for patient participation were indulged every time a patient spoke, regardless of whether the content of the patient's statement indulged or deprived the staff. Similarly, silence may be regarded as deprivational to staff members (in favor of patients), and a silence factor calculated to express staff deprivation.

Taken in their entirely, the meetings subjected staff to more deprivation than patients, unless the staff is regarded as having incorporated a demand for the success of patient-staff meetings into their value systems.

Power Indulgences and Deprivations

The dynamic character of the meetings becomes clearer when the flow of indulgence and deprivation is examined in detail in reference to the value categories. The results of studying the phases of the decision process in the six meetings have been presented; however, the power process itself considered as specialized practices (which were indulgent or deprivational) remains to be examined. The task of describing the role of power in patient-staff meetings is complicated by the absence of formal voting procedures which would provide relatively unambiguous records of outcome. A recorded vote permits the political scientist, in characterizing a forum, to note those who win (are indulged), lose (are deprived), and remain uncommitted (inflicting deprivations on both winners and losers). By examining votes taken at various points during the decision process, it is possible to assess the weights of participating individuals and groups at the intelligence, recommending, prescribing, invoking, applying, appraising, and terminating phases of coping with a continuing problem. When formal votes are omitted, the strength of individual

TABLE 7   The Values: *Power* Indulgent and Deprivational
Statements[a]

Meeting	1	2	3	4	5	6	Average (%)
By Patients							
+	3	.5	5	1	3	3	2.6
—	0	0	5	0	0	6	1.8
+ and —	3	.5	10	1	3	9	4.4
By Staff							
+	0	0	1	0	0	1	.3
—	.5	0	0	0	0	1	.2
+ and —	.5	0	1	0	0	2	.5
By Patients and Staff							
+	3	.5	6	1	3	4	2.9
—	.5	0	5	0	0	7	2.1
+ and —	3.5	.5	11	1	3	11	5.0

a. In the tables concerned with indulgences and deprivations of values in patient-staff meetings (Tables 7, 11–17), percentages shown are of all statements categorized under a value.

participants, groups, and coalitions cannot be measured directly. Inferences can be made by observing expressions of support or non-support for proposed lines of group action; but this is difficult since a minority may do most of the talking. Occasionally, however, there is no doubt about the unanimity of a group or a discernible subgroup.

When contrasted with the extensive authority and control exercised by the staff in the pre-innovation period and earlier, the patient-staff meeting can be interpreted as a continuing power indulgence of patients and a chronic power deprivation of staff. However, to the extent that staff members incorporate the demand for power sharing, they do not perceive themselves as deprived by the adverse references made to them at meetings.

Directly pertinent to power indulgence and deprivation are assertions of approval or disapproval of staff or patient policy, recommendations of alleged hospital prescriptions, and proposed or executed invocations or applications. Of all value indulgences or deprivations in the meetings, five per cent are in terms of power (Table 7). If the category is limited to statements explicitly related to collective policy, the role of power is understated. Many assertions categorized under values other than power bear upon policy alternatives and are put forward in the expectation that they may influence hospital decisions. All the time spent in patient-staff meetings may be regarded as relevant to power (in addition to other values), and weights may be assigned to the number of participants, the amount of meeting time, and the percentage of time spent in communication (in addition to the percent of communications specialized to power in the more restricted sense). Every interaction involves all values to some extent; each classification describing a particular interaction may be amplified in this way. We shall not, however, proceed in this fashion.

The statements specialized to power are closely balanced; the overall ratio was four positive to three negative statements made by all participants (statements by patients were 2.6 positive to 1.8 negative; staff statements, .3 positive to .2 negative). The number of statements categorized under power was relatively small (5 per cent), primarily because of the restrictions imposed by the definitions used. Patients made more power statements; of the five per cent recorded, much less than one per cent came from staff.

In the absence of any voting procedure, a positive assertion may be viewed as equivalent to a vote in support of a policy, group or individual, and a negative statement as an opposing vote. Such interpretations cannot be accepted unequivocally, for the crystallizing of policy alternatives, characteristic in most forums prior to the taking of a vote, was rare in patient-staff meetings.

It might be asserted that power is divided as talk is divided, that if patients and staff talk the same amount it is probable that they exercise equal power. As noted, eighty per cent of talking was done by patients, twenty per cent by staff. However, this "equal talk" criterion may be rejected since in these meetings the top power elite encouraged the rest of the community to talk; and talk by patients may reflect powerlessness rather than power. In this perspective, patient-staff meetings are comparable to a gathering in which a king graciously condescends to hear the petitions of the populace. Lengthy expositions by petitioners are to be expected; judgments are more concisely expressed.

There is, however, some validity to the equality theme. The proposition may be phrased, "equal power, equal participation," construing participation to include style, purport, and frequency. Participation by patients and staff may be unequal because staff members seek to maintain a directing and therefore superior role, either by

TABLE 8   Comparison of Staff Participation in First and
Second Halves of Meetings[a]

Meeting	1	2	3	4	5	6	Average
First Half	2	10	12	9	5	17	9.2
Second Half	1	9	10	5	6	17	8.0

a. The frequency (number of participations by staff speakers) does not include acknowledgements or brief speeches by chairman (less than two units).

talking too much, or holding back to encourage more patient participation. If staff holds back, it might be indicated by their being more active in the last half of the meeting; a comparison of the first as against the second half of the transcripts reveals, however, that staff speeches were spread equally through the two halves of each meeting.

It might be predicted that residents would be less active in early meetings of the year because they were unfamiliar with the hospital and not yet identified with it. True enough, more residents spoke and spoke much more often in Meetings 3 and 4 than in Meetings 1 and 2 (see Tables 2, 3). However, they were again less active later in the year (Meetings 5 and 6), perhaps with a renewed sense of estrangement in anticipation of the end of their YPI service. The relationship between participation in meetings and the individual's familiarity and identification with the community, is reflected in the fact that patients who had been in the hospital longest are the ones who participate most actively.

We might predict a direct relationship between the sense of equality that exists in patient-staff relations and the extent to which true discussion occurs. All categories of participants would then exhibit the same patterns of participation to the extent that equality was felt. If A were criticized he would reply, neither ignoring the challenge nor responding in brief, cryptic, or dismissive fashion; staff and patients would make speeches responsive to one another and of similar length. As the year proceeded, we discover that the length of staff and patient speeches tended in fact to become the same (Table 9), in part because residents and other newcomers became more confident about their roles in the YPI.

Where parliamentary bodies are dominated by two parties, the practice of "equal time" is approximated, especially on important policy issues. In courts, judges try to give equal opportunity for contending parties to state and justify their claims; judges may say little until they announce a decision (and they may or may not justify it

TABLE 9   Average Length of Participations in Patient-Staff
Meetings (minutes)

Meeting	1	2	3	4	5	6	Average
Patients	3'5"	1'35"	4'5"	1'54"	1'55"	1'38"	2 min. 22 sec.
Staff	0'47"	2'42"	2'33"	1'22"	1'23"	1'36"	1 min. 43 sec.

with an opinion). The pattern of power exhibited in patient-staff meetings does not conform to the model of a court or an organized legislature. We have suggested that patient-staff meetings most closely approximate an advisory council in which the director invites anyone to bring up any matter of common interest, with the tacit assumption that a more detailed and definitive outcome will be worked out elsewhere.

Style

Committal and Noncommittal

Psychiatrists and specialists on communication draw inferences about conscious and unconscious processes from scrutinizing the style as well as the purport of messages. For example, attention is directed to length of words, length of sentences, ordering of qualifying clauses, frequency and ordering of adverbs and adjectives, occurrence of mispronunciations or grammatical errors, and stammering or stuttering.

Individual and group differences in style may indicate an equalitarian or nonequalitarian approach to participation in patient-staff meetings. One mode of statement contains clear, straightforward commitments by the statement-maker. For example:

"I think, ah, Edward's suggestion is excellent" (5, 101).

"I told everybody what her age was" (4, 109).

"I'm, I-I just feel so terribly strongly about what's happened with Kent" (3, 33).

The indirect statement, in contrast, obscures or softens the proposition put forward. For example: "Well, I wonder, ah, whether we can, ah, find ah, ah, solution to a problem if we look at it in terms of who's to blame" (3, 26).

"I just sorta had the feeling that I sorta think I brought both of 'em up" (1, 136).

"I would like to say, if it doesn't seem presumptuous, that this lady, Dr. Dunn is it, does speak French" (2, 119).

TABLE 10   Committal and Noncommittal Statements[a]

Meeting	1	2	3	4	5	6	Average (%)
COMMITTAL							
by patients	71	66	48	74	74	52	64.1
by staff[2]	3	28	15	9.5	12	16	13.9
NONCOMMITTAL							
by patients	17	1	18	10.5	7	17	11.7
by staff[b]	5	1	17	3.5	5	12	7.2

a. Calculated as per cent of all units in each patient-staff meeting.
b. Does not include chairman acknowledgements of participants seeking the floor.

"It would seem here, ah, that for instance where the advisory committee might have been useful, I wonder what the patients do think about this" (4, 24).

The record reveals that staff members are less explicit than patients. In the six meetings analyzed, staff members made about twice as many *committal* as *noncommittal* statements (Table 10). Patients, however, used the committal style six times as often as the noncommittal (64.1 per cent to 11.7 per cent). In the second meeting, patients were particularly unequivocal; practically every assertion was committal (66 per cent to 1 per cent). This difference suggests that physicians (by far the most active staff participants) carry the indirect modes of utterance they use in psychotherapy into patient-staff meetings. In psychotherapy the therapist, although unmistakably the authority, characteristically tries to avoid interfering with the autonomy of the patient and to encourage him to talk freely, in part by avoiding unnecessarily discouraging, argumentative, or critical statements. This may contribute to the vague, verbose, fumbling verbal style of physicians in the meetings. It may be predicted that with time, as staff and patients achieve more equality of outlook, differences in style will diminish. Patients, trying to maximize their well-being, will tend to incorporate staff characteristics, particularly those which appear connected with therapeutic skill. As doctors come to regard their distinctive communication practices as less necessary in their work, they will use the standard forms of the common culture. Such a change already occurred in the psychiatrist's garb when he abandoned his white coat.

In discussions among equals a certain bluntness is part of the

American norm. Physicians may eventually become more outspoken in style, although the noncommittal pattern—with its distinctive, evasive modes of speech—both reflects and sustains staff members' favorable power position. (The implication is not that the noncommittal style will have no abiding effect. Members of our society are increasingly perceptive of subtleties in human interaction. Bluntness may itself be modified, as in the past urban culture exerted a refining influence upon "rustics" and "pioneers.") Changing speech patterns are not evident in a single year; they could not be discerned in the analyzed transcripts. The averages for committal and noncommittal statements by both patients and staff were about the same when the first three analyzed meetings were compared with the last three. No differences in committal-noncommittal usage between old and recent patients, or between old and recent staff members, were evident.

The Practice of Informality

Discussion in patient-staff meetings remained largely at the phases of intelligence and appraisal, consisting in an exchange of information, comment upon the inclusive value goals of the hospital, assessment of the extent to which aims were achieved in fact, and the consideration of individual proposals. The course of discussion might make it clear that nearly everybody favored doing something definite about specific issues; however, such a consensus was rarely summarized as a formal outcome or registered in a directive. In addition to the avoidance of formal votes, emphasis upon any particular solution was diluted, with the effect that physicians and others who were obligated to act in a concrete case were protected from policy guidance that was too explicit, and also from subsequent censure.

Absence of explicit formality was reflected in other features of patient-staff meetings, notably in the omission, for example, of an announced agenda of regular committee assignments or reports, a codebook containing rules of parliamentary order, fixed seating assignments or a rigid arrangement of chairs, the requirement that one stand when speaking, rituals such as standing when the director arrives or leaves the room, a fixed sequence of arrival or departure, or of marching to or away from the assembly room. (Beyond 1957–58, such evidences of formality were increasingly present. Reports from the residents on duty the previous evening or weekend were presented in meetings on days when staff meetings were not held; later, the recommendations of patient-staff advisory committee and of activities committee were also regularly presented.)

Seriously disturbed patients felt tolerated in this informal atmosphere and therefore able to participate. The director sometimes attempted to halt repetitive statements which might result in boredom and distracted attention, and to forestall prolonged discussion of assertions whose relevance was negligible. But more often he sought to elucidate the meaning of distracting conduct and apparently irrelevant comments. He encouraged the expression of a wide range of diverse viewpoints and the participation of the reticent, timid, and slow speaking. The chairman usually refrained from interrupting a speaker who was irrational, incoherent, irrelevant, or provocative. A disruptive participant was not ejected; instead, his behavior and its effects in the meeting were discussed in his presence with his participation. His conduct outside of meetings was also considered in the effort to understand his motivation, make constructive recommendations to him and his therapist, and formulate ways in which staff and patients could be useful to him. If a patient tried to avoid attending a meeting because he was particularly troubled, his absence would be discussed; a group would then sometimes leave the meeting and return with the patient, insisting that his upset state be talked about rather than evaded by his withdrawal from the community.

The permissive, informal atmosphere of the meetings was also indicated by the frequency of laughter and wisecracks. Although tolerant, the chairman nevertheless tried to prevent the development of a collective mood of irresponsibility.

Informality and Ideology

Occasional prolonged discussions of relatively abstract issues diverged from the informal pattern of patient-staff meetings. However, basic assumptions shared by participants, including a preferred dialectical pattern, tended to protect the meetings. In our culture more is required of a speaker than naked assertions of demands, personal threats, or promises: proposals must be justified and related to common goals. Whenever a participant stepped outside this prescriptive framework and asserted demands that he did not attempt to relate to anything more persuasive than his own perspective, these arbitrary expressions were listened to but did not rally support from others. Naked expressions of hostility to rules were experienced by the group as too egocentric for the meetings.

It is characteristic of the proceedings that appraisals, recommendations, and invocations are explicitly formulated in reference to allegedly common goals and standards. Applications are assumed to be within a framework of prescription. Hospital news and estimates of the future are shared with the expectation that such intelligence is pertinent to the evaluation of policy alternatives open to the group in the pursuit of common interests.

In the July meeting, the discussion of the unauthorized departure of Mr. Ives proceeded within this frame of reference: "I think much of the discussion I've listened to centered around the question of what is discussed at this meeting. Ah, What sort of things can be brought out?" (1, *132*).

In the second meeting, the problem of how to introduce new patients to the YPI was discussed. Testimony about the past reflected the following frame of reference:

"I know that with my own entrance to the hospital, as soon as convenient for the other patients so that it would not disturb the rest, I was welcomed to the room that I now have, the nurse was available to talk to me and answering questions, ah, apparently with unlimited time on her hands, with nothing to do but to talk to me" (2, *128*).

In the third analyzed meeting, discussion centered on Kent, who had also run away. The group dealt extensively with patient and staff responsibilities in fulfilling the objectives of the hospital:

"But in, ah, looking back, in my effort I tried to act as the hospital should've acted, namely, that the hospital stood for authority" (3, *84*).

At Meeting 4, Bob sought support for his opposition to a staff ruling. The discussion made explicit certain previously vague assumptions about prescriptive obligations:

"A lot of people feel that Bob has been, ah, given a dirty deal here . . . he didn't talk to his doctor openly about it . . . and I think if that's the case, he wasn't being very open with his doctor, he doesn't have any, ah, grievance" (4, *156*).

The fifth analyzed meeting was engrossed with Vic's predicament: his family had told him that they could not continue to support his stay at YPI. The deliberations again dealt with the responsibilities of patients and staff:

"It seems, ah, part of the problem is the vagueness on the part of the staff. But there's something else. Vic's leaving in three weeks. He still only goes out in a couple of groups. And I don't feel this is any way to prepare a patient who's going to leave" (5, *65*).

The sixth meeting was more scattered, but eventually focused on the adequacy of arrangements for impending "separation difficulties" connected with the change of staff. The question of patient-staff responsibilities emerged in many statements:

"Just about everything there is that I could do within the rules has

been done at least, ah, a hundred times. And, ah, you get bored stiff
. . . I think even the spontaneity to a degree is becoming habitual.
And, ah, I think if they could find some new things to do, everybody
could use their imagination then maybe we'd get outta this hole, or
this mess" (6, *188*).

The chairman at times tried to restrict protracted exercises in justification. Among participants, there was a wide range of technical
competence. The patient group sometimes included lawyers, acad-
emicians, and theologians; of all professional groups they are
among the most specialized to the elaborating of symbols in the pattern we call demand-justification. If the chair were to permit these
skilled individuals to monopolize the floor, the meetings would be
endangered by the accumulation of resentment among neglected
participants. The clarifying, testing, and stabilizing of reality performed in the meetings are at times threatened when patients permit
others to dominate the meetings or attempt to avoid the social reality
by flights into abstraction.

Values Other Than Power

It is possible to show the relatively wide limits of discussion at
patient-staff meetings by summarizing the frequency of statements
whose reference is to values other than power.

The *well-being* value is of principal concern to the professional
staff. The innovation was initiated to facilitate the understanding and
treatment of severely disturbed psychiatric patients. To what extent
does the preoccupation with this value emerge in the manifest content of statements made by patients and staff? In this narrow sense,
individuals refer to themselves or others as "anxious," "disturbed," or
"improving," for example, in about thirteen per cent of all the evaluative statements in the transcripts (Table 11). For every two indulgences in well-being, 10.7 statements refer to deprivations in this
value.

In addition, other communications were perceived by all concerned as explicitly relevant to the well-being of patients. Many of
these, however, are categorized as *enlightenment*, which emphasizes
the role of giving, withholding, or receiving information in the flow
of value indulgences and deprivations. Many of the statements that
perform an intelligence or appraisal function in the decision process
are, in value terms, classified as acts of enlightenment. When a patient purports to offer a factual account of an incident, he enlightens
other patients and the staff. To categorize the account as enlightenment does not allege that the assertion is factually true, but only that

TABLE 11   The Values: *Well-Being* Indulgent and
Deprivational Statements

Meeting	1	2	3	4	5	6	Average (%)
By Patients							
+	1	0	3	2	2	1	1.5
—	11	3	5	6	11	15	8.5
+ and —	12	3	8	8	13	16	10.
By Staff							
+	0	0	2	0	0	1	.5
—	0	.5	3	5	2	3	2.2
+ and —	0	.5	5	5	2	4	2.7
By Patients and Staff							
+	1	0	5	2	2	2	2.
—	11	3.5	8	11	13	18	10.7
+ and —	12	3.5	13	13	15	20	12.7

the statement was made in "fact form," that is, as though it were true. If a statement is challenged, both the original statement and statement maker are thereby deprived. If the statement is confirmed by others, the assertion and the asserter are indulged. A prediction of future events, similarly, may be challenged or accepted.

Participants in the meetings are always acquainted with facts or plausible estimates of the future that they do not disclose, whether from lack of capacity or unwillingness to speak. Hence all participants suffer from enlightenment deprivations whose magnitude they are unable to assess. It is sometimes possible for observers after the event to explicate the degree to which such deprivations of enlightenment occurred. To some extent it is possible for the group to supply its own corrective to inaccurate or insufficient information.

Because of these limitations, the analysis understates the role of enlightenment in the meetings: 31.9 per cent of participations in the six transcripts (Table 12). There were two positives for every negative enlightenment reference. The topics of meetings which evoked the most enlightenment participation were concerned with the introduction of new patients (the second), and a patient being forced to leave the hospital (the fifth).

In patient-staff meetings, references to *skill* consisted mostly in assertions about the excellence or inefficiency of staff members. Such

TABLE 12   The Values: *Enlightenment* Indulgent and Deprivational Statements

Meeting	1	2	3	4	5	6	Average (%)
By Patients							
+	9	24	5	9	27	8	13.6
—	9	10	7	14	8.5	10	9.7
+ and —	18	34	12	23	35.5	18	23.4
By Staff							
+	1	15	4	9	6	2	6.1
—	1	3	1	6	2	1	2.3
+ and —	2	18	5	15	8	3	8.5
By Patients and Staff							
+	10	39	9	18	33	10	19.8
—	10	13	8	20	10.5	11	12.1
+ and —	20	52	17	38	43.5	21	31.9

TABLE 13   The Values: *Skill* Indulgent and Deprivational Statements

Meeting	1	2	3	4	5	6	Average (%)
By Patients							
+	4	1	1	1	2	2	1.8
—	6	3	5	2.5	6	7	4.9
+ and —	10	4	6	3.5	8	9	6.7
By Staff							
+	0	0	0	1	0	0	.1
—	0	1	2	0	0	3	1.
+ and —	0	1	2	1	0	3	1.1
By Patients and Staff							
+	4	1	1	2	2	2	2.
—	6	4	7	2.5	6	10	5.9
+ and —	10	5	8	4.5	8	12	7.9

statements are also closely related to well-being and enlightenment. The continuing development of skill in the observation of the self and others is highly valued in the YPI for both staff and patients:

TABLE 14 The Values: *Respect* Indulgent and Deprivational Statements

Meeting	1	2	3	4	5	6	Average (%)
By Patients							
+	4	6	1	1	0	0	2.
—	8	2	3	14	4	3	5.6
+ and —	12	8	4	15	4	3	7.6
By Staff							
+	0	0	0	0	0	0	0
—	0	0	0	0	0	1	.1
+ and —	0	0	0	0	0	1	.1
By Patients and Staff							
+	4	6	1	1	0	0	2.
—	8	2	3	14	4	4	5.8
+ and —	12	8	4	15	4	4	7.8

skill in self-enlightenment which serves well-being. With this rationale the number of references expressly related to skill may be added to the totals for well-being and enlightenment. About eight per cent of all evaluative statements were in the skill category (Table 13). For every affirmative skill reference, three were negative.

Respect values are at stake in every interaction, although distinctions according to social caste and class so permeate society that they are often outside the conscious focus of attention. The influence of social class upon patterns of interaction is reflected in the slightly patronizing tone sometimes adopted toward social inferiors, the deferential manner accorded superiors, and the mode in which admiration is expressed for a meritorious individual achievement. Congratulations to a social inferior may be a trifle hearty, whereas to an established figure in the respect system, heartiness may be inapposite. Distinctions of this kind elude quantification when the verbatim record does not include accompanying vocal patterns and body gestures. The transcripts contain explicit expressions of admiration and contempt, but results based only on the manifest record understate the important role of respect indulgences and deprivations. About eight per cent of the communications were in this category; for every three respect deprivations there was one indulgence.

Further, standardized status expressions are used by patients in addressing the director, other physicians, and some other staff members. Identifying labels are often informal when one patient alludes to another; but the first name or nickname is not invariably used, as when a patient is relatively mature and looked upon as distinguished ("Mr. Ives"), or when he is still a stranger. The traditional respect hierarchy of the hospital persists, although it is attenuated in the pattern of innovation.

The opportunity to hold the floor and speak itself constitutes a value indulgence, most obviously in respect. A factor expressing this dimension may be used in calculating respect indulgences experienced by participants; it would reflect the number of those present who spoke and the number of times they spoke and would therefore be derived from the material summarized in Tables 2 and 3. Another index which may be used in calculating the respect indulgence-deprivation balance is negative: absence of freedom from interruption by the chairman or others. Related positive indices are the frequency with which a participant is mentioned by others, and also specifically replied to by others in the meeting.

In some social situations, direct criticism of a participant is preceded by respect indulgences of the target ("my honorable colleague," "my revered senior"), and such verbal tags are employed as "if I may be so bold," or "with your kind permission." Although examples of such patterns appear in patient-staff meetings, an observer unfamiliar with the setting might be startled by the seeming disrespect expressed in open criticism, often on "delicate" topics. Standards here differ greatly from the norms of respect regarded as appropriate in many other circumstances. Practices characteristic of individual psychotherapy which, like these meetings, emphasizes the acquisition of enlightenment and skill in the service of well-being, exempt participants from many conventional respect demands.

The value *affection* is also at stake in every interaction; no human contact is conceivable without some stirring, however faint, of positive feeling or aversion. Affection is referred to in characterizing people as "warm and outgoing," "cold and withdrawn," or "hostile," and in describing the positive relationship between the individual and groups of which he is a member as "deeply involved" or "loyal."

A verbatim record incompletely reflects the play of affection among participants in a meeting. Voice tones and gestures are lost, and the subtler interplay of positive and negative expressions among participants is not available to the observer. Laughter, for example,

TABLE 15   The Values: *Affection* Indulgent and Deprivational
Statements

Meeting	1	2	3	4	5	6	Average (%)
By Patients							
+	1	4	2	0	2	0	1.5
—	0	0	3	0	4	1	1.3
+ and —	1	4	5	0	6	1	2.8
By Staff							
+	0	0	0	0	.5	0	.1
—	0	0	0	0	0	0	0
+ and —	0	0	0	0	.5	0	.1
By Patients and Staff							
+	1	4	2	0	2.5	0	1.6
—	0	0	3	0	4	1	1.3
+ and —	1	4	5	0	6.5	1	2.9

may constitute a warmhearted, enthusiastic response to a popular
figure, or express the contempt of the group (disrespect).

Of the manifest content of communication in the meetings, three
per cent of the total were specialized to affection; statements categorized under the value affection were positive for every 1.3 negative (Table 15).

As the year proceeds and participants get better acquainted, formal expressions of respect decline. An important and elusive issue
in considering such changes is whether this greater informality
means disrespect or increasing affection, and whether the basic appraisals in terms of respect are not actually rising rather than falling.

A number of communications were specialized to *rectitude*, reflecting the use of ethical or religious standards (Table 16): twenty-nine
per cent of total evaluations were categorized under the value rectitude; for every three negative, only one positive rectitude statement
was made.

A conspicuous feature of the patient-staff meeting pattern is revealed in the *wealth* analysis. Few references are made to money,
cost, income, or the hospital budget. The contrast with deliberations
of a legislative committee on revenues or appropriations, or, indeed,
to meetings in other institutional contexts, is striking. Although free-

TABLE 16   The Values: *Rectitude* Indulgent and Deprivational
Statements

Meeting	1	2	3	4	5	6	Average (%)
By Patients							
+	9	3	9	0	.5	6	4.6
—	22	10	10	25	11	14	15.3
+ and —	31	13	19	25	11.5	20	19.9
By Staff							
+	0	2	13	0	1	1	2.8
—	2	11	9	2.5	3.5	8	6.
+ and —	2	13	22	2.5	4.5	9	8.8
By Patients and Staff							
+	9	5	22	0	1.5	7	7.4
—	24	21	19	27.5	14.5	22	21.3
+ and —	33	26	41	27.5	16	29	28.7

dom to talk about any issue and most particularly any feature of the
YPI is explicit in the meetings, and although economic issues are of
great importance to the participants and the hospital, they were
rarely alluded to; the strictly financial aspects of problems were
evaded and not discussed in detail.

The result of tabulating economic references is a misleading indicator of the importance of wealth (Table 17). The financial situation of the YPI as a whole, and of individual patients, is important
in private conversations and administrative deliberations. The role
of the economic factor is also understated, in part, because the criteria used for categorizing wealth statements are primarily money,
income and expenditures, without including resources and technolo-
gies used in production and consumption.

What Is the Innovation?

The overall balance of indulgence and deprivation of values (Table
5), the role of power (Table 7), and the phases of the decision process (Table 4) in the manifest content of the analyzed patient-staff
meetings have been presented as they appear. When the profile of all
values shaped or shared in these meetings is examined, enlightenment is most prominent (Tables 12, 18). This reflects concentration
upon sharing information, emphasis upon the intelligence and ap-

TABLE 17   The Values: *Wealth* Indulgent and Deprivational
Statements

Meetings	1	2	3	4	5	6	Average (%)
By Patients							
+	0	0	0	0	0	0	0
—	0	0	0	0	2	0	.3
+ and —	0	0	0	0	2	0	.3
By Staff							
+	0	0	0	0	0	0	0
—	0	0	0	0	0	0	0
+ and —	0	0	0	0	0	0	0
By Patients and Staff							
+	0	0	0	0	0	0	0
—	0	0	0	0	2	0	.3
+ and —	0	0	0	0	2	0	.3

praisal phases of the decision process, and the important position accorded enlightenment in both the treatment process and psychotherapeutic ideology.

Rectitude is also very prominent in the meetings (Tables 16, 18). Rectitude is the most emphasized value in staff participation: almost half (43. 2 per cent) of all value statements made by staff members are concerned with it. This finding stands in contradiction to the deemphasis on moralistic considerations in the psychotherapeutic ideology, and to the conventional image of the psychotherapist as refraining from interventions in rectitude terms.

Values other than enlightenment and rectitude are less important in the meetings. The objectives of the Yale Psychiatric Institute, of individual psychotherapy, and of the patient-staff meetings are all conventionally characterized primarily in terms of well-being; however, the analysis demonstrates that the well-being value is not expressly prominent in the meetings.

The importance of rectitude in the value profile of patient-staff meetings suggests that the staff applies the therapeutic ideology in vigorously moralistic terms. It is clear from the record that staff members (especially the director) used strategies in patient-staff meetings which maintained their power. The situation was approached as if it were a therapeutic session; the physician invited the

TABLE 18   The Value Profile in Patient-Staff Meetings

Value	Calculated as per cent of all value statements made by patients and staff combined[1]			Calculated as per cent of value statements made by staff only
	Patients	Staff	Patients and Staff Combined	Staff
Enlightenment	23.4	8.5	31.9	34.7
Rectitude	19.9	8.8	28.7	43.2
Well Being	10.	2.7	12.7	12.1
Skill	6.7	1.1	7.9	5.6
Respect	7.6	.1	7.8	1.0
Power	4.4	.5	5.0	2.2
Affection	2.8	.1	2.9	0.5
Wealth	.3	0	.3	0.2

1. Summary of Tables 7 and 11–17.

patient to take the initiative in bringing up any topic "on your mind"; interpretative remarks or evocative interrogations were introduced in the hope of aiding "insight." These strategies permitted a moralistic application of the psychotherapeutic ideology which assured staff dominance without seeming to do other than inquire and explore. For example:

At the July meeting the chairman took advantage of the discussion of the Ives case to reiterate the importance of sharing information on all topics of common concern (1, 65 ff. also *132*).

The second meeting illustrated the efforts of the staff to stimulate patients to play a more responsible part in such hospital activities as the orientation of new patients. Dr. Leary employed the tactic of offering a direct and adverse appraisal of the "group spirit" (2, *97*). The chairman returned to this theme, stating "it's easier not to be involved" (2, *155*).

In the third meeting a patient raised the question, had anything been done about "freeing the second floor?" (3, *4*). The chairman (the assistant director) took the lead in elaborating the theme of patient responsibility (3, *10*). When discussion focused on the treatment of a patient who had run away, the residents kept the accent upon the role of patients in helping their fellows.

Instead of waiting for patients to initiate discussion in the fourth meeting, the chief resident used a strategy which emphasized ther-

apeutic issues: "This is my second Chritmas and, ah, there are similarities in some respects between last year and this year. Everybody
seemed to me at that time, ah, to be rather undecided whether they
got depressed or not" (4, 19). Patients brought up grievances about
hospital practice, but the chief resident did not permit the topic he
had initiated to be ignored. "We may go home but we don't really
feel like it because we know that it's going to be something that's not
exactly pleasant. And I think these are the problems which are much
more disturbing than that the hospital says you are not supposed to
go or you are supposed to go" (4, 49).

Early in the fifth meeting, Vic brought up his departure from the
hospital, but immediately succeeding speakers did not pursue this
issue. Dr. Bennett saw an opportunity to steer the meeting toward
insight, understanding, and realism: "It seems in the last few minutes
there's been more participation around the question of cigarette
butts than there has been around the question of giving Vic advice
on how difficult it is in leaving the hospital. And . . . I wonder if it's
because one is, ah, more anxiety-producing" (5, 38).

At the sixth (June) meeting, a time of high anxiety associated with
the imminent departure of residents, the chairman took the initiative
in directing the attention of the group to the need for self-
examination. He repetitively emphasized the topic of lateness to
meetings, interpreting this behavior as in opposition to the therapeutic ideology: "Well, that's one of the difficulties we have all over
the hospital, there's somebody anxious or uncomfortable or a little
diffident about doing something. We act out" (6, 71).

The psychotherapeutic emphasis—and the concomitant ascendancy of the staff—is further reflected in remarks addressed to individuals by staff members. In the fifth meeting, Dr. Bennett addressed
a patient: "Sam has told me several times now how he's made an
effort to try to stay . . . stay awake at these meetings. I'm wondering
why he has his eyes closed now."

SAM: "I don't have my eyes closed."

CHAIRMAN: "Come to the meeting, Sam" (5, 23, 24, 25).

Members of the staff utilized their role as arbiters of what is therapeutic as a mode of exercising control; hence rectitude is employed
in the service of power. The importance of this value in patient-staff
meetings invites an eventual examination of the position of rectitude
in individual psychotherapy.[2]

2. We plan to make a later report on value profiles in psychotherapeutic
situations. For verbatim texts and modes of analysis see M. Gill, R. Newman,
and F. C. Redlich, *The Initial Interview in Psychiatric Practice* (New York,
International Universities Press, 1954); E. J. Murphy, A Content-Analysis

The staff, especially the director, employ their therapeutic skill as a base value for maintaining their predominant role in the decision process. Although patients participate in the total process, especially in intelligence and appraisal, the final word rests with the staff, most particularly with the director. Ascendancy is retained by insisting on therapeutic techniques and objectives in which skilled physicians, especially the director, retain authority and control. The goal of the hospital emphasizes therapy as interpreted by psychoanalytically oriented psychiatrists. At the YPI this includes the expectation that psychotic patients will acquire the capacity for effective, responsible social participation in their movement toward health. In the hospital context, behavior in conformity with this conception includes engaging in problem-solving activities, individual and collective, displaying candor in probing for explanations of conduct, clarifying goals of action, inventing and assessing alternatives of behavior, appraising trends toward or away from goal attainment, and estimating future capability. Such problem-solving emphasizes the performance of intellectual tasks which may be expressed in the following summary questions: What are my (our) goals (preferred events)? To what extent have I (we) been moving toward or away from their attainment? What combinations of conditioning factors help to explain degrees of success or failure? What is the probable course of future capability in realizing goals? What are the behavioral options most likely to lead to this result at least net cost in terms of all values?

Conclusion

From the evidence summarized it is possible to draw together a description of the patient-staff meeting innovation and to separate the innovation proper from its subsequent effects. Patients participate actively in the flow of talk in the meetings; discussion is relatively rational and realistic. The principal question is to what extent power is genuinely shared by patients and staff. The analysis reveals that the functions of intelligence and appraisal are conspicuous in patient-staff meetings; promotion plays a modest role; the other phases of the decision process, invocation and application, and especially prescription and termination, are much less visible.

The category of decision structure with which patient-staff meet-

---

Method for Studying Psychotherapy; O. H. Mowrer, ed., *Psychotherapy: Theory and Research* (New York, Ronald Press, 1953); J. Dollard, F. Auld, Jr. and Alice M. White, *Steps in Psychotherapy* (New York, Macmillan, 1953); M. I. Stein, ed., *Contemporary Psychotherapies* (Glencoe, Illinois, The Free Press 1961).

ings can be most directly compared is an advisory council or assembly that refrains from pressing its advice on general prescriptions or concrete situations to the point of formal resolution. Although patient-staff meetings played a part in making and executing hospital policy, they failed to achieve far-reaching power sharing during the period. Their role in the making of "laws" (prescriptions), and in applying the authorized norms of the hospital, was limited.

This impression may be modified when other decision structures in the YPI are examined. Once patient-staff meetings were established in the life of the hospital, a new and vital hospital institution, the patient-staff advisory committee, was inaugurated. It was actively involved with invocation and application. Although patient-staff meetings abstained from formal votes, they provided an arena in which a consensus might emerge on specific problems of patient management which could then be put into effect by the advisory committee. Therefore, although patient-staff meetings did not vote on prescriptions or applications, they became important in these phases of the policy process.

Patient-staff meetings can be characterized in more definite terms by analyzing the extent to which all values were shared in the meetings. They were preponderantly value indulgent of patients. This finding was also sustained in regard to power. The situation was more complex for residents, senior physicians, nurses, and other staff members.

The power realities of the situation emerged more clearly when content analysis was used to disclose the style as well as the purport of patient-staff meeting communications. The staff used an approach adapted to individual psychotherapy in which noncommittal forms of expression encourage the active participation and free associations of patients. The physician, in asking the patient to contribute more openly and intimately than he does, assumes a superior position of which the noncommittal style is a manifestation.

Despite the informality which characterized patient-staff meetings, the ascendancy of the director was maintained. The comments and interpretations employed, emphasized the effective control exercised by the director and senior staff over policy toward individual patients and hospital issues.

How was this retention of staff power reconciled with the emphasis upon free discussion and equality that became part of the YPI ideology? Discrepancies between the articulated ideal of power sharing and overt performance were justified by giving precedence to another aspect of the ideology, the prime importance of the facilitation of therapeutic objectives. "Is it therapeutic?" is the recurring question to which all policy options are subordinated and according to which behavior is moralistically judged. This frame of reference tends to obscure as well as justify the extent to which the staff continues to exercise power. No serious objection was offered to the assumption that physicians, especially the director, were primarily responsible for adapting prescriptions of the ideology to concrete circumstances.

By means of the technique of content analysis it has been possible to describe patient-staff meetings in ways that permit the broad issue of power sharing to be discussed with some precision. It has also been possible to raise detailed questions about the value shaping and sharing significance of any meeting, especially when part of a formal process of decision. We have begun to explore decisions by the systematic use of techniques that begin with the manifest content of a verbatim record and gradually become more intensive, revealing the true complexity of the process.

Part III

The Hospital in Transition

8. The Patient as Participant

The post-innovation hospital no longer acquiesced in the tacit family conspiracy in which the patient was the scapegoat for its failures. The predicament of the patient, however, remained complex and full of ambiguities. Although he was not wholly responsible for hospitalization and the disruption of his life, could he be induced to take responsibility for coping with the situation and finding his way out of it? In the home context he had lost the power struggle and suffered expulsion. What if conditioning within the family had induced the patient to make demands that others were neither willing nor able to accept and imposed a way of life in conflict with the perspectives and strategies required for effective functioning in the larger society? Must he seek to reconstruct himself completely? Would the hospital context be any better adapted to the task of rehabilitation than the family?

The intelligence function of the decision process, with particular reference to self-observation, was emphasized in the post-innovation hospital. The new ideology of incessant participation created a working model of some features of the larger society. But the contradictions between the phrases of the ideology and the performances of the YPI were sufficiently drastic and inexplicit to sustain the conflicts characteristic of any unclarified social process.

Predispositions and Perspectives

The post-innovation patient's predispositions reflected changes in his preparation for and orientation to hospitalization. Perspectives were now influenced by the hospital's reputation as a psychotherapeutic facility. The overall complexion of the patient group and the nature of patient relationships with one another, doctors, and nurses changed markedly after the innovations.

Applications for YPI admission greatly increased because very few private hospitals of high reputation both emphasize psychotherapeutic treatment and work primarily with adolescents and young adults. Admissions were therefore more frequently planned in advance. The age range of patients changed from twelve to sixty-five, with most patients between twenty-five and forty-five, to a predominantly adolescent and young adult population (most between sixteen and thirty, with only an occasional patient over forty-five). Most patients were now high school, college, or graduate school students or recent graduates, unmarried, and neither financially independent nor settled in work. Formerly, men and women who enjoyed established social and professional positions predominated. Because of obligations of the YPI to the Yale and New Haven communities, and to psychiatrists and psychoanalysts in the New Haven and New York areas, many patients continued to be admitted on an emergency basis.[1] However, more patients were not acutely disturbed on entering the hospital because of planned admissions of long-standing applicants.

It is difficult to separate the effects of the innovations from the impact of tranquilizing, antidepressant, and other drugs increasingly used in the hospital during the last years of this study. Whereas a pre-innovation patient who was disturbed on admission often required isolation for more than a week, it was now more common for such a disturbance to pass within twenty-four hours, after which the newcomer was involved with others and living on the ward. Whether this was the result of drugs, changes in the patient population, the modified admission procedure, or alterations of the total context, including changes in the responses of other patients and staff to the new patient, is difficult to evaluate. Dramatic resolutions of such initial disturbances have been observed when drugs were not used at all, or when drugs were administered, but before their levels reached a therapeutically effective range. Because of the prominence accorded the psychotherapeutic ideology and uncertainty about the role of drugs, there was an inclination to de-emphasize their importance in these cases.[2]

All admissions to the hospital were now voluntary; committed patients were no longer accepted. The "voluntary" character of admission was often specious, however, since prospective patients were sometimes threatened with commitment to another hospital if they refused to enter the YPI voluntarily. Care was now taken to be explicit that YPI hospitalization involved intensive psychotherapy over

1. The decline in average age of patients on admission to the YPI is consistent with recent trends in state and other private psychiatric hospitals. The described changes in admission policy did not result in a less troubled YPI patient population: the majority were either acutely psychotic on admission, or came to the YPI after lengthy unsuccessful courses of outpatient and hospital treatment elsewhere.

2. Despite this uncertainty as to the impact of drugs, the knowledge that effective tranquilizing and antidepressant agents are available is important to the staff's sense of confidence about being able to manage acutely psychotic behavior.

a period of months and more probably years. The staff was more alert to the importance of clarifying the nature of the hospital, the character of treatment, and probable length of stay to the referring doctor, the patient, and his family. Financial implications were thoroughly explored to avoid the possibility of admitting a patient whose treatment would be interrupted for financial reasons. The prospective patient was presented with a brochure prepared by patients, which included a complete description of the hospital. In addition to interviews with the admitting physician, the prospective patient was shown the hospital by patients, and talked freely with them alone about being a patient in the YPI. On the new patient's admission, the patient-staff advisory committee routinely appointed a suitable "sponsor" to introduce him to other patients and staff members, orient him to procedures and activities, and answer questions arising during the first weeks of hospitalization. If the patient was acutely troubled on admission or had special difficulties about entering into hospital life, the problem was discussed and plans for coping with it were formulated in hospital meetings. For example, if protective measures were required to prevent the newcomer from hurting himself, patients might take turns spending time with him in the isolation area.

Hospitalization continued to be precipitated by the same deprivations of well-being, power, and affection experienced by pre-innovation patients, and by comparable secondary deprivations of other values (enlightenment, skill, wealth, respect, and rectitude). The patient still felt victimized upon admission, but the experiences of learning about and preparing for hospitalization, being admitted, and entering into hospital life, no longer sustained this perception. From the beginning of his contact with the hospital, the newcomer increasingly experienced indulgences rather than deprivations of affection, respect, enlightenment, and well-being. He tended to be apprehensive about limitations of power, but reassured by his initial experiences affecting respect, affection, and well-being, including efforts to share responsibility and invite participation in the decision process.

The YPI Experience

The post-innovation patient's day, in dynamic contrast to the interminable sitting of his predecessors, included a rich schedule of meetings, classes, work, recreation, and other activities. On admission the patient might be confined to his room and the closed ward (or the isolation area if acutely disturbed), and his activity limited to hours of individual psychotherapy, some work in occupational therapy, and informal contact with his sponsor, other patients, and staff members. Within a day or two, even if acutely disturbed initially, he would begin to participate in group therapy, patient-staff, and patient-government meetings. Within a week he would usually attend calisthenic and adult education classes. If of high school age, he would soon spend some hours each day in class and evening studyhall, and would later attend school outside the hospital. After a time he would also undertake regularly scheduled volunteer work in the general hospital and, later, paid work in the community. He might also participate in a small study or activity group concerned with a special interest he shared with its other patient members. Activities continued to include films in the hospital and group visits to theaters, restaurants, and the beach. Musicales, plays, game nights, dances, and cooperatively prepared weekend breakfasts and cook-outs were arranged by the patients themselves.

Hence a patient might get up, read the newspaper, have breakfast, work for two hours in a general hospital stockroom, meet with his doctor in psychotherapy for an hour, have lunch, go to calisthenics for half an hour, attend high school classes in the hospital, participate in group therapy, attend a patient-staff meeting, read or chat informally, have supper, attend an adult education class, participate in a musicale, and go to bed tired. Patients also attended meetings of patient-staff advisory committee and patient government committees concerned with planning hospital activities and orientating new patients, received visitors, met regularly with the social worker or doctor who was assigned to members of their family, and often participated with their therapist, social worker, and wife or parents in regularly scheduled family meetings.

The extent of contact between the post-innovation patient and the nurse depends on the degree to which he is troubled and needful. When acutely disturbed, the patient leans heavily upon the nurse for contact and reassurance, and the nurse is able to respond to such clear and direct expressions of need warmly and helpfully. She appreciates the opportunity to be useful in this more conventional nursing role for which she is well prepared. When not acutely upset, the post-innovation patient is less likely to engage the nurse in ways she can respond to, and as he becomes occupied with the hospital program, tends to have less direct contact with her. He checks in with the nurse on leaving the ward and most of their other interactions have a similar routine character; she hands him medications, helps serve his meals, and is available on the ward for greater contact. She is present with him at hospital forums and group therapy, but usually only chief nurses participate actively on these occasions.

Individual therapy remains the core of the patient's experience in the hospital, eclipsing other therapeutic aspects of the YPI. In the initial phases of psychotherapy the orientation of the patient to the therapist and the work of treatment is strongly influenced by elements outside the therapeutic relationship itself. New patients have always received an informal rundown on the doctors from other patients, including the therapists' distinctive modes of operation and how each conducts himself in his psychotherapeutic contacts. They are also orientated to their doctors by contact with them during their nights on duty. A new patient's image of his doctor evolves from experience during their work together, contacts with him on other occasions, and the doctor's reputation among other patients, particularly those assigned to him. The patient's overall picture of the hospital is influenced by his relationship with his psychotherapist: the hospital is perceived as hostile and unfriendly and its staff as arbitrary and unfeeling, when the therapist is experienced as aloof and unconcerned; it is warm and nurturing when the therapist seems considerate and helpful. The essential change in the mode of introducing a new patient to his therapist in the post-innovation hospital is the active participation of the therapist, other doctors, the rest of the staff, and patients in this orientation. Problems and complaints can be talked through openly in forums where the reality-testing functions of the group are more likely to be exercised. New elements make their appearance in this process. At times a patient observes his therapist's reactions to being criticized or maligned by other patients, or disagreed with by seniors and colleagues.

A patient vigorously attacks Dr. A, who is not her therapist, because of his "unfeeling, perfunctory" response to her complaints in talking with her at her request late the previous evening as the doctor on duty. She had asked to see him because she "felt depressed." It took him a long time to come down to see her and when they talked together he seemed impatient and critical. She complained in the meeting that he did not hear her out, was sarcastic, seemed to make fun of her, and ended their talk abruptly. Some patients commented on their contacts with Dr. A when he was on duty in which they also experienced him as impatient, sarcastic, and abrupt. Other patients described experiences with Dr. A in which he had been understanding and helpful. Other patients and a nurse commented on their contacts with the complaining patient in which they found themselves feeling impatient and abrupt with her. They talked about the rapidity with which she shifted from conveying a sense of desperation and helplessness to appearing in control and provocative. Drs. B and C talked about having been called late at night or early in the morning to see this same patient and described their puzzlement with her and their notions as to what was involved in her asking to see a doctor at such times and in the way in which she presented herself when they talked with her. Dr. A acknowledged that he had been impatient with her, described their talk and how he had subjectively experienced the contact.

Such complaints about the behavior of a doctor on call are not new; this forum, however, permits fuller discussion of the complaint and a greater sharing of pertinent information. The querulous patient cannot get away with a damning attack and let it go at that. In such a forum she is called upon to offer a more complete account, including her behavior with the doctor, expectations, and feelings about his responses. Discussed in this context, the complaint is more likely to be related to problems for which the patient entered the hospital, problems she has encountered in adapting to others in the hospital community, and what is happening in her individual psychotherapy. Ideally, the colloquy would not become argumentative or defensive. Patients would not be criticized for the content of their complaints or for complaining. The tone of the discussion, set largely by the chairman, would retain a consistently therapeutic character: attempting to understand what happened and its meaning to the participants, what can be learned that might be useful in resolving conflicts that brought the patient to the hospital, and informing other patients and staff members of means by which they can be helpful.

This optimal picture of what might be realized in patient-staff meetings was rarely achieved. But the existence of such forums, in conjunction with other innovations, provided conditions under which the ideal was approached. Matters previously assumed to be undiscussable were in fact discussed. Ways were found of talking about problems together, openly, and frankly, and with the participation of the entire hospital community.

The patient's emerging picture of his therapist was now influenced by observations of his behavior in patient-staff meetings. An image of the doctor as assertive, strong, and clear-headed may be confirmed or contradicted by observations outside individual psychotherapeutic contacts. Since the power of the director is emphasized in these meetings, the patient is often inclined to experience him as more important than his own therapist. For some, talking with their therapist becomes "just talking"; anything of importance can only be clarified and settled with the most powerful figures in the community, especially the director.

A graduate student became acutely depressed. Hospitalization involved separation from his wife and recently born son. As therapy proceeded, his depression began to lift and he repeatedly emphasized to his therapist the importance to him and his wife of his visiting her at their apartment outside the hospital. As he absorbed the psychotherapeutic ideology, his request emphasized his capacity to handle this responsibility and its therapeutic usefulness. Although the therapist constantly met this demand by emphasizing the need to clarify all its emotional ramifications for the patient, he gradually felt that such a visit would be useful in treatment, and that this was important for both the patient and his wife. The therapist also felt comfortable about the request since the patient appeared sincere and his assurances that he would handle these visits responsibly seemed valid. The therapist shared these impressions with the patient and implied that bringing the request up in patient-staff meeting would just be a formality. When discussed in patient-staff meeting, nurses emphasized that although the patient had been in the hospital for some months, none of them felt they really knew him yet. Other patients emphasized his distance from them and his persistent reluctance to become involved in hospital activities. The chief resident, assistant director, and the director saw the request as premature and insisted that basic issues still remained unclarified. They questioned the advisability of a patient on the closed ward leaving the hospital on such visits. They asked why he pressed to visit his wife when difficulties with her which were still not understood had been important in his initial depression. They also questioned his wish to be close to his wife at a time when he found it difficult to be close to anyone. The patient was not permitted to make these visits. He was angry with the hospital, the director and other senior staff members, and most particularly with his therapist. The questions raised in the meeting made some sense to the patient. His anger with his therapist centered on his having failed to raise these questions and having given him the impression that he would be able to make these visits. He was disillusioned with his therapist and saw him as a secondary figure; the director saw the issues more clearly, and his judgment prevailed.

Both patient and therapist may learn from such discussions. Issues that must be dealt with in treatment are delineated. The limits of the therapist's powers are made explicit. The need to work out the implications of the patient's request thoroughly are emphasized. However, the therapeutic relationship may suffer, despite the fact that discussion facilitated the overall therapeutic objectives of the hospital.

Participating with his therapist in these meetings, the patient sometimes experiences him as a sibling rather than as a parent figure. The chairman addresses a patient by his first name and sometimes uses first names in referring to residents and other staff members, but he and other senior staff members are usually addressed formally. The appearance that residents and patients constitute a single peer group distinct from the hierarchically superior senior staff lends another dimension to the complaint of residents being oriented to the hospital: "It's impossible to tell the patients from the doctors." Being bracketed together as members of a group of inferior status may contribute to their sharing a perspective that devalues their psychotherapeutic work. Meaningful clarification and decision-making seems to come only from powerful figures who stand outside and above the relationship between therapist and patient, both of whom are subject to the authority of these more powerful figures. Their decisions may be reversed, policies modified or halted, judgments censured or contradicted. Tacit agreements which depend upon this shared view of the hospital sometimes develop between patients and their therapists, and mutually protective attitudes are assumed in opposition to their more powerful seniors. These problems arise in any hospital. Do they become more difficult where many contacts are encouraged between therapists and patients outside individual treatment, and where therapists, patients, and other staff members participate actively together in the community? In this setting the play of forces between director, residents, and patients is brought into sharp relief.

The innovations affected the impact on patients of the annual change of residents and made the importance of the relationship with the senior staff more obvious. The patient has greater contact with the director and other staff members who remain on the staff year in and year out; feelings develop toward them which in some ways supersede the relationship with the individual therapist. Sometimes the patient, while working with his therapist, maintains a more important relationship with the director, assistant director, or chief resident, seeing them on rounds, participating with them in patient-staff meetings and other regular forums, and often speaking with them informally. In these contacts with more durable senior staff members it sometimes appears that more important issues are talked about, more important impressions made, and since these doctors have greater power in the community and will continue to be around, decisions arrived at and paths of action determined in a way that departs markedly from the indecisive character of contact with his therapist. Anxiety is high whenever the director is absent and someone else chairs patient-staff meetings; anxiety is highest when residents are changing. Having endured severe emotional deprivations repeatedly, patients are exceedingly sensitive to the loss of a trusted confidant. Patients hospitalized for a long time protect themselves against further loss by holding back in their work with their new resident therapist. They do not want to get involved and hurt again.

The post-innovation hospital is experienced as utopian by some severely deprived patients who have been hospitalized for years. The patient finds an opportunity to pursue his wishes, needs, and interests in an atmosphere conducive to his emotional, social, and intellectual growth. He is surrounded by people with whom he can talk and share in activity, people who understand and care about him. The hospital appears to meet his needs in all that affects safety, health, and comfort. It is concerned about his emotional health and psychological growth and development, it provides asylum from the pressures, involvements, and responsibilities which proved too stressful and burdensome in the outside world; it respects his needs and responds to them with thoughtfulness and consideration, thus rendering conflicting needs of others less important; it provides an atmosphere tolerant of the unusual, reacting with compassion and the effort to understand; it protects him from self-hate and the aggression of others; it helps him find a way to get on with his life, clarify what he wants and needs, and fulfill himself; it provides opportunity for active participation in deciding the affairs of the community. Many feel they can never hope to find such a model society elsewhere and dread getting lost again in the larger world.

Although hospitalization, which removes the patient from family and community, imposes deprivations of affection, power, and wealth, the prospect of leaving the hospital is envisioned by many as inflicting even more comprehensive losses (in affection, respect, skill, enlightenment, power, and well-being). To the extent that the new hospital does become a comprehensively psychotherapeutic environment and approaches a model society, patients are motivated to remain. The problem is compounded for long-hospitalized patients and youngsters to whom the pressures of the outside world appear particularly dreadful. The patient knows he will receive the dubious reward of exile when he achieves the capacity for full participation in this community. However, if he has faced his problems, he knows the shortcomings of this utopia, perceives the deprivations of continued hospitalization, and knows that he can only fulfill himself in the larger world.

Psychotherapy And Its Setting

The YPI innovation provides pertinent insights into the place of psychotherapy among the therapeutic procedures within the total context of hospital and community. Psychiatry is concerned with the relationship between individual psychotherapy and the context in which it is conducted. In out-patient treatment the psychotherapist seeks to structure the work with his patient so that the process of investigation and explication is not compromised by any involvement of the therapist in struggles for power between the patient and his family or others. The scope of the psychotherapist's interactions are limited to the patient; contacts with family, friends, colleagues, or other individuals of importance to the patient are avoided. The explication of the patient's feelings, wishes, and needs, his goals and strategies is undertaken (the intelligence and appraisal phases of the decision process), but some outcome phases of decision-making (prescription and termination) are deferred during psychotherapeutic work. The autonomy of the patient is central to the process; the therapist carefully abstains from influencing the direction of the patient's associations, offering advice, imposing any power deprivations, or otherwise interfering with the patient's determination of his own destiny.

When individual psychotherapy is conducted in a psychiatric hospital, the setting has a direct, sustained impact on the character of the interaction. As a member of the hospital staff, the therapist of necessity participates in subjecting his patient to major deprivations of power. This issue may be obfuscated, but whether acknowledged or not, it is of great importance in the doctor-patient relationship. When patient-staff forums are introduced, they do not necessarily result in a modification of the balance of power between patient and therapist; however, as a result of such forums, aspects of the therapeutic interaction which involve deprivations of power may be brought to the forefront and explicated more readily. The therapist exercises power over his hospitalized patient whether or not forums exist in which such matters are openly discussed; the presence of forums invites a more comprehensive investigation of the patient's predicament, including his power position.

The nature of the political structure of a hospital and the role of the therapist within it are reflected in individual psychotherapy. If the setting is severely authoritarian, but the therapist in contrast responds to the patient with respect, he may be experienced as a savior; if he is clearly identified with the power elite of an authoritarian hospital, his patient may experience him as a remote oppressor; if he participates with his patient in power-sharing institutions, he may be experienced as a sibling. The extent to which the therapist has an investment in the hospital establishment and is defensive of its practices will be reflected in limitations on his capacity to examine freely his patient's predicament. If the therapist insists that he plays no role in the power structure of the hospital, his patient may experience him as indifferent and the interactions with him as inconsequential. If the mode of therapy confirms the existence of a marked discrepancy between practice and the spoken ideology of the hospital, the therapist may be viewed as hypocritical and dishonest. The therapist must clarify for himself just where he stands in the political structure of the community in which he and his patient undertake their work together before he can usefully facilitate the explication of how the patient experiences the therapeutic relationship.

Formal separation of psychotherapists from the political structure of the hospital is one available strategy. The treatment program may be organized so that psychiatrists working with patients in individual psychotherapy have no other connection or responsibilities in the hospital, and all decisions about patient management are made by other psychiatrists and staff members and or patients. Such an arrangement exists in the YPI when the patient works with both an "outside therapist," a psychiatrist in the community or in the department of psychiatry not on the hospital's regular staff, and an "administrator," who meets with him regularly and is responsible for his overall treatment program. At the Cassell Hospital near London, psychiatrists (including the medical director) and other staff members who participate with patients in hospital activities and forums do not work with patients in individual psychotherapy; patients see their psychotherapists only in treatment hours, and these psychiatrists avoid any other participation in the affairs of the institution. This strategy may provide the hospital psychiatrist with the outpatient therapist's freedom to explore the patient's experience without the burden of also participating in the determination of the nature of that experience, including the imposition of power deprivations. However, because this arrangement excludes the psychotherapist from a more comprehensive role in the hospital, it deprives the resident of experience important in his training and has therefore been regarded as not suitable at the YPI.

Power Position

The post-innovation patient enjoys a clearly more responsible position in the hospital decision process: he has the opportunity to participate directly in shaping the character of his experience in the hospital. Information about issues of common concern is shared by patients and staff in a continuing dialogue (intelligence); patients, doctors, social workers, nurses, and aides have the opportunity to suggest policy alternatives for dealing with community problems (recommendation or promotion); all may, at times, participate in establishing hospital policies or procedures (prescription); all have the opportunity to participate in assessing whether conduct of patients and staff members complies with established policy (invocation), applying agreed-upon procedures (application), judging the success or failure of policies (appraisal), and, with common consent, to discard policies and procedures (termination).

The new hospital provides an environment where the patient is relatively unhampered by the negative expectations implicit in the passive role and the sense of victimization sustained in the pre-innovation hospital. In the effort to make the hospital comprehensively therapeutic, indulgences of the patient in enlightenment, skill, respect, power, and well-being are to be consistent in individual psychotherapy and the rest of his experience. But is this ideal achieved? The ideology of the therapeutic community is accepted, and all participants strive for its fulfillment. Nevertheless, the basic structure of the hospital remains authoritarian to the extent that substantial power is retained by the director and those in his staff to whom he delegates responsibility. Although power is genuinely shared on some matters, the director may at his discretion withdraw power which he has once delegated. Hence democratic claims of the new hospital may be experienced as a sham, and the therapeutic

community as a society in which the ruler benignly permits his subjects to play at democracy.

The reserve powers of the director are sometimes visibly exercised,
not always under circumstances clearly understood by the patient.
Decisions made at staff and patient-staff meetings are sometimes
overruled. Policies are sometimes established unilaterally by the
director without consultation or discussion. A conflict is stimulated
within the patient: he strives to participate in the full realization of
the therapeutic community; he is confused and exasperated by the
knowledge that power is incompletely shared on grounds which remain ambiguous.

Realistic conflicts between the ideal of the therapeutic community
and obligations of the director to the larger community were not
explored in patient-staff discussions. Hence an opportunity to explicate a difficult and complicated issue in the real world was not taken
advantage of; patients were asked to support an ideology whose
limitations were not explicit.

The patient is both excited and frightened by his new position of
responsibility. As he strives to fulfill the challenge of full participation in the hospital community, he finds himself hampered by all the
inner obstacles which led to his being characterized as "ill." Intrapsychic conflicts which found expression in pre-hospital relationships
and interfered with clarifying and fulfilling his objectives also oppose his efforts to participate responsibly within the hospital
community. Gaining mastery in the struggle within himself, in the
attempt to cope with "illness," is also a necessary achievement and
precondition to assuming the responsibilities of citizenship in a community. In this perspective the individual psychotherapeutic effort
and the processes of the therapeutic community supplement one
another.

The inner forces against which the patient struggles are reinforced
by the inadequacies and fears of models to whom he looks for guidance. They are severely tested and too often found wanting by the
rigorous demands intrinsic to full citizenship in a democratic society.
Staff members are also limited by personal immaturity, long exposure to and incorporation of authoritarian values, and the resulting
conflicts when confronted with freedom, responsibility, and opportunities to create and sustain constructive action with others. These
individual limitations of the members of the staff, operative despite
good intentions and conscious adherence to the ideology of the new
hospital, impose constraints upon the patient's vision of what is
actually possible.

9. The Ambiguous Role of the Post-Innovation Nurse

Predispositions and Perspectives

Of all those in the hospital whose role and activity have been modified, the nurses have been most drastically affected by the developing therapeutic community. The doctors are still primarily engaged in the work of psychotherapy; social workers are still largely occupied in work with patients' families; the patients, for all their increased freedom and responsibility, still look to the staff for treatment and care. But for the nurse the question now arises in this changing atmosphere: does she still nurse? Every aspect of her role and work has been affected by the innovations: the clothes she wears, the character of her relationships with patients, doctors, and fellow nurses, the extent of her authority and responsibility, her tasks, what others expect from her and what she expects of herself.

These changes are symbolized by the young and energetic director of nursing appointed in the post-innovation period. She received some of her training in the YPI from oldtimers she then directed. Her preparation also included extensive work as an educator in psychiatric nursing and instruction in the social sciences related to psychiatry. Her primary interest in undertaking work at the YPI was to investigate problems in psychiatric nursing and develop a more comprehensively psychotherapeutic hospital. Her perspectives thus contrast markedly with the image offered earlier of the pre-innovation nurse.

The effort to transform the YPI confused the nurse's role by devaluating the clearly structured tasks with which she was occupied earlier, and placing new emphasis on her most important responsibility—direct, more clearly psychotherapeutic interaction with patients. Her former sources of gratification and power have been undermined by the innovations. Her secrets are now shared with all the patients; the rules, which she kept and about which others deferred to her as an authority, are now vigorously scrutinized and continuously modified by forums in which patients participate more actively than nurses. Residents, social workers, and, most particularly, patients themselves are increasingly active in assuming direct responsibility for patients; patronizing and authoritarian elements in nurses' behavior toward patients, previously sanctioned and encouraged, are criticized; physical treatments, about which nurses were the most knowing, experienced staff members and which offered them a basis for feeling competent in their work, are only rarely employed. The nurse's preferred role as the doctor's helpmate has increasingly become a position which she can earn only through demonstrating her comprehension and mastery of the tasks intrinsic to active professional participation in the therapeutic community. The innovations, the new research and psychotherapeutically oriented director of nursing, and the gradual addition to the staff of other nurses who share her curiosity and excitement about the changing role of the psychiatric nurse, have stimulated others in the nursing staff to try to understand what is happening and to take part in it.[1] Most remarkable has been the reaction of the oldtimers: although discomfited and threatened by these changes, they have tried to comprehend them, have demonstrated their flexibility in reexamining assumptions which guided their work for years, have sought more training, and have been enthusiastic about, as well as resistant to, some aspects of the new emphases in the hospital. Members of the core group describe their experience in the post-innovation hospital as much more satisfactory, minimize the disruptive impact of their altered position and tasks, and emphatically state their preference for the new regime.[2] These complacent responses are most difficult to understand or accept as wholly accurate. Although the nurses are offered the possibility of a new, more substantial professional status by the innovations, the price is a drastic redefinition of who they are and what they do. These new perspectives entail great confusion and insecurity.

In characterizing the hospital's treatment philosophy and orientation, all post-innovation nurses referred to both individual psycho-

1. A comprehensive investigation of nursing at the YPI has been undertaken by Anne Baziak, former Director of Nursing.

2. Core-group members were asked to compare their work in 1961 with working in the hospital prior to 1956. They said they were now "more contented" (7; 2 said they were "less contented now"); that they now work under "less stress" (7; 3 said there was "more stress now"); they saw themselves as "now having more responsibility" (6; 1 reported "less responsibility now"); they think they are "now more important to the residents" (5; 1 felt "less important to the residents now," and 4 reported "no change" in their importance to residents); they have "more say" now than earlier (7; 3 felt they had "less say now"); "more free to talk to the doctors" than before 1956 (7; 1 felt "less free" to talk to them now); and they felt that "the residents are more receptive to their ideas about patients than they were before 1956" (5; 3 described residents as now "less receptive" to their ideas).

therapy and the increasing therapeutic use of the community of patients and staff, and they present themselves as more fully committed to the new emphases in the hospital than the residents.[3]

The YPI Experience

The post-innovation nurse's day is primarily occupied in activities which depart from traditional nursing. She arrives at work in either a starched white uniform or street clothes—an indicator of where she stands in her struggle with the ambiguities of her new position. She is free to wear what she pleases.[4] The director of nursing wears street clothes all the time; most oldtimers wear uniforms and discourage the wearing of street clothes. Wearing a uniform may communicate to patients, "I am different from you, superior to you, separate from you," and to residents, who no longer wear white, "I am reluctant to shed the clearly defined role for which I have been trained and in which I have experience to join in this disturbing, confusing adventure." Shedding the uniform makes the nurse more vulnerable to patients and other staff members and invites a greater involvement as an equal without special protection.

Most nurses have no awareness of what is symbolized by what they choose to wear and account for wearing uniforms on practical grounds (cost and ease of laundering). Respect and wealth considerations are probably important here, for street clothes reveal identifying status characteristics that wearing a uniform does not.

The nurse's confidential reporting of patients' behavior has become much less important. Her elaborate notes and reports were the object of intense curiosity by patients who wanted to know what was being thought and said about them. The nurse's notes are much briefer, and only a concise weekly summary is retained in the clinical record; they also require much less of her time. With the advent of patient-staff meetings, material that used to be hidden in the nurses'

3. When asked about "the approach most valued in a resident" by those running the hospital and by nurses themselves, most nurses saw those running the hospital as preferring residents who regard individual therapy as most important (10, including 5 members of the core group); others felt those running the hospital favored residents who regard involvement in the community of patients and staff as most important (8, 4 in the core group). However, most nurses stated they themselves most valued "community involvement" by a resident (10, 5 in the core group); seven, including four in the core group, most valued the residents' emphasis on individual psychotherapy.

4. When asked what they wear to work, 17 nurses (10 in the core group) stated they wore a uniform. Four (including only one member of the core group) said they wore street clothes, reflecting the strength of the nurses' reluctance to change.

notes is now shared openly by nurses, doctors, social workers, and patients. The nurse's domain is also intruded upon by doctors and other staff members who have many more opportunities to observe directly and interact with all patients in the hospital, not just those with whom they work in individual treatment. The nurse's secrets are no longer secret, and the doctors are less dependent upon nurses for information. The nurse is encouraged to share her observations with the entire community and is thus deprived of respect and power.

The nurse's former position in dealing with patients' disturbances is now shared with patients and other staff members. A patient who becomes agitated and troublesome to others is not dealt with by the nurse, or nurse and doctor, working alone to quiet him with medications, restraints, or isolation; patients express concern, plan constructive action with the staff, and pitch in and try to help.

A young adult woman patient had become relatively compliant and passive as she became involved in hospital treatment, but her earlier agitation now returns as her doctor departs from the hospital staff; she is again provocative and demanding. This behavior disturbs other patients, especially those on her ward, the doctors and nurses, and all participants in a patient-staff meeting of which she is disruptive. She sits beside the director-chairman during the meeting, interrupts frequently without having the floor, and repetitively intrudes her own problems into the discussion of other matters. Her behavior becomes the focus of the meeting, and observations are shared by nurses and doctors, her individual therapist, the social worker who has contact with her family, student nurses, and the aides. Activities workers describe her behavior under their supervision. All contribute, delineating conditions under which she seems to get worse and in which she is less troubled. A picture of what is happening and how it might be dealt with emerges. Recommendations are made about periods of isolation for her, medication, the possible usefulness of other patients taking turns spending time with her, and the advisability of visits from family and friends; a complete management regimen is worked out by the community in concert, the patient herself participating in this assessment and planning. In subsequent patient-staff meetings, plans are appraised and revised, new observations reported, other opinions about management expressed; the entire community approaches her disturbance as a community problem. Because of elaborate discussions which have already taken place in patient-staff meetings, little is added in staff conferences. These problems are also discussed in individual and group psychotherapy and in patient-staff advisory committee, where further management recommendations are made.

The nurse participates in such planning discussions on an equal footing with patients and other staff members. She is deprived in power and confused as to just what her distinct role is within the hospital community.

Most of the elaborate procedures for policing the safety of patients, formerly carried out by nurses, have been modified or eliminated as each has been scrutinized in the continuing dialogue of hospital forums. Table knives are no longer counted; radios, clocks, and lamps are no longer locked away at night; patients use their own electric razors or locked razors which are available without supervision. The nurse still polices some safety precautions, for example, smoking in bed. However, patients as well as other staff members share these responsibilities. The nurse has become one among many in the community concerned with such precautions and has lost another previously exclusive function which helped delineate her role.

A residue of the extensive, time-consuming precautions characteristic of the pre-innovation hospital persisted in the chore of locking closets at night. Patients complained in patient-staff meetings about this holdover as unnecessary and reproached the staff for sustaining a useless procedure which undermined their dignity and treated them as childlike and irresponsible. After discussion in a series of meetings, the director and others in the staff agreed to leave closets unlocked at night. However, it was emphasized that patients would have to share responsibility for any consequences of closets being unlocked, a responsibility the staff felt patients could successfully assume. More discussions of what would be involved in unlocking closets followed. Patients emphasized their fear that it would be easy for someone to hang himself in a closet; despite their earlier complaints and the approval of the staff, it was decided at their insistence that nurses would continue to lock the closets at night. Patients shared the nurses' reservations about giving up those protective functions which were a part of her authoritarian, parental role.

The pre-innovation nurse monitored patients' use of the telephone on the closed ward. Patients complained about this in patient-staff meetings as a useless procedure which should be terminated;

again the director and others in the staff agreed, if patients would assume this responsibility themselves. This arrangement was accepted. Patients now oversee the use of the telephone on the closed ward. They keep one another informed of the extent to which they have permission to use the telephone. If a patient attempts an unauthorized call, he is restrained from doing so by other patients. If he is insistent and difficult, patients remove the telephone from the ward. A patient who misuses the telephone no longer has the alibi, "the nurse failed to stop me." Another of the tasks which helped the nurse define her role was eliminated.

The pre-innovation nurse nursed patients, the passive recipients of her tender care and prodding direction, to get them well. In the new hospital, however, most patients are physically healthy adolescents and young adults; they rarely sit in ward lounges or their rooms passively awaiting the nurse's intervention. Through much of the day there are few patients present on the closed wards, and the open wards are often bare. Some patients are at work or school outside the hospital; others are involved in activities and work within the hospital. Even the most disturbed of closed-ward patients participate in an elaborate schedule of meetings and therapy and, as soon as they are able, in the other activities. The efforts of troubled patients who struggle to isolate themselves and evade such participation are vigorously opposed by other patients, social workers, and doctors, as well as nurses. On the wards, patients are more often involved in games, homework, and other structured activities. They increasingly prefer interactions with staff in which they participate on more of an equal footing: ping-pong or bridge, discussing politics, and going over homework. Interactions in which patients assume a passive role and invite the ministrations of the nurse are increasingly regarded as alien to the hospital atmosphere. The nurse who would occupy herself with conventional nursing tasks finds few patients willing to participate.

When a nurse becomes closely involved with a patient, few of the safeguards present when a psychiatrist or social worker enters into such a relationship protect nurse and patient. Encouraged to interact more with patients, she sometimes finds them telling her about their earlier experiences, the intimate details of their private lives, about their parents, marriage, children, and work. She is uncertain about what to do with this information, how to respond to it, and about whether or not she is intruding upon matters appropriately left to individual psychotherapy. She is concerned that her relationship with the patient may consist in a mutual "acting out," an uninspected quest for the direct, immediate gratification of the needs of both nurse and patient.

In considering functions now demanded of the nurse, the question must be asked: What constitutes a psychotherapeutic relationship? It may be defined as one in which the effort is made to investigate and clarify (enlightenment) what one individual (the patient) needs and wants (in all value dimensions), and what he does (the strategies he employs) in his relationships with others, especially with the other person in this interaction (the therapist). This is a careful working over of current and past experience, identifying how what is needed and wanted is sought and has been interfered with, and how gratification might be obtained. Such a therapeutic relationship requires of the therapist that he be clear about where his gratification comes from; classically, he obtains satisfaction of his intellectual curiosity (enlightenment) and is concretely rewarded with money (wealth); he is obligated to scrutinize any gratification of these and other of his wishes and needs in the relationship. It is particularly in this latter undertaking that the therapist's personal psychoanalysis is indispensable; continuing or periodic supervision of his work by experienced colleagues is helpful in identifying his sources of gratification in therapeutic relationships, alerting him to the need for self-examination. In the new effort to maximize the psychotherapeutic aspects of every relationship, the nurse is encouraged to spend more of her time directly with patients and to participate in the continuing examination of all such interactions. This task includes helping the patient to identify in his current behavior and relationships the expression of problems that brought him to the hospital. In the psychotherapeutic interaction, the patient constantly presses for direct gratification in the relationship itself (all values, particularly affection), and the therapist uses his technical skills to channel the energy behind this quest into the investigatory effort (enlightenment in the service of well-being). If needs are directly gratified in the relationship, the patient's motivation to modify his behavior and mode of relating to the external world is undermined (indulged in affection in treatment, he may be less motivated to seek such indulgence outside treatment). Important in this therapeutic skill is a continuing appraisal of the patient's capacity to tolerate a deprivation of need, and the effort to effect a balance between analyzing as against indulging need (the extent to which enlightenment can be indulged at the same time that a relative deprivation in affection is imposed).

The nurse does not meet the criteria for this therapeutic role. She lacks personal psychoanalytic experience, technical training, and the opportunity for continuing or periodic supervision (she is deprived in enlightenment and skill, and because she has not had personal treatment is more vulnerable to deprivations in well-being); she tends to seek fulfillment of her needs directly in the relationship, and her gratification remains unexamined. This characterization of the intellectual and investigatory aspects (enlightenment) of a therapeutic relationship underemphasizes the warmth, tolerance, understanding, and appreciation of what the patient is feeling (respect and affection), which are important in the therapeutic process and which the patient does receive from the nurse. This kind of involvement requires that the nurse, like her psychiatrist and social worker colleagues, be alert to what such a relationship means to her: what needs she brings to it, how these needs are met, and the specific nature of her impact on the patient's psychotherapeutic course. Confronted with this delineation of the nurse's task, it is not difficult to appreciate the increased emotional burden of her work and her resistance to the demand that she interact more with patients.[5]

As part of their training, student nurses spend periods ranging from a few weeks to several months in the YPI. Some have had prior experience on psychiatric wards in a large, nearby state hospital, work in some respects comparable to the experience of the preinnovation nurses in the YPI. They are confused about what they are meant to be doing in the YPI and are more comfortable with clearly structured tasks, assisting the nurse in the dispensing of medications or accompanying a patient on an errand. But their time on the wards presents problems, more difficult because most patients are late adolescents and young adults. They cannot see what is sick about most patients they encounter and experience them more readily as friends of their own age than as patients requiring their ministrations. When student nurses are encouraged to spend most of their time "interacting" with patients, they are extremely uncertain about their role. Adolescent and young adult patients tend to prefer the oldtimers, with whom their problems about relating to peers are not stirred up. They feel more comfortable leaning on and being helped by the older nurses.

5. The nurses' recognition of this problem is expressed in their responses to the question, "What are the most frequent mistakes that inexperienced nurses make with patients?" The majority replied, "they get too involved" (14, including 8 of the core group), are "too social" (9, 6 in the core group), and "too eager to please" (8, 3 in the core group). The nurses least often designated the inexperienced nurse's tendency to be "too distant" with patients as a problem.

Nurses' resistance to the demand that they interact more with patients is illustrated by their response to the reconstruction of the closed-ward nursing station. The former station was on the women's side of the second floor, a location that was not accidental; the nurses clearly felt more comfortable relating to female than male patients and spent most of their time on the women's side. (The male aides felt more comfortable with male patients and spent their time on the men's side.) The nurse's station was simply a room with a door. Whenever a nurse wanted to talk privately with another nurse or with a doctor, the door was closed. It was also closed when the nurse was preparing medications or writing observation notes and when the resident was writing orders.

A new nurse's station was built between the men's and women's sides of the closed ward to promote more interaction between nurses and patients, especially the avoided men. It was constructed with large plate-glass windows protruding into the hallway, permitting nurses to observe both sides of the ward, and enabling patients to look in and see the nurses. Another room was constructed in the rear where notes could be written and conferences held without interruption. The new nurse's station did not work; the nurses continued to spend most of their time with women patients. When nurses wanted to be alone the new station made it even easier than before. Nurses tended to stay in the back room with the door shut, or in the front section behind the glass with the door locked, making conversational contact more difficult. This solution proved inadequate because it did not cope with the question of why nurses find relating to male patients difficult or their reluctance to interact with all patients.

The post-innovation nurse further evaded the demand to increase interactions with patients by busying herself with whatever less exacting tasks she can find, for example, working with kitchen helpers setting tables and serving meals. She was unmistakably threatened and discomfited when unable to evade the new imperative.

The Nurse and Other Staff

The nurse's preference for viewing herself as the doctor's helpmate, assisting him in ministrations to patients, and in assessing their behavior, de-emphasizes direct work with patients and gratifies her wish for camaraderie and respect. Because the post-innovation nurse is ill-equipped for the full participation now demanded of her, residents and other doctors are less accepting of her as helpmate. She has few opportunities in the new hospital to be as helpful as in the past, when her skills were necessary in physical treatments and patients were encouraged to be the passive recipients of her care and direction (her deprivations in enlightenment and skill now contribute to deprivations of affection, respect, and power).

Nurses' relationships with one another did not change in the post-innovation period.[6] A new clique began to develop among newer nurses who embraced the innovations and the psychotherapeutic hospital more enthusiastically than oldtimers; however, they were outnumbered and outranked by the core group. Some were transient, soon accepting positions in other hospitals attempting similar innovations.

The post-innovation nurse's relationship with social workers is influenced by the fact that they are better prepared than the nurse for participation as professional equals with the physicians in the comprehensive psychotherapeutic effort. The nurse's losses in the new hospital are the social worker's gains: her traditional skills are not used; in the performance now demanded she is inadequate in enlightenment and skill and consequently also deprived of affection, respect, and power. The social worker's skill and enlightenment are increasingly acknowledged, opportunities for application are greater, and she is indulged in affection, respect, and power. The work of the nurse is disrupted as tasks alien to her training and experience are emphasized; the social worker has long sought to participate more fully in the very tasks she is now authorized and encouraged to undertake.

The Nurse and her Seniors

Residents and senior doctors are now less ready to exercise authority and power directly and are disinclined to supervise nurses in their tasks. This apparent indulgence of nurses in power, which confers upon them an increased measure of autonomy and responsibility, simultaneously deprives them of a source of role-definition available during the pre-innovation period.

In the post-innovation period, because the director, assistant director, and chief resident participate directly with patients in patient-staff meetings and other forums, more of their information is derived from direct contact than from nurses' reports. They have an opportunity for continuing, meaningful relationships with each of the patients without relying upon residents or nurses as intermediaries. Since the nurses are now in this sense bypassed, occasions

6. When core group nurses were asked whether "nurses at the YPI tended to relate to one another more closely or less closely than they did prior to 1956," four said they were "more close now," and five said they were "less close now."

for close contact between nurses and senior doctors have been drastically reduced. Residents are the only physicians with whom they are now likely to have much individual contact, and this reinforces their view of themselves as having less power and authority in the post-innovation hospital.

At the same time, there has been an effort to heighten the nurse's respect position by helping her to recognize the importance and usefulness of her contacts with patients and the valuable contribution she can make in providing information and assessments of the patient's status. In every discussion in staff, patient-staff, and advisory committee meetings, nurses are encouraged to participate actively, often with the question, "Is your experience with this patient consistent with what has been said or recommended?" However, nurses tend to compare their understanding and capacity to speak in groups unfavorably with that of doctors, social workers, and well-educated patients and to deprecate the quality and usefulness of their contributions. In these circumstances deficient training limits their ability to take advantage of a potentially increased respect position.

The commitment of the post-innovation director of nursing in investigation and psychotherapy offered an alternative model to what had been valued in the traditional, pre-innovation nurse. Her high enlightenment and skill position brought her emphatic indulgences in affection, respect, and power, gratifying to all nurses who identified with her. At the same time, however, she was envied and experienced as remote from the rank-and-file nurse because of her intellectually superior preparation, diverse interests, and greater involvement with others in the staff. She also evoked respect and gratitude from the nurses for the training she was equipped to provide, as well as skepticism of her capacity to appreciate their predicament. Because they felt distant from the director of nursing, some nurses turned to the chief nurses for guidance and support.

Decision-Making and Power

Post-innovation nurses are more conservative than others on the staff about patient participation in the hospital decision process.[7] Nurses vigorously opposed patient participation in decisions on issues con-

7. Asked whether or not patients should participate in deciding nine common management issues, the majority of all nurses opposed their participation on four issues; the majority of the core group opposed patient participation in deciding six of the nine questions. Nurses were most accepting of patient participation in determining whether or not a given patient should be on the open ward. Patients "should" participate, said sixteen (7 in the core group); "should

ventionally regarded as medical.[8] Most nurses favored patient-staff
meetings,[9] opposed patient participation in discussing and deciding
many issues in which they already constructively participated,[10]

---

not," said five (3 in the core group). Most also favored patients having a voice
in "whether or not a given patient may make phone calls at will": "should" said
twelve (6 in the core group); "should not" said nine (4 in the core group).
There was less agreement about patients participating in deciding how much
time a given patient should spend outside of the hospital unaccompanied:
"should," said eleven (6 in the core group), "should not," said eleven (5 in the
core group); how late all patients on a given ward may stay up: "should," said
twelve, "should not," said eight (6 in the core group were opposed), and
whether or not a given patient is ready for discharge: favored by twelve nurses,
opposed by eight (5 in the core group).

8. Twenty, including all members of the core group, opposed patient participation in deciding "whether or not a given patient should be given a tranquilizer" (only one nurse said patients should participate). Nineteen, including
all in the core group, opposed patients participating in deciding "whether a
given patient should be given EST" (2 said "should"). Eighteen, again including all core group members, opposed patient participation in deciding "whether
or not a given patient should be taken off bedtime sedation" (4 said "should").
Fifteen (7 in the core group) opposed patients having a voice in deciding
"whether or not a given patient should be physically restrained" (4, including
2 core-group members, favored patient participation in deciding this issue).
When the nurses responded to these questions (in 1961), patients were already
actively participating in the decision process on all of the issues. However, on
issues regarded as "medical," patient participation tended to be limited to the
intelligence and appraisal functions; information they shared with staff, including their assessment of the effectiveness of the treatment regimen of a given
patient, was influential in determining and modifying therapeutic plans. This
opposition of nurses, particularly the core group, expresses their wish to return
to earlier modes of decision-making and the political structure in which patients
exercised less power in the hospital.

9. Asked, "Do you think the business conventionally conducted in staff meetings could be conducted in joint patient-staff meetings?," eighteen (including
10 core-group members) said, "no" (one core-group member was undecided),
two (neither in the core group) said, "yes." However, the majority agreed that
decision-making meetings at the YPI should include both staff and patient-staff
meetings (18, including all members of the core group; 2 favored "staff meetings only"; one favored "patient-staff meetings only"). When presented with a
series of arguments for and against patient-staff meetings, the majority stated
that on balance they agree with arguments in favor of patient-staff meetings
(16, 7 in the core group "for"; 5, 3 core members, "against"). Of these arguments, they gave greatest weight to giving the patient "an opportunity to assume greater responsibility for the way the hospital is run and for his own conduct in the hospital," and providing "a continuing opportunity for patients and
staff to share information." Of arguments against these meetings, nurses were
most impressed with "undermining the patient's view of the therapist by seeing
him challenged by colleagues and patients, and their thus interfering with the
patient's image of the therapist" (an argument given little weight by resident
therapists).

10. The nurses were presented with a list of thirty "topics which might be
discussed at joint patient-staff meetings," all of which had been discussed in

and further, acknowledged the very limited extent of their own participation in these meetings.[11]

All the sources of the pre-innovation nurse's power have drastically changed: she is less the doctors' professional associate and helpmate; if she is now to reestablish such a position, professional criteria, for which her training and experience have not yet prepared her, must be fulfilled. Secrets she told doctors about patients are no longer secrets, but shared with the entire community. She continues to participate in making decisions in staff meetings from which patients are excluded, but issues formerly discussed and decided in these meetings are increasingly the business of forums which include patients. Her former role as keeper of the rules and other less formal hospital prescriptions is now shared with all members of the community, including patients. The post-innovation nurse is discouraged from assuming an authoritarian position. Goading, reproaching, and disciplining patients, sanctioned in the pre-innovation period, is questioned and criticized. Patients increasingly assume the responsi-

---

such meetings, and asked whether they should be. In contrast to residents, most of whom favored discussion of twenty-nine of the thirty topics (except for "staff salaries"), a majority of nurses opposed discussion of twelve topics. They opposed discussion of "staff salaries" (20, including all core members), "religion of a staff member or patient" (20, including all core-group members), "validity of a resident's judgment as questioned by staff" (18, 10 in the core group; 4, one in the core group, favored discussion), "whether a patient should be put on a tranquilizer" (17, including all members of the core group; 5 were in favor of discussion), "whether the hospital should use EST at all or not" (opposed by 17, including all core-group members), "a resident's treatment of a patient" (14, 9 in the core group), "the director's running of the hospital" (14, 9 in the core group), "the hospital budget" (14, 7 in the core group), "the prognosis of a given patient" (14, 6 in the core group), "a patient's financial problems" (13, 8 in the core group), "sexual indiscretion of a staff member" (13, 8 in the core group), "use of daytime or bedtime sedation" (12, 8 in the core group).

Nurses were willing to discuss in patient-staff meetings "bedtime hours," "a patient's holding a job, attending school," "the value of group therapy," "a patient's refusal to attend meetings," "the ability of a given patient to head patient government," and "the advisability of compulsory attendance at education classes."

11. When asked about the extent of their participation in patient-staff meetings, nurses tended to be more accurate than residents, who overstated their participation. However, some nurses not in the core group described themselves as speaking much more frequently than they actually do. Most nurses said they spoke in less than one out of six patient-staff meetings (11, including 6 in the core group). A few said they spoke more frequently: five, one in the core group, said they spoke in one out of three meetings; three, one in the core group, said they spoke in one out of six meetings; none said that they spoke "in almost every meeting." Nurses are thus aware of speaking infrequently in these forums. A majority added, however, that they had found participation "less difficult" than they had anticipated (10, 5 in the core group); seven (3 in the core group) said it was "more difficult" than they anticipated.

bility of monitoring the behavior of one another. The administration of physical treatments and the nurse's role in the physical care of patients is largely over; the dependency of patients intrinsic to these functions has thus been modified. The psychotherapeutic emphasis and the infrequent use of physical treatments have decreased the nurse's job of orienting and instructing residents. The camaraderie formerly enjoyed with senior doctors, an important source of affection, respect, rectitude, and power indulgences for the pre-innovation nurse, are substantially decreased as senior doctors have more direct contact with patients, are less dependent, and have less meaningful individual relationships with nurses.

Their most powerful representative, the director of nursing, now shares the investigatory and psychotherapeutic interests of others in the staff which remain alien to the nurses as a group; they are less confident of her ability to understand and appreciate their predicament. The oldtimers remain in the majority and hold all chief-nurse positions. Although striving to comprehend and comply with the psychotherapeutic ideology, largely in the service of pleasing and being approved of by the senior staff, they continue to prefer a traditional delineation of the nurse's role and devalue the direct interaction with patients now emphasized as their primary function.

The post-innovation nurse experiences deprivations in power, for which she is no longer compensated by affection and respect. Her relative deprivation in wealth is sustained. She is subjected to new deprivations in rectitude as she resists innovations enthusiastically supported by patients, most colleagues, and her seniors. Her deprivations in enlightenment and skill appropriate to the new hospital sustain her increasingly deprived position in respect and power. She is presented with the opportunity to enjoy a position of greater autonomy and responsibility, but it requires that she achieve the capacity for full professional participation. The gratifications, availble to the post-innovation nurse are contingent upon her success in meeting this challenge and finding a way to join in building and sustaining the therapeutic community.

10. The Impact on Resident Physicians

Predispositions and Perspectives

After the inauguration of patient-staff meetings at the YPI in 1956, the staff of the Veterans Hospital became increasingly interested in such forums and in the concept of the hospital as a community. Later, similar meetings were held regularly on some of its wards. The larger patient population and shorter hospital stays discouraged the VA staff from turning over as much responsibility to patients as was done at the YPI, and the overall character of VA hospital life was not markedly changed. However, the VA came to provide the resident with an introduction to such forums during the first year of his training and some familiarity with this new emphasis in treatment prior to his work at the YPI.

In 1961, during the last months of this study, a new department clinical facility was established, a ward within the Yale Medical Center's general hospital. In line with a trend throughout the United States, its objective was to provide treatment for acutely disturbed patients within the local general hospital for a period of one to three months, and then effect their return to the community with continuing outpatient care. This ward's initial director had been a resident and chief resident at the YPI and an important participant in changes effected in the YPI. He tried to apply its forums and community emphasis to the treatment program in the ward. Since the goal was brief hospitalization, drugs, physical treatments, and explicitly authoritarian interventions were frequently employed. Individual psychotherapy was less prominent in treatment than at the YPI. In this setting, patient-staff meetings assumed a different character. An atmosphere was created in the YPI which permitted the patient to put aside his craziness with the understanding that he would have the opportunity for long-term definitive treatment in the hospital. The ward, in contrast, asked the patient to put aside his craziness in order that he could return promptly to his family, work, and the larger community. YPI patient-staff meetings constituted a continuing forum, with a relatively stable group of participants subjecting to general appraisal their interactions with one another and the policies of their community. The patient on the ward was a relatively transient participant in such forums, and the emphasis was on his promptly attuning himself to the tasks intrinsic to his return to the larger community. Because of the need for brief hospitalization, conformity to demands made by family and society were sometimes reinforced without benefit of a thoroughgoing investigation of the deprivational impact of such demands upon the individual, and without the exploration of possibilities for the patient meeting his needs within the limits of these socially imposed demands.

The training of the resident, prior to his year at the YPI, was therefore changed as a result of the innovations at the YPI; both the VA Hospital and the newly established psychiatric ward in the general hospital were affected and provided some experience with patient-staff meetings for those who later worked in the YPI.

The expectations of the resident beginning his YPI year also changed; he now wanted to learn about, to participate in, and to acquire the skills of community treatment as well as psychotherapy. The innovations and their accompanying atmosphere of excitement and promise interested the resident and appealed to his curiosity. Although becoming a competent psychotherapist remained the most important objective of the YPI resident as in pre-innovation years, the opportunity to master this new mode of treatment assumed great importance. Participation in a therapeutic community joined intensive psychotherapy in the residents' view of the most rewarding aspect of their YPI year,[1] the hospital treatment philosophy and orientation,[2] and the approach to his work he and his

1. Asked to describe "the most rewarding aspect of your YPI training," most post-innovation residents (12 of 28, or 41 per cent) emphasized intensive psychotherapy, as did pre-innovation residents. However, ten post-innovation residents (10 of 28, or 35 per cent) described working in a therapeutic community as the most rewarding aspect of their YPI training, emphatically documenting the impact of the innovations upon their experience. Some residents who referred to this aspect of the year as most rewarding described it in a way that separated them from actual participation: two spoke of "learning about," two described "gaining insight into the dynamics of," and two talked of "observing" the therapeutic community.

2. When asked to characterize "the treatment philosophy and orientation of the YPI during your training year," most emphasized intensive, individual psychoanalytically oriented psychotherapy, as did pre-innovation residents. A shift is revealed with particular clarity when pre- and post-innovation residents' responses are compared, especially when pre-innovation residents who worked at the YPI during the present director's term are separated from those who worked in the hospital earlier. The earliest group of pre-innovation residents (at the YPI between 1950 and 1953) characterized the hospital as emphasizing intensive individual psychotherapy (11 of 11); only two of these residents added any reference to milieu treatment. In the next group of pre-innovation residents (who worked under the present director, but prior to patient-staff meetings and other innovations, 1953–56), ten of twelve characterized the hospital as emphasizing intensive psychotherapy; four of the ten added a concern with the community

seniors most valued.[3] Although the residents still considered individual psychotherapy and nursing care the most important aspects
of the hospital treatment program "in determining whether or not
patients get better," the innovations modified their assessment of the
importance of other aspects of the program, shifting patient-staff
meetings and the work program upward and decreasing the importance of activities, patient government, and later, group psychotherapy.[4] Participation in a therapeutic community and psycho-

---

of patients and staff in treatment; two of twelve spoke only of the community in
characterizing the treatment orientation. One resident said, "It was a therapeutic
unit in the process of finding itself." Another added, "It was the beginning of
the community concept in the hospital, but it was still quite bumbling." In the
post-innovation group (those who worked in the YPI after the inauguration of
patient-staff meetings, 1956–61), twenty-one of twenty-eight (75 per cent)
emphasized "community treatment"; fifteen of the twenty-one also mentioned
intensive individual psychotherapy, and six referred only to the community emphasis in treatment; only three characterized the hospital's treatment orientation
as concerned with intensive, individual treatment and made no reference to
community treatment. These changes in characterization of YPI treatment
philosophy and orientation clearly reflect the influence of the current director
and the impact of patient-staff meetings and other innovations. Of the twenty-
nine residents who referred to intensive individual psychotherapy and specifically
described the treatment as "psychoanalytically oriented," the majority (18)
were in the pre-innovation group; as the YPI became more concerned with the
community of patients and staff, there was some tendency for residents to view
intrapsychic and psychodynamic considerations as less important in the hospital's treatment philosophy and orientation.
     3. Asked whether they valued "individual psychotherapy," "involvement in
the community of patients and staff," or "research" as most important, the majority of both pre- and post-innovation residents emphasized "individual
psychotherapy" (38 of 55, or 69 per cent); ten (18 per cent) most valued
"community involvement"; four viewed "individual therapy and community
involvement" as equally important; only three selected "research." Of the ten
who most valued "community involvement," only two worked in the YPI in the
pre-innovation era; eight were in the post-innovation group.
     When residents were asked which of these approaches by a resident was most
valued by the senior staff, they replied that their seniors most valued "individual
therapy" (27 of 54, or 50 per cent) and then "community involvement" (19, or
36 per cent); three saw the senior staff as valuing "individual therapy and
community involvement" equally; four felt that their seniors emphasized "research." The residents view their seniors as valuing "individual therapy" less,
and "community involvement" more than they do. In fact, post-innovation residents believed their seniors put "community involvement" (15 of 29, or 53 per
cent) above "individual therapy" (11, or 38 per cent), an evaluation which the
residents do not share. However, residents' weighting of "community involvement" has risen markedly, a most important change in the perspectives of residents observed in relation to the innovations.
     4. When asked to assess ten different aspects of the treatment program in
determining "whether or not a patient gets better," post-innovation residents
agreed with pre-innovation residents, rating individual psychotherapy as far and
away the most important, and nursing care as clearly the second most important.
The activities program, put next by pre-innovation residents, was decisively

THE IMPACT ON RESIDENT PHYSICIANS

therapy were both important in the resident's value objectives; he now sought skill and enlightenment about this community concept, rectitude and respect in fulfilling his new perceptions of what he and his seniors most valued, and power and well-being in pursuing his professional development by becoming competent in this new mode of treatment.

Post-innovation residents were more optimistic than those who served in the YPI prior to 1956 about the effectiveness of psychotherapy in schizophrenia and the possibility of effecting something like a cure in schizophrenia. This difference may be explained by the fact that when these responses were obtained, pre-innovation residents had worked with schizophrenic patients for a longer time than later residents. However, it is possible that the post-innovation resident's greater optimism derived from their observations of the remarkably integrated behavior of schizophrenic patients in the new hospital.

The post-innovation resident's expectations on beginning his YPI year are tempered by new concerns expressed by others who have worked in the hospital, as illustrated by the following excerpt from an interview with a 1960 YPI resident:

> When I was first deciding whether or not to spend a year at the YPI, I talked with some residents who were already here and one of the things they talked about was patient-staff [meetings]. It had for me an already established tradition as being a potential hot-box for residents. This was the place where you would find yourself exposed to criticism, the hostility of patients, and it was a pretty uncomfortable situation, an arena where you got thrown to the lions daily, if not weekly. It was something that I heard about as the outstanding part of the experience as a resident, so I came with some expectations of what this might be like. But I was told about them in pretty general terms, mostly that it might be a pretty embarrassing situation, or a pressure situation where you might get turned upon, and usually with a kind of a leer and a wink, you know, "wait until you get there, you'll really be in for it and see what this is like."

---

demoted by post-innovation residents, who regarded patient-staff meetings and the work program as next to individual therapy and nursing care and placed both of these above activities. Group psychotherapy, begun in 1954, was perceived as less important by post-innovation residents, probably because its functions now overlapped patient-staff meetings as well as individual psychotherapy. Patient government was also downgraded by post-innovation residents; it was relatively more important before the innovations as the only aspect of the program which encouraged patient participation in hospital affairs.

The YPI Experience

In the post-innovation period, patient-staff meetings and other innovations add to the resident's burdens by demanding that he be a participant in the life of the hospital rather than only a psychotherapist
working on its periphery. His work is now subjected to greater scrutiny by patients as well as colleagues and seniors, his performance
publicly appraised and, at times, criticized, his private life even
more frequently intruded upon.

All the many tasks and obligations of the pre-innovation resident
persist in the post-innovation calendar. However, his day may now
begin with a patient-staff meeting in which issues, observations, and
plans (previously confined to staff meetings) are discussed. In the
patient-staff meeting he is a participant with all his patients and all
other hospital patients. They observe with whom he sits and chats
as the meeting begins, how he reacts to comments by patients and
others, and the responses of others to his comments. He may be confronted by a patient describing, complaining about, and demanding
that he account for the way he handled a patient's distress when on
duty the previous evening or how he dealt with an agitated patient
the previous afternoon. He may be asked to explain why he isolated
or restricted a patient, or opposed a patient's request to work or
attend school. His colleagues and seniors may side with the complaining patient and imply that he was unwise or unfair. A nurse,
social worker, or the director may offer observations which contradict the resident's assessments and decisions. He may feel vulnerable, ridiculed, and unsupported.

Such pressures challenge the therapist to think through carefully positions he takes with his patients. In subsequent individual
treatment hours, a patient may chastise him for not effectively advocating in patient-staff meeting a request he had accepted in their
discussions. Patients may be contemptuous of him because he was
criticized or ridiculed by the director or his fellow residents, or they
may comfort or support him in his struggles with the rest of the
staff. The patient sees how others view his doctor and how he is appraised by colleagues and seniors; a more complete picture of how
his doctor operates is available to him on the basis of his behavior in
these forums. He may see his therapist intimidated by criticism and
readily backing down, or holding to his position despite opposition
from both patients and staff. The patient may determine from his
own observations and participation in these forums whether his

therapist takes a position or remains noncommittal, is concerned about pleasing everyone, or whether he appears to have a consistent set of guiding principles in his work. If his doctor's values and expectations are very different from those of the rest of the community, they will be discernible more readily than before and may be discussed in forums in which the patient participates.

The resident's daily calendar, in addition to seminars, conferences, staff meetings, hours of supervision, and his own analytic hour, may now include attending a patient-staff advisory committee at that committee's request to explain, for example, why he supports the request of a patient to move from the closed to the open ward. In this meeting patients may, with or without the support of a nurse or the chief resident, convincingly document their impression that the patient remains too troubled for such a move, continues to need the larger staff available on the closed ward, and has remained withdrawn on visits to the open ward. The resident may again feel vulnerable, incompetent, and unprotected. He cannot lean upon his authority as physician or expert; unlike the traditional physician his judgment and power do not remain unquestioned. He must now justify his actions and decisions to the community of patients and staff.

In evenings and weekends on duty, in addition to handling hospital affairs, talking with patients who require his attention, and doing his paperwork, he is now encouraged to have supper with patients, play bridge or ping-pong with them, and go through the wards chatting with them before they retire.

The impact of the innovations upon YPI residents is suggested by the residents' responses to a list of thirty topics which might be discussed at joint patient-staff meetings and asked whether they should be discussed. These included the "director's running of the hospital," "request by a patient for a change of therapist," "whether a given patient should be placed in special [isolation]," "a patient's request that a staff member be fired," "a nurse's or a resident's handling of a patient," "a patient's readiness for discharge or to hold a job or attend school," "promiscuous behavior by a patient," "a patient's financial problems," and fourteen other comparable topics. Seventy-five per cent or more of both pre- and post-innovation residents felt that twenty-four of these thirty topics should be discussed at patient-staff meetings. Residents were less amenable to the discussion of six other topics, but a majority opposed discussion of only one question, "staff salaries." Why is the discussion of this one topic opposed by a majority? The value analysis of patient-staff meeting transcripts demonstrates that statements concerned with economic issues (wealth) arose far less frequently than other values, and much less frequently than in many other kinds of meetings in our society. Residents express their readiness to talk about "a patient's financial problems" in joint meetings of patients and staff,[5] but oppose discussing staff salaries. Residents' salaries are very low ("grossly so," said a resident who listed it as a complaint he did not feel free to bring up with his seniors), in keeping with medicine's tradition of apprentice bondage. Their salaries do not correspond with their responsibility, power, and respect in the hospital. Since money is regarded as an indicator of prestige and competence in American culture, it may be expected that the discussion of salaries might undermine the respect accorded the resident, particularly where most patients and their families are of high socio-economic position. As perennial students, in their late twenties or early thirties, with wives and children, often dependent financially on parents or wife, they are likely to be sensitive about their salaries. A related consideration is the traditional medical school policy which emphasizes the "confidentiality" of staff salaries. This restriction refers only to positions beyond residency, however. Information about resident salaries is readily available and generally known to patients.

Other topics which residents are relatively less willing to discuss in joint meetings of patients and staff (although a majority favor their discussion) are in two related groups: issues traditionally regarded as "medical," to be decided exclusively by the physician as an expert in caring for patients;[6] and issues which concerned the private life of the resident, the disclosure of which might upset the resident and disrupt his work with patients.[7]

The degree of mutuality in patient-staff meetings acceptable to

5. Forty-two of fifty (84 per cent) felt that such an issue should be discussed.

6. "Medical" topics included "whether a given patient should be put on a tranquilizer": "should not be discussed," said a majority of pre-innovation residents, eighteen to fifteen, but post-innovation residents favored discussion seventeen to nine; the "prognosis of a given patient": discussion opposed by twenty-two residents; and "whether the hospital should use EST at all or not": opposed by fourteen.

7. Among "personal issues" were the "validity of a resident's judgment as questioned by staff." Post-innovation residents were evenly split on whether this issue should be discussed, fourteen to fourteen; of pre-innovation residents, never subjected to such discussions, twelve were in favor and ten opposed it. Discussion of "sexual indiscretion of a staff member" was opposed by fourteen residents; pre- and post-innovation responses were in agreement.

residents is limited,[8] but the extent to which residents are willing to participate candidly with patients in these meetings is impressive. Their reluctance reflects their seniors' judgment about what constitutes optimal conduct in these meetings, discomfort from intrusions into their personal affairs, and the threat these meetings and increased participation of patients in all phases of decision-making in the hospital now pose to their traditional medical role.

When patient-staff meetings were first considered, and later when decision-making began to shift to these meetings, residents were confused, troubled, and threatened. At each point of transition the question was raised, "How are you going to tell the patients from the doctors?" Their support of these forums and readiness to discuss freely most topics indicates that the new hospital environment did not undermine their position as much as they feared. However, the physician, particularly the relatively inexperienced resident, is reluctant to abdicate much of his traditional authority and power until he is convinced that his fears are exaggerated and the changes serve him and his patients.

During the years 1954–58 the majority of residents (13) personally felt "enthusiastic," six felt "contented," and none felt either "discontented" or "very dissatisfied" with their YPI year. This remarkable era of enthusiasm and contentment, preceded and followed by considerable discontent and dissatisfaction, was the period of the innovations. Discontent returned when experimentation and innovation began to subside and policy and procedure were again relatively stable.

The Resident and the Patient

The innovations modified the annual change of doctors at the beginning of the hospital year for both resident and patient. Patient-staff meetings provided an opportunity for the expression and discussion of feelings, fantasies, and rumors about the shift, as well as its implications for individual patients, and made them available to the real-

8. The residents' readiness to discuss with patients "promiscuous behavior by a patient" (45 to 4) and "homosexual behavior among patients" (43 to 7) contrasts with their being less willing to discuss a "sexual indiscretion of a staff member" ("should be discussed" said 32 residents, "should not," said 14). The residents' readiness to talk about "the ability of a given patient to head patient government" (48 to 1) contrasts with their reluctance to discuss "the validity of a resident's judgment as questioned by staff" ("should be discussed," said 26, "should not," 24). And their feeling that "a patient's financial problems" should be discussed (42 to 8) contrasts with their opposition to discussing "staff salaries" (29 to 18).

ity testing which staff participation facilitated. The resources of the entire hospital community were mobilized more effectively during the changeover crisis to cope with what was now recognized as a problem faced by all. Incoming residents attended patient-staff meetings in late May and June, prior to beginning work at the hospital on July 1. Their initial observing, and then gradual taking part actively, facilitated the mutual orientation of resident and the hospital community. The deprivational impact of the shift was further modified by the increased contact and the more substantial relationship each patient had with senior physicians and other members of the permanent staff. The loss of the resident with whom the patient worked in treatment was tempered by the continuation of these important relationships now possible in the hospital. Contact with physicians other than the resident therapist was not discouraged, and a broad transference extended beyond the individual therapist to include the entire hospital and its permanent staff.

Physical attacks on residents by patients were less frequent in the post-innovation period.[9] This may reflect the increasing availability of tranquilizers and other mood-affecting medications, changes in the hospital population, and the new hospital climate which made war less necessary.

The innovations encouraged more informal interaction between residents and patients. Although this often meant increasingly meaningful contacts and gave the resident greater knowledge about the patients' hospital experience, this emphasis at times jeopardized the resident's position in psychotherapy. It was more difficult for the therapist to sustain the relative anonymity that was possible in the pre-innovation hospital. As a participant in community forums, his actions, responses, his strategies, their effectiveness or failure, the positions he is committed to, the issues he cares about, and his inactivity were all available to observation by patients. His conduct might influence patients in their individual struggles with problems of assertiveness. His personal conflicts about taking a stand, now more readily evident to the patient, might interfere with the thorough exploration of the patient's own related difficulties in individual treatment. However, it may be argued that if the therapist is not able to handle problems involved in participating in a democratic society,

9. When residents were asked whether they had ever been attacked by a patient, thirty-one (54 per cent) replied "yes" (17, or 60 per cent, of pre-innovation; 14, or 48 per cent, of post-innovation residents) and twenty-six, (46 per cent) said "no" (11, or 40 per cent, of pre-innovation; 15, or 52 per cent, of post-innovation residents).

he cannot be helpful to his patients with their similar problems, whether or not his conduct in forums is visible. In patient-staff meetings, other models are available to the patient; he may learn effective alternative strategies from other participants who are less troubled in areas where his individual therapist is limited.

The availability of others in these meetings can be used by the patient to evade what he may come to experience as a threatening closeness in his relationship with his doctor. Leverage traditionally available to the psychotherapist may thus be undermined. The patient may experience the individual therapist as the one person in the hospital who understands, appreciates his predicament, and cares, in contrast to the indifference of other patients and staff members. In the new hospital this important spur to the development of an intense relationship with the therapist was less likely to occur.

The issue of confidentiality is difficult to clarify in the post-innovation hospital, where sharing information with the entire community, including patients, is insisted upon. Just what information confided to the resident by patients should be shared with others? Can confidences be shared without jeopardizing the patient's relationship with the resident? The extent to which discreet, yet useful, means of sharing information were found which were both protective of the patient and adequately responsive to the requirements of other members of the hospital community in their efforts to live and work together was most impressive.

The therapeutic efforts of the resident are perhaps jeopardized by his more clearly secondary position in the staff. The patient may be encouraged to regard relationships with the director and other seniors, who clearly have more power and are not transient, as more important: contact with the director on rounds and in patient-staff meetings may seem more crucial than the individual psychotherapy.

The patient's image of the therapist, now derived from more informal interaction and regular participation together in patient-staff meetings, as well as contact in individual psychotherapeutic work, is less likely to be determined largely by the patient's wishes, needs, and prior experience. The transference may be diluted and its analysis interfered with by frequent, intense extrapsychotherapeutic contact. The assessment of whether or not this risk is worthwhile depends on the conception of what constitutes effective psychotherapy in the psychoses. In certain phases of such treatment, the analysis of the transference is central. However, a context must first be established in which the patient can actively bring his capacities and resources to bear and effectively participate in this phase of psychotherapeutic work. The preliminary stages of treatment are terribly difficult: engaging severely disturbed patients in meaningful contact requires patience, hard work, and thoughtful therapeutic activity for long periods. The resident may cope with extrapsychotherapeutic contact by means not inconsistent with the objectives of individual psychotherapy. He may walk with the patient, be defeated by him at ping-pong, or join him over a cup of coffee, and then discuss and clarify the patient's feelings and thoughts about these events in the psychotherapeutic exchange. Work with psychotic patients demands that the therapist "be there," that he emerge as a real figure with whom the patient has continuing active contact; the silence and inactivity of the therapist appropriate at times in the treatment of the neuroses cannot be sustained by the psychotic patient.

The Resident and Other Staff

As a result of the innovations, the functions of residents began to overlap those of nurses and social workers. The resident on the wards interacted directly with patients more often; the nurse moved closer to the resident's role as she tried to fulfill the demand that her work be more clearly psychotherapeutic. Residents were encouraged to be involved with patients' schooling and work activities and to meet with their families, previously the exclusive concern of the social worker. The social worker's increased contact with all patients was encouraged; her classically psychotherapeutic mode of interacting encroaches upon the resident's territory and is more threatening to him. Because of her professional training, longer experience, and the fact that she remains on the staff after the resident has departed, the social worker is an articulate, well-armed competitor for patients' respect, and an authority in community forums. Her role now duplicated the resident's to the extent that a staff social worker, particularly successful in engaging a difficult patient in the course of working with his family, was sometimes assigned as the patient's therapist. Such stimulating confusion accompanied the reexamination of role designations and functions in the hospital: the resident, on the wards more, is often the patient's companion; the nurse tries to work with the patient psychotherapeutically; the resident talks with members of the family; the social worker may see the patient in individual psychotherapy.

An important source of the social worker's power in collaborating and competing with the resident, and in sustaining a professional image superior to nurse and patient, has been the information she obtains in interviews with patients' families, her secrets: history of the patient and his family, how they interacted in the past, and how the family responds from week to week to the patient's hospitalization and treatment. This source of power was now diluted by the resident's information gathering in his contacts with the family. The social worker's deprivation was outweighed, however, by the opportunity to apply her training and experience with greater freedom; her work was increasingly determined by the psychotherapeutic contribution she is equipped to make, rather than the conventional characterization of what the social worker does.

The nurse is no longer the resident's confidante; her secrets, derived from observations of patients and information the resident confided to her, are now shared with the entire community. The nurse struggles to gain competence in working psychotherapeutically with patients, turns to the resident for guidance, is less awed as she becomes better informed about the once mysterious work of psychotherapy, and begins to assume a professional status closer to and in some ways competitive with that of social worker and resident.

The described blurring of roles and functions was only a beginning. The innovations opened the way for the unfettered use of nurses' and social workers' individual talents, training, and experience, and encouraged their greater participation in the fulfillment of the overall psychotherapeutic goals of the hospital. They stimulated a new sense of freedom and fostered a new, vigorous, intellectually curious pursuit of professional growth and development. Nurses and social workers began to awaken to the challenge of the new hospital and may eventually become the residents' co-workers, rather than his helpmates, in the psychotherapeutic task.

An effect of the innovations upon the residents' relations with one another was the use of patient-staff meetings as a public arena in which to compete for the respect of patients and seniors, particularly the director. As the analyzed transcripts demonstrate, residents as a group were sometimes not active participants in the meetings. However, when a resident spoke, particularly when he was articulate and effective, other residents became more active, vying for the community's approval. Some residents learned that silence served them most effectively in this competition and refrained from speaking, assuming that more profound thoughts would be attributed to them if they refrained from some of the awkward things they found themselves saying when they participated.

Patient-staff meetings made feelings between the director, other senior staff members, and individual residents, clearer to the entire community: all could know that residents A and B see things the same way and would support one another; that residents C and D were antagonists; that the director and chief resident favored resident E, respecting and supporting his positions; and that they did not respect Dr. F and contradict or dismiss his comments in the meetings. Competition among residents now included attempts to demonstrate their greater involvement in the hospital community; they employed the strategem of trying to engage more actively than their fellows in informal contact with the patients. Despite their competition, post-innovation residents were increasingly aware of their vunerability as a group, especially in hospital forums, and reported feeling closer to one another.

The Resident and his Seniors

Just as the director and other members of the senior staff are now more directly engaged in the affairs of the hospital community, and more informed about each patient from day to day, their opportunities to scrutinize the resident's work and to engage with him in a continuing dialogue on his assessments, decisions, and plans have been greatly increased by the innovations. Their remarkably detailed observation and supervision of the YPI resident's work during the pre-innovations period was described earlier; patient-staff meetings and other innovations carried this process even further. The resident's need to be well-regarded by his seniors, particularly as a competent psychotherapist, persists in the post-innovation era. However, the demands made upon him by his seniors, and the demands he makes upon himself to live up to what is expected of the proficient resident, now include the quality and extent of his community participation.

The conditions which have developed in the hospital as a result of the innovations constitute a trying work setting for the resident. Changes in expectations include new and different criteria of competence and effectiveness. Critical areas in the resident's performance, such as his capacity to lay down the law and stick with it, to temper his judgments and modify his decisions when presented with new information, to sustain his curiosity and investment in understanding what is going on despite demands for prompt action, and thoughtfully and flexibly to coordinate his own contributions and efforts with those of patients and colleagues, are all far more available to the scrutiny of the entire community. This also applies to the inclination of an individual therapist to be either overly assertive or noncommittal and inactive. When topics which evoke a high level of anxiety are discussed in the group, the doctor's interventions are available to observation and assessment of all present. When sexual acts among patients are talked about in these forums, the doctor's views about sexual behavior and sexuality in general, as well as any manifestations of comfort or anxiety regarding his sexual role, are open to appraisal; so, too, is his total self-image in sexual and aggressive terms. Far more observable is the extent to which he is dependent upon the views held of him by colleagues and seniors or is relatively independent and self-assertive, his efforts to rely upon demagogic popularity or his emphasis upon the substance of issues under discussion, and his capacity to stick his neck out, taking whatever deprivations result from asserting himself because he believes that his goals justify enduring these deprivations.

The heavy investment of the senior staff in patient-staff meetings is evident to residents, and it is clear that an important means of pleasing these teachers and bosses is to invest in this program. Sometimes residents make an effort to approve and respect these forums but are unable to do so in a thoroughgoing, substantial way. For example:

A resident therapist feels that it makes good sense for one of his patients, an adolescent girl, to move from the closed to the open ward. He puts aside any reservations about this shift with the rationalization that she will find a positive response to this request by him and others in the hospital community encouraging and supportive. He tells her that he thinks the shift makes sense but suggests that she bring the matter up in patient-staff advisory committee and attends the meeting in which this issue is raised himself. He speaks a lot, asserting that it is important in his therapy with the patient for this request to be granted. His active participation in the meeting effectively silences any opposition to the request. In the next meeting of the larger hospital forum, patient-staff meeting, in which it is not so easy for a resident to have his way because seniors and colleagues are also present, patients silenced in the advisory committee meeting speak up about their reservations, express their concern about this girl being isolated on the closed ward, and question whether she is ready for the less protected, more independent existence demanded of patients on the open ward. Members of the senior staff, other staff members, and patients actively support these reservations, as does the patient herself, and it is decided that she should remain on the closed ward.

The resident is deprived of the opportunities to hide and protect himself that are characteristic of conventional psychiatric hospital work. He can no longer work as if conducting a private practice on the periphery of the hospital, seeing a series of patients in his office and having his work assessed by his teachers and bosses on the basis of his own reports. His individual psychotherapeutic work remains central to his seniors' appraisal of his competence, but activities outside the office, particularly in patient-staff meetings, now compound the demands made upon him and are critical. In examining the heavy responsibilities of the pre-innovation resident it was not easy to see how anyone could adequately carry through the tasks intrinsic to his predicament. The burdens which the demand for community participation place upon the post-innovation resident, his greater vulnerability in this setting, and the different resources and strategies required of him render the new situation even more demanding and stressful. He undertakes both individual psychotherapy and active participation in the hospital community, struggles with the hardships intrinsic to each, as well as the still greater difficulties which arise from the effort to do both at the same time.

When asked about "the least satisfactory part of your YPI training," post-innovation residents put greater stress upon difficult conditions of work and their relationships with the senior staff as the least satisfactory part of their YPI training.[10] Pre-innovation residents had emphasized deficiencies in instruction and supervision.

10. "Harrassment," "strain," "personal anxiety," "on duty too much," "lack of support," "not enough time for reading and thinking," "the work was too hard": such complaints about difficulties in work appeared as the least satisfactory part of the year in the responses of eighteen, or thirty-one per cent (4, or 14 per cent, of pre-innovation; 14, or 48 per cent, of the post-innovation residents). Dissatisfaction with their relationship with the senior staff ("the director was too involved in everything," "there was not enough contact with the director"), and with the direction by senior staff was the least satisfactory part for twelve [or twenty-one per cent (4, or 14 per cent, of pre-innovation; 8, or 27 per cent, of post-innovation residents)]. Their instruction and supervision was least satisfactory for twenty-one [or thirty-six per cent (15, or 53 per cent, of pre-innovation; 6 or 20 per cent of post-innovation residents)]. Other aspects of YPI training singled out as least satisfactory were "not allowed to make decisions" (2), "competitiveness among residents" (1), "group therapy" (1), "therapeutic community too limited" (1), "patients kept too long" (1), "having to physically restrain patients" (1), and "not enough variety of patients" (1).

The Chief Resident

Because of the director's greater opportunity to scrutinize the residents' work directly, the chief resident's functions as an intermediary who runs interference for and protects them are now less necessary, and much of his role as overseer of their day-to-day work has been usurped. The director is less dependent upon the chief resident for information about residents, and he contributes less to the director's assessment of their work. The chief resident is less occupied with residents' activities, more attentive to the overall affairs of the hospital, and more directly engaged with patients. He no longer chairs daily staff meetings but is an active participant in patient-staff advisory committee. These changes remove residents from their former closeness to the chief resident; he is less available to guide and support them, and they are less inclined to view him as especially appreciative of their predicament. However, they continue to bring problems and complaints to him more frequently than to other seniors. Since greater opportunities for direct communication with the director now exist and he is more involved with day-to-day decisions, more problems are worked out directly with him. To the residents, therefore, the chief resident is less useful and important in the new hospital.

The Director

Whereas the contacts of the pre-innovation resident with the director consisted in administrative supervision, his chairing of staff meetings, infrequent appearance on the wards, and participation in departmental conferences, these contacts are now augmented by his seeing each patient regularly on rounds, a more active and direct involvement in the treatment of each patient, and participation with residents and all patients in the continuing dialogue of the patient-staff meetings. Although these changes bring the director and residents into one another's presence more often and provide many more opportunities to communicate directly, he must be shared at such times with the rest of the staff and patients, and the residents' wish for greater individual contact with him is still frustrated. The occasions on which the resident is liable to criticism by the director multiply, and the emotional stress of adverse criticism is heightened by the public context in which it occurs.

Residents' responses to the director were consistent throughout the pre- and post-innovation periods: they tended to criticize him as "authoritarian," "dogmatic," and "vague"; these complaints were made increasingly through the term of the present director, and most heavily after the innovations. Residents emphatically recommended that the solution was to be found in increased personal contact between the director and themselves. However, it was noted that he successfully maintained communication with residents: next to fellow residents and the chief resident, they most frequently brought their complaints to him. In the residents' appraisals of overall performance, the present director consistently received the highest rating of any staff member. The inauguration of patient-staff meetings, which seemed to facilitate greater communication between director and residents and to encourage a greater sharing of decision-making power by all members of the hospital community, did not change the residents' perception of the director. They still complained that he was too authoritarian, continued to press for increased personal contact with him and to regard his overall performance as superior to that of any other staff member. The director's greater participation in the affairs of the hospital did not silence the residents' demand that he be more intimately concerned with them.

Supervisors

The supervisors remained aloof from changes in the hospital, including the community emphasis. They continued to meet with residents individually, concern themselves exclusively with the formal psychotherapeutic exchange between resident and patient, and operate as if this interaction were the sole determinant of the patient's course. They did not participate in patient-staff meetings or other forums and remained skeptical about the innovations and apprehensive that a shift away from the emphasis upon intrapsychic exploration in treatment might be encouraged. Post-innovation residents experienced supervisors as even more remote from, and unfamiliar with, the affairs and procedures of the hospital than their predecessors did. They recommended even more emphatically that supervisors participate more in the life of the hospital.

Dissatisfaction with the curriculum, with insufficient supervision, and with the calibre of supervisors and teachers was consistent for both pre- and post-innovation residents. After the innovations, however, complaints about supervisors increasingly referred to their unfamiliarity with operation of the hospital, particularly its forums and efforts at power sharing. The director's and other senior staff members' direct observation and participation with the resident caused more opportunity for discrepancies between appraisals made by senior staff and supervisors, and estimates more often diverged in reference to individual residents and the treatment of specific patients. Opportunities for the resident to invite and exploit differences between supervisors and other senior staff members about treatment were greater; the resident could attribute them to the supervisor's ignorance of the new hospital or use such conflict as a justification for dismissing the director as having abandoned a genuinely psychotherapeutic position.

Decision-Making and Power

The patient continues to be deprived of certain freedoms, and the hospital staff remain the expert agents sanctioned by the community to exercise extraordinary power over the patients in their care. The director continues to be authorized to deprive patients of rights and privileges ordinarily regarded as their prerogatives as citizens in a democracy—in the service of their treatment. Although he delegates some of this power to members of the staff, he is viewed as personally retaining full responsibility. Since these powers are now increasingly shared with staff members other than physicians, and patients are encouraged to participate with the director and his staff in decision-making, a potentially hazardous departure in the delegation of power has now been undertaken by the director. While he now shares more of his authority with residents, social workers, and nurses, and makes the critical step of encouraging patients to assume more responsibility themselves, his caution in delegating power to relatively inexperienced residents extends to all members of the hospital community.

The resident's basic responsibility for determining the extent to which the rights and privileges of a given patient are limited or usurped continues. However, this responsibility is now more directly shared with patients as well as the director and other members of the staff. Patients participate in discussing, deciding, and assuming responsibility with the resident for such questions as whether a patient should live on the locked or open ward, make phone calls, receive visitors, go out into the larger community to work or attend school. The patient continues to discuss such issues with his therapist, but action requires that he raise the issue himself in patient-staff meeting: approval and implementation require the assent of the patient-staff advisory committee. The resident's approval remains important—his opinion is sought when the proposal is considered— but the decision results from discussion initiated by and participated in by the patient. He is free to raise questions, challenge arguments opposing his request, and demand explanations. Although, when he offers his proposal to the group, his therapist may support or oppose him, or remain silent, the patient is now less dependent upon his therapist. Prior to the innovations, the patient could not himself raise such issues for approval and implementation. He had to rely upon his doctor to raise them on his behalf at staff meetings and to report staff responses to him. If the patient's request was rejected he had no recourse other than complaining to his resident and persisting in efforts to convince him, or to press him to act again and more effectively.

These changes unburden the resident from much of the pressure exerted by patients and of feelings of guilt about confining and in other ways controlling his patients, and decrease his power. The resident is therefore also deprived of some of his former prestige. His moral conflicts about limiting the freedom of patients with whom he is emotionally involved are less intense; affection and rectitude conflicts are resolved in ways that carry the cost of decreased power and respect in the community. To the extent that the resident values the traditional image of the physician as an expert who makes the decisions and heals the patient, he suffers a deprivation of self-esteem; if this is accompanied by anxiety or symptom formation, the resident is also deprived in well-being. To the extent that he is unambivalently committed to democratic process and has the capacity to share authority with the patient, the resident's self-esteem is increased, his preferred image of himself as physician and citizen is fulfilled, and his well-being is served.

The residents' perspectives about their power in the post-innovation hospital are expressed in their pointing to the director when asked, "Who tended to make decisions about your patients that you should have made,"[11] viewing him as the only staff member with a

11. When asked "who tended to make decisions about your patients that you felt you should have made?," thirty-two, by far the greatest number, replied "the director." Among other choices, sixteen singled out the chief resident, six said "chief nurses," and four "the assistant director." As for other residents, supervisors, director of nursing, nurses, department chairman, referring doctor, and other outside doctors, two or less residents felt that people in each of these categories made decisions he should have made about his patients. Of those contending that the director interfered, the majority were post-innovation residents (24 of the 32); the chief resident was referred to more frequently by pre-innovation residents (10 of 16). This confirms the shift which coincided with the innovations toward experiencing the chief resident as less and the director as more interfering and usurping of their power. In patient-staff meetings, the director can make direct observations, ask questions, and bypass the resident in offering opinions and actively promoting his views on the care and management

great deal of influence over the way things go at the hospital,[12] and complaining that they are overruled when he disagrees about a patient's readiness for discharge.[13] Residents imply that the hospital remains essentially authoritarian; decisions are not arrived at through democratic process. At the same time, the residents view themselves as most influential in "determining whether or not pa-

---

of each patient. He assumes some aspects of the role previously held by the chief resident: he is the senior doctor, informed about the resident's care of his patients, who is experienced as intruding, disagreeing, and countermanding his decisions. In this sense, the innovations not only combat fantasies about the director as aloof; they render him far less remote, and make the degree to which he is controlling substantial and explicit.

12. When pre- and post-innovation residents were asked to assess "how much influence" staff members had "over the way things went at the YPI," a majority saw the director as the only member of the staff having a "great deal" of influence, and all others viewed his influence as "considerable." They rated the chief resident, chief nurses, and the residents as the only others exerting substantial influence over the way things went. The relative ratings made by pre- and post-innovation residents differed: after the innovations, residents viewed patients, residents, and chief nurses as more influential, the chief resident as less influential. Most pre- and post-innovation residents viewed the department chairman, outside doctors, business manager, supervisors, relatives of patients, the chief social worker, the director of nursing, and the assistant director as having little or no influence over the way things went. Post-innovation residents saw the department chairman and supervisors as still less influential than did residents who worked in the hospital earlier. Although this assessment by residents of who controls the hospital shows some change in the direction of more power exercised by patients, residents, and chief nurses, the director is consistently seen by both pre- and post-innovation groups as *the* powerful influence; others of titular importance are consistently seen as having relatively little substantial power despite the innovations.

13. The residents were asked whether "they had as much say as they should have had in deciding" questions involved in patient management. As reported earlier, the great majority of residents (81 or 98 per cent) felt they had enough say on all issues, except "whether or not your patient was ready for discharge." Here thirty-five [or sixty-five per cent (21 pre-innovation and 14 post-innovation residents)] felt they had "enough say" and nineteen [or thirty-five per cent (6 pre-innovation, 13 post-innovation residents)] felt they did not. Eighteen of the nineteen who felt that they did not have enough say about discharge worked at the YPI during the current director's tenure (from 1953). Assessing a patient's readiness for discharge increasingly became a matter of dispute about which the resident felt he did not have enough say. This change coincided with the current director's period of service rather than with the innovations. The shift may reflect the director's greater involvement in the management of each patient as a result of the innovations, and the concomitant undermining of the resident's autonomy in making the critical decision about his patient's readiness for discharge. However, the more important determinant is probably independent of the innovations: the current director's commitment to ambitious treatment goals and his regarding lengthy hospitalization as often necessary to their fulfillment. When the director is firmly committed to a position, he is clearly able to determine policy, despite efforts at power sharing and opposition from his subordinates.

tients get better,"[14] feel they have "as much say as they should have" in deciding most issues important in patient management, and emphatically state that they have "enough power" in making decisions about patients.[15] Residents are still content with the degree of their power despite the innovations and complaints about the authoritarian director. They continue to say they have enough power and influence in the face of evidence documenting the increased power of the director, social workers, and patients, and a concomitant decrease in their power within the community. They are enthusiastic about those changes in the hospital structure which have furthered the sharing of power with patients.

Residents resoundingly support patient-staff meetings; those who participated in them favor them unanimously. They emphasize opportunities provided for patients to assume more responsibility and for patients and staff to share information and compare views. The most heavily weighted reservation about the meetings concerned the possibility that they offered only the appearance and not the reality of shared power and responsibility.[16] Although most pre-innovation

14. The residents were asked to assess the influence of staff members over whether or not patients got better. Their replies distinguish this issue sharply from the matter of who exerted influence over the way things went; efforts to eliminate discrepancies between "administration" and "therapeutic considerations," to have all determinations of hospital policy rest upon the single question, "Is it therapeutic?," are not seen by the residents as effective. They consistently view themselves, the resident group, as having by far the greatest influence upon the patients' therapeutic course in the hospital. They rate nurses, patients, and the director, in that order, as next most influential. Pre- and post-innovation residents saw their own influence and that of the director in about the same way, but after the innovations, nurses were regarded as less influential and patients as exerting much more influence on whether or not patients got better. Most residents held that the director of nursing, assistant director, and activities workers exerted little or no influence; residents unanimously rated the department chairman as having little or no influence; the influence of relatives of patients, chief nurses, aides, supervisors, social workers, and the chief resident, in that order, were rated of intermediate importance in determining the course of treatment.

15. Asked to assess their power in making decisions about patients, the great majority of pre- and post-innovation residents (41, or 73 per cent) said they had enough power in this regard; eleven (or twenty per cent), said, "not enough," four (or seven per cent), replied, "too much." All those replying, "too much" were in the pre-innovation group; those who replied, "not enough" increased in the post-innovation group. However, the emphatic response, "we had enough power in making decisions about patients," was consistent for both pre- and post-innovation groups.

16. The residents' feelings about patient-staff meetings are reflected in their responses when presented with arguments made for and against these meetings. "They give the patient an opportunity to assume greater responsibility for the way the hospital is run and for his own conduct in the hospital," was the positive argument most heavily weighted (referred to in 34 of 75 responses by 16 pre-

residents did not think the business conventionally conducted in staff meetings could be worked out in patient-staff meetings, a majority of post-innovation residents believe that it can be done.[17]

---

and 18 post-innovation residents). "They provide the patient with a way of comparing his views with those of other patients and staff," was considered most important by twenty-nine (11 pre- and 18 post-innovation) residents. The third argument, "they provide a continuing opportunity for patients and staff to share information" was also heavily weighted (26, 10 pre- and 16 post-innovation residents). Two residents emphasized the opportunity provided for the clarification of disagreements within the staff. Other positive arguments included, "patient-staff meetings counter regressive tendencies" (1); "they provide an opportunity for the vicarious expression of feelings by non-verbal patients" (1); "they constantly reinforce the attitude that growth and development can proceed in the face of illness" (1).

The most heavily weighted argument against patient-staff meetings was, "they give the impression of sharing power and responsibility while not in fact doing so" (15 of 24 responses by 6 pre- and 9 post-innovation residents). Pre-innovation residents were more concerned about the possibility of confidentiality being violated than were residents who had actually participated in the meetings. The argument, "they violate the therapeutic compact by revealing to the larger group information obtained in individual treatment," was subscribed to by eight residents, but only one of them worked at the YPI after the meetings were inaugurated. The argument, "they undermine the patient's view of the therapist by seeing him challenged by colleagues and patients; they interfere with the patient's image of the therapist" was selected by only two (1 pre-, 1 post-innovation) residents. Negative arguments included the difficulty of discussing and resolving staff differences in meetings in which patients participated (3 responses, 1 pre- and 2 post-innovation residents); "they limit the possibility of exploratory psychotherapy" (1); "they provide a ground for acting out between patient and therapist" (1). Residents were then asked, "On balance, do you tend to agree with the arguments for or the arguments against patient-staff meetings?" Forty-three [or ninety-one per cent (16, or 80 per cent, of the pre-innovation; 27, or 100 per cent, of the post-innovation residents)] replied "for;" four [or twenty per cent (all were pre-innovation residents)], replied "against."

Residents were asked for "suggestions as to how patient-staff meetings might be modified." Three pre-innovation residents suggested that the meetings be "limited to discussion with the explicit understanding that the patients' safety and treatment are staff responsibilities and that the physicians must make the decisions." One pre-innovation resident suggested that "confidentiality must be maintained except in community matters." Neither of these issues found expression in the suggestions of post-innovation residents. They were concerned with procedure: "the chairman should not always be the director. The chair should rotate among residents and patients" (4); "meetings should be held more frequently" (3); "they should be shorter" (2); "shorter meetings daily with one longer meeting each week" (1); "should be held at the same time of day" (1); "some topics should be ruled out" (1); "some matters should be discussed without the feeling that decisions must be arrived at" (1); "there should be no staff meetings" (1); "the staff should do its business in patient-staff meetings, not save it for staff meetings" (1); and "strictly staff meetings are also necessary" (1).

17. The question, "Do you think the business conventionally conducted in staff meetings during your YPI year could be conducted in joint patient-staff meetings?" was asked of both pre-innovation residents who had never partici-

Most residents stated that they found participating with patients in discussions of their problems and management less difficult than they had anticipated.[18] The great majority of residents believe that decision-making meetings at the YPI should consist of both staff and patient-staff meetings.[19] Residents who participated in patient-staff meetings describe themselves as participating actively much more than they actually did.[20] A majority favor the discussion of almost all topics in meetings with patients but oppose patients participating in the making of decisions conventionally regarded as medical.[21] Although the residents describe themselves as bringing their com-

---

pated in patient-staff meetings, and post-innovation residents who had. Twenty-five [or fifty per cent (8, or 38 per cent, of pre-innovation; 17, or 58 per cent, of post-innovation residents)] replied, "yes;" twenty-three [or forty-six per cent (12, or 57 per cent, of pre-innovation; 11, or 37 per cent, of post-innovation residents)] said, "no;" two (1 pre-innovation; 1 post-innovation) said, "I don't know." Thus residents collectively are not at all sure that business transacted in staff-meetings could be conducted in patient-staff meetings; pre-innovation residents doubt it strongly (12 to 8), post-innovation residents are more inclined to think it possible (17 to 11).

18. When residents were asked, "Did it prove more difficult or less difficult than you had anticipated to participate with the patients in discussion of their problems and management in patient-staff meetings?," most replied "less difficult" (18, or 62 per cent); nine, (or thirty-one per cent), said "more difficult"; two said "neither," implying that their assessment of difficulties involved proved accurate.

19. When asked "What do you think decision-making meetings at the YPI should consist of?," only two (both pre-innovation) residents replied, "staff meetings only," and only two (both post-innovation) replied, "patient-staff meetings only." All forty-four other residents (or eighty-nine per cent), preferred "staff meetings plus patient-staff meetings." Although not convinced that the business usually transacted in staff meetings could be done in forums with patients, residents do not favor staff meetings to the exclusion of patient-staff meetings; they want both kinds of forums.

20. Post-innovation residents were asked "how frequently did you speak at patient-staff meetings?" Their replies do not conform with observations made at these meetings and suggest a distorted perception of the extent of their activity: twelve (or forty-one per cent), replied that they spoke in "almost every meeting," sixteen (or fifty-five per cent), said they spoke in "one out of three meetings," one said he spoke in "one out of six meetings," and none replied that they spoke in fewer meetings than that. This overestimation by residents of the frequency with which they spoke in patient-staff meetings is contradicted by the analyses of six meetings described; only one resident spoke at all of the meetings, and one resident did not speak in any of them.

21. The effort was made to clarify what issues residents felt patients should participate in deciding, and what topics they felt staff should and should not discuss with patients in joint meetings. They distinguished sharply between "patients participating in deciding" and the "discussion of topics with patients in joint patient-staff meetings"; they viewed the sharing of information as separate from the decision-making process, regarded the discussion of most issues with patients as satisfactory or desirable, but were less willing to have patients participate in making decisions. When presented with a list of thirty topics which "might be discussed at joint patient-staff meetings," most residents (more

plaints and criticisms to staff meetings, they said that they virtually never speak up about matters of particular concern to them in patient-staff meetings.[22]

In describing the predicament of the pre-innovation resident, the moral and ethical conflicts with which he struggles in exercising extraordinary power over his patients is emphasized. He feels guilty about depriving his patients of their rights as citizens and about the anger which his distrustful and provocative patients evoke in him. He regards his patients as objects toward whom it was forbidden to acknowledge or express anger and tends to direct such feelings to his seniors. He tries to cope with this guilt by evading and externalizing responsibility for the use of power. The resident's abdication of power was motivated by conflicts engendered in him concerning his preferred self-image as a psychiatrist and as a citizen in a democratic society. In the pre-innovation period he viewed his seniors as the wielders of power and felt victimized and deprived when they overruled him or exercised power when he failed to act. But he is not dissatisfied about the limited extent of his power, although he complains about the authoritarian and dogmatic behavior of his sen-

---

than 75 %) favored the discussion of twenty-four of them; they were less willing to discuss "medical" issues ("whether a given patient should be put on a tranquilizer") and issues which concerned their private life ("sexual indiscretion of a staff member"). However, a majority favored the discussion of all topics except staff salaries. The residents' opposition to patients' having a voice in "medical questions" was more emphatic when they were asked if "patients should participate in deciding" rather than "discussing" the issue: the majority of both pre- and post-innovation residents opposed patient participation in deciding "whether a patient should be given EST" (43 to 10), "whether a patient should be given a tranquilizer" (38 to 13), and "whether a patient should be taken off bedtime sedation" (37 to 13).

22. Residents were presented with a series of common situations in which they were critical of their working conditions, a hospital policy, or another staff member, and asked, "What did you characteristically do in the way of bringing [the situation] to someone else's attention?" They tended to bring their complaints to fellow residents, the chief resident, or the director. Among alternative choices were raising their criticisms and complaints in staff meetings and patient-staff meetings. Staff meetings were frequently used for complaints about the chief resident, a resident, a social worker, or a hospital policy, but less frequently for complaints about working conditions, the director, or a supervisor. Only one resident, and in response to only one of the eight situations ("critical of the chief resident's decision in a staff meeting"), said that he brought the matter up in patient-staff meeting. The residents are clearly reluctant to use this forum to discuss matters about which they are concerned. Some of the situations presented would clearly not be appropriate for discussion with patients ("a criticism of an absent psychotherapy supervisor"), most of the situations are of concern to all members of the hospital community and have profitably been discussed in patient-staff meetings with patients participating (a criticism of "a nurse's handling of a patient," "a social worker's handling of a patient's family," or "a patient having to leave the hospital for financial reasons").

iors. The residents' sense of deprivation stems largely from feeling that their seniors do not invest enough in them. Their major complaints in this predicament concern the behavior, particularly the authoritarianism, of their seniors, especially the director. They emphatically recommend increased personal contact between themselves and the director and other seniors as the means of improving this situation. In effect, residents are willing to accept the superior power of the director and other seniors, asking only that they be cared for and respected.

Post-innovation residents have less power. The director, through greater involvement in the day-to-day affairs of the hospital and more active, direct participation in the treatment of each patient, is more powerful. Other staff members, notably social workers, are also more powerful; their greater participation in treatment and decision-making is authorized and encouraged. Much of the residents' power has been relinquished to patients who now assume more responsibility. Residents welcome the sharing of power with patients: it lessens their conflicts about exercising extraordinary control over patients and unburdens them of pressures from patients who now bring complaints and demands to community forums. They complain more vigorously about the director's still greater power but continue to view the extent of their own power as adequate, and make even stronger demands for the director's affection and concern. The innovations have not modified the central importance of intensive psychotherapeutic work, nor have they affected the residents' continuing preoccupation with seniors, although the demands made upon them in order to win their seniors' approval and respect are now even greater.

11. The Incipient Revolution

Why Wasn't the Revolution More Revolutionary?

Although we affirm the proposition that power was both authoritatively and effectively shared, it is at once necessary to take a further step and ask why the revolution wasn't more revolutionary. The pre-innovation hospital was authoritarian. Decisions about fundamental and pressing issues in the lives of patients were decided by others than the individuals most concerned. Despite the modifications introduced, the basically authoritarian character of the hospital was substantially unchanged. The staff, particularly the director, retained the decisive voice.

The impact of the fact that power sharing remained incomplete was intensified by a sense of constraint on the part of all concerned about acknowledging the degree to which the democratic ideology was not put into effect. Staff and patients alike were not, however, unaware of the facts. Senior doctors could still, and at times did, make decisions arbitrarily, and without consultation. They at times vetoed decisions made individually or collectively by other staff members or patients. They sometimes acted unilaterally, without utilizing the institutions which had been established in part to prevent this, and without consulting or obtaining the consent of the governed. Such arbitrary actions tended to abrogate the therapeutic ideology. Although the new forums provided opportunities for the open, direct examination and criticism of such authoritarian, undemocratic behavior, and occasional discussion did tend to chasten the offenders, the decisions, once made, could rarely be undone or modified. The collectivity remained unprotected against the repetition of such acts, and as a consequence patients and most staff members continued to view themselves as relatively powerless. The effective power of the director and other senior doctors either did not decrease or was limited only enough to permit an appearance of democracy.

The burden imposed on the community by the fact that effective power was retained by the senior doctors was compounded by the new, largely implicit, demand that all now pretend that the hospital was democratic. Any acknowledgement of the limited character of power sharing constituted a violation of the ideology. Two factors are important in the relatively fictive quality of democracy in the post-innovation hospital: first, senior doctors were never bound by explicit agreement to adhere to the newly established pattern of democratic practice or to use its institutions. The senior staff retained power to make decisions arbitrarily outside the hospital forums and decision-making institutions (staff meetings, patient-staff meetings, and patient-staff advisory committee); they were not obliged to account for their unilateral decisions.

Second, the limits of democratic process in the hospital community were not openly acknowledged, explicated, discussed, or challenged. Perhaps the senior staff was not confident of the patients' capacity to face and deal with the presence of such limits. Perhaps the senior staff sought the appearance of democracy without being ready to surrender actual power. An explicit step might have been taken: the fact that there were limits on power sharing could have been stated publicly. The justification of these limits (including the demands made by the larger society, particularly on the director) could have been specific. The hospital community might have examined and considered these declarations, probing for possible changes, acknowledging that preliminary steps would be required before modifications could be introduced, and perhaps accepting some limits as unmodifiable.

The avoidance of open discussion of the limits of achieved power sharing did not cause much furtive discontent with the decision-making primacy of the director and senior staff. There was, in fact, little pressure exerted publicly or privately in favor of a sweeping change toward more general power sharing. No one demanded a firm commitment from the director and other senior doctors to the effect that all decision-making would occur in patient-staff meetings. Indeed, the necessary preliminary step of demanding that all major decisions be discussed and decided in staff meetings was never put forward. Our examination of each component of the staff in addition to the senior members shows that they were concerned with maximizing values other than power (residents, for example, emphasized skill and enlightenment and sought affection and respect rather than power). The hospitalized, long acquainted with defeat and submission, did not take the initiative.

It is of course possible that incomplete power sharing is preferable, that the problems inherent in administering a psychiatric institution and conducting a responsible and effective treatment program for severely disturbed patients absolutely require such limits. The following arguments support such a position: the director must be able, despite opposition from other staff members and patients, to transfer a patient from one psychotherapist to another if in his judgment the treatment will be facilitated. In the face of opposition from the therapist involved and others, the chief resident must be able to shift a patient from the open to the closed ward, to cancel a patient's visit with his family, or to order the administering of medications if he regards such steps as serving the needs of the patient. If in his judgment a given patient cannot be effectively treated in the hospital, the director must be able to insist that he be transferred to another facility, or that a patient whom he considers unready for discharge remain in the hospital for further treatment. The occasional necessity for urgency in coming to a decision, the possible irreversible and destructive effects of incompetent judgment, and the fact that the director remains ultimately responsible for whatever is done in the hospital are additional justifications for the retention of extraordinary power by the director. Failure to discuss such decisions as they arise with patients and other members of the staff is, however, more difficult to justify.

The YPI physicians were reared in a society whose ideology was democratic, but which also took for granted the legitimacy of exempting directors of mental hospitals from adhering to full democratic practice. Individuals who suffered from mental illness were, after all, considered dangerous to themselves and others, and failure to take the measures required to save the patient from doing harm to himself and other people would be a breach of professional obligation. Hence society was justified in allowing physicians to administer the affairs of patients as dependents. The doctors of the Institute were in no doubt about this, nor were the doctors of the department of psychiatry, the medical school, or the larger medical community. This position was supported by the relatives of patients and the general public.

Our inquiry suggests that the crucial event in the YPI environment which triggered the innovation was the emergence of the idea of a therapeutic community and the beneficial effects of patients' active participation in the hospital treatment program. The impact of this view was revolutionary and set in motion a process which can be found in all revolutionary movements, the evoking of conflicts of conscience within those exercising power. The power elite, the senior doctors, knew, but had not previously been forced to acknowledge to themselves or others, the necessity of extending to all the patient's experience the dignity, respect, responsibility, autonomy, and self-determination long acknowledged as central to psychoanalytic treatment. Rectitude standards, hitherto assumed clear, were rendered uncertain. The doctor's double obligations as a democratic citizen and a therapist were not in conflict according to the previous interpretation. He was morally obligated as a citizen and a doctor to make decisions *for* and not *with* his patients. If the new version of reality was correct, it was immoral to continue to violate the canons of shared power, and these deviations were no longer justifiable on therapeutic grounds.

However, although the concept of the therapeutic community was stimulating and plausible, members of the staff were not sure that it could be applied effectively in the YPI. As exploratory steps were initiated, the responses of patients of a great range of pathology, and of staff members of divergent levels of professional preparation and readiness for such change, and the effects upon the training as well as the therapeutic and research objectives of the hospital were carefully scrutinized. The director, particularly alert to his extraordinary responsibility and to potential risks, tempered his enthusiasm for these changes with caution.

Why did not the patients and various staff members press more intensely to curb the director's power and to create a small body politic in which the decisions formerly made by the director were subject to explicit limitations? The reply to this question is of particular concern to students of democracy since an important weakness of systems of popular control is the lack of the motivation necessary to translate doctrines of freedom into service devoted to the common good. Such weakness of motivation is variously conceptualized as alienation, lack of identity, or unwillingness to assume responsibility, and is allegedly exhibited in nonvoting, unwillingness to run for public office, or cautious conduct in the presence of corrupt and arbitrary acts. What was the constellation of factors present in the YPI context that inhibited vigorous demands for fuller democratization?

So far as the senior doctors were concerned, the uncertainties described were of great importance. The conflicts of conscience the doctors experienced when confronted with the significance of the idea of a therapeutic community were assuaged by the limited steps toward power sharing that were taken. The doctors were then able to convince themselves that they were not being excessively arbitrary or going too far in usurping the power of others. If the pressures from patients for greater freedom and a greater share in responsibility had been less easily satisfied, and if the patients had constantly pressed harder for more, the doctors' inner conflicts would not have been so easily stilled, and power sharing might have gone further.

The extent to which the doctors' personal power strivings account for their reluctance to give up power remains uncharted. That power is an important source of the doctors' personal gratification is to be inferred from the observation that their assumption of positions of extraordinary power over the lives of others was not a passive process imposed from outside. Moreover, the doctors sought and retained power in the face of some pressures to give it up. Power is granted and exercised by doctors in the service of healing; it is justified only because it is deemed necessary to the facilitation of the work of healing. In the absence of substantial documentation of that rationale (or when it appears to threaten their strivings to be loved), doctors are in inner conflict about their power. The doctors were reluctant to give up more power because: (1) it was necessary for the expiation of guilt; (2) if they had less power they could not be so sure of being able to meet demands made upon them by those to whom they were responsible; (3) they sought to gratify inner strivings for power.

That changes at the YPI were not more far-reaching reflects the difference between the dynamics of reform by consent and of revolution, whether by consent or not. Among specialists on politics and history it is notorious that, in a well-established social setting, drastic innovations are unlikely unless the effective decision-making elements are confronted by a threat or opportunity of remarkable dimensions. A research hospital is, in a sense, a social institution specialized to revolution or reform. It strives to make major contributions to the advancement of knowledge, and such turning-points in enlightenment are, hopefully, revolutionary. Psychiatric hospitals are restricted by their obligations to serve the immediate needs of current patients, whose interests cannot be sacrificed to the long-range community objective of developing more enlightened ways of coping with mental illness. Hence there are built-in limitations on revolution, and although revolutionary objectives may be proposed, the first steps of any program of innovation are reformist.

Revolution carries major implications for the distribution of power and other values. However, some innovations of a drastic character can be tried out on a small scale without threatening national or international power elites or their established ideological systems. Small-scale tryouts conducted in comparative obscurity by scientists is a strategy of public policy that prepares the way for eventual interventions in the great arenas of public life. It is important to underline the point that the factors militating against revolution in the larger arenas of society are present in the lesser ones, not excluding situations explicitly specialized to the advancement of knowledge.

Thus a medical director who seeks to initiate drastic changes in a functioning context is limited by the predispositions of participants who are indoctrinated in the prevailing ideology and oriented toward established power processes. To assert that the whole ideology is wrong or a fraud is to create a situation which demands either that the participants be almost entirely reconstituted or that the director modify his strategy and identify himself with fundamental aspects of the established perspective, accept the overriding goals of, and otherwise affirm confidence in the present institution. The YPI was not in a state of conflict about its objectives or operations; on the contrary, participants were committed to its exploratory role. But members of the staff were far from willing to agree, if anyone had urged the thesis, that by failing to share power with patients they had been acting immorally. A revolutionary doctrine of this magnitude could not be sought directly by open strategies. Limited changes were effected and tolerated since they were made within a framework of confidence in the capacity of the institution to fulfill its objectives without revolutionary reconstruction. Reforms could be accepted because they did not arouse the fear that they might threaten the sources of security. Once some changes were made, the innovators tended to oppose further modifications, delivering on their implicit promise not to go too far. Further innovations must then await the coming to power of others. The innovations effected in the YPI probably reflect such a state of affairs, indicating that any changes required to widen the degree of power sharing would have to await new leadership.

Several factors appear to explain why the residents accepted their comparatively modest role in the decision process. They were transient and mobile and would leave in a year. They were lacking in self-confidence concerning their professional skill and enlightenment and fearful of the consequences to themselves and others of inept performance. Hence they were willing to assume a dependent role, recognizing that they would be able to play much more self-determining roles in their work once this last training year was finished.

Residents, nurses, and other staff members were vulnerable, as were patients, to the atmosphere of guilt created by the vigorously moralistic application of the psychotherapeutic ideology characteristic of the hospital and of patient-staff meetings. This emphasis upon rectitude, of which the director was clearly recognized as the appropriate major arbiter, served primarily as a mode of control by the director and senior staff over other members of the staff and patients, and secondarily as a control used by the rest of the staff, particularly residents, over patients.

The nurses had no expectation of exercising major responsibility. Tradition had long assigned them a role ancillary to the doctors. The social workers were beginning to see themselves as members of a profession whose behavioral training was in some ways more comprehensive than the doctors'. They were uncertain about how to use their skills most effectively in the treatment of severely ill patients, and remained largely acquiescent in the structure of the hospital.

The patients were ambivalent about further power sharing, settled for less than necessary under the circumstances, and did not press for more. Why? Their past experience as losers, victims, and sufferers contributed to low expectations regarding their capabilities and to relatively modest demands. They were ready to be passive, dominated, and victimized, to have others assume responsibility, take care of them, and direct them, to view themselves as incapable of caring for themselves, to accept the usurping of their power by others as justified and necessary, and to expect defeat and deprivation. Recall in this connection the "locked closets" issue. Patients complained about the locking of the closets in their rooms at night and convincingly documented the futility and irrationality of the practice. The staff was convinced, stated their readiness to give up the practice, but stipulated that patients would have to assume responsibility if the closets were left open. The matter ended there; patients were not willing to assume that responsibility. They could participate effectively in the intelligence and appraisal phases of the decision process on this question but were reluctant to move on to new prescription, which increased their responsibilities. They did, however, take the next step occasionally: patients were willing to assume responsibility for monitoring the closed-ward telephone. The risks involved on this issue were not so great. Although a telephone call might have destructive consequences, it was not likely to approach in severity the feared result of leaving closets unlocked (suicide). Patients imposed limits on the extent to which they sought shared power on the basis of their fears of assuming, and their positive wish to have others assume, difficult and demanding responsibilities; they resisted abandoning the role of the deprived and the defeated.

The innovations involved patients in the joint consideration of issues individually and collectively important to them. They did in fact participate in sharing information (the intelligence phase of decision-making) with the rest of the hospital community on matters which had not previously been discussed together. They engaged in the joint evaluation of the way things were and of what they, patients and staff, were doing (the appraisal phase), with a view toward improving hospital policies designed to fulfill the therapeutic objective (the decision phases of recommendation, application, and invocation). Prescription and termination, the more assertive and definitive outcome phases of decision-making, were largely avoided in patient-staff meetings, although the expression of views on a specific issue would sometimes lead to a consensus which was acted upon. The director-chairman would at times, and at other times would not, explicitly participate in such a consensus; definitive summary statements of what had been decided were rarely formulated. Given a consensus supported by the director's stated or tacit agreement, the implicit prescription would sometimes be put into action or viewed as accepted policy. However, these actions and policies were subject to later arbitrary reversal. The consensus might be declared ambiguous or merely tentative, and subject to further discussion.

Patient-staff advisory committee meetings were largely occupied with the promoting phase of decision-making. The committee offered recommendations for further consideration by the staff regarding changes in patient status (going out unaccompanied, moving to the open ward, taking a job or resuming school) or measures to meet pressing and current hospital problems (for example, suggesting a program for keeping a troubled patient in contact with others). Since most of their recommendations were accepted, the committee was in fact often engaged in prescription and termination. However, because the staff retained veto power over committee decisions, staff participants on the committee were sounded out carefully on each possible alternative in the effort to avoid the exercising of that veto. The committee's sense of responsibility was weakened by their awareness that further consideration would be given each issue and that the final decision would be made either by the staff or the director alone.

The Possibility of Genuine Power Sharing in the Hospital

How much further could power sharing have gone? A firm procedure for decision-making to which all were committed, clearly stating what decisions were to be made, where, and by what means, could have been established. For example, patient advisory committee recommendations could be subject to consideration by the staff, but after hearing the views of the staff, the committee could be empowered to override the staff and make its own final, binding decision. Agreements arrived at by consensus in patient-staff meetings could be explicitly formulated by the chairman and, in the absence of opposition, declared binding. Members of the staff, including senior doctors, could expressly commit themselves to use established community institutions for the making of a defined range of decisions. Certain exceptions might be agreed upon after discussion by the hospital community, including decisions requiring such prompt action that prior consultation would be difficult, and possibly some outcomes carefully defined as "medical" and regarded as outside the competence of the collectivity. Any exceptions would require rigorous and continuing scrutiny by the community, however, since it is evident that all too many decisions can be made arbitrarily, unilaterally, and impulsively under the guise of urgency or of lying outside the ken of nonphysicians.

Such an extension of power sharing would mean that the collectivity, consisting mostly of patients, could at times supercede the judgments of some, or even all, staff members, occasionally overriding their vetoes. They could, at times, move a patient from one floor to another, transfer him from one therapist to another, discharge a patient from the hospital, or eliminate a procedure intended to assure safety which they regarded as irrational or unnecessary. The collectivity would thus have great power, subject to persuasion and influence by dissenters among patients and staff, but not to their domination.

The community would then no longer be playing at democracy. Power would be genuinely shared, and the stakes and responsibilities of all members of the community, including patients, would be great and real. Such decision-making procedures might result at times in taking risks presently avoided by the retention of power by the director and senior doctors. To innovate power sharing on such a scale would require genuine reliance upon the patients' capacity for judgment and courage to accept and act upon community decisions, despite potential reservations and inherent risks.

This more revolutionary revolution would require the acceptance of the formidable responsibilities of full democratic citizenship by every member of the community, doctor and patient alike. The patient would have to face and perhaps struggle all the more vigorously with his reluctance to assume responsibility for his destiny and the affairs of his community. The staff would have to face and struggle with their personal power strivings and inclination to assume too much responsibility for others. They would need to find the courage to work cooperatively with their patients at a far more demanding level. At times it would be necessary to tolerate less expert judgments, and at all times the task would be to persuade the community rather than arbitrarily override decisions. The larger community would need to be prepared for these shifts in allocation of power. It would be necessary for civic, university, and professional representatives to agree to the exercise of greater power by the patients and accept the risks involved. They would need to modify the traditional pattern by which community supervision has been administered, shifting from reliance upon their appointed expert agents (the doctors), and allowing patients to participate with staff in the control of the hospital community. The fact that in the course of YPI innovations such arrangements were not sought from representatives of the larger community attests once more to the modesty of the changes introduced.

The assumption of power by patients could conceivably be carried even further. We can imagine a dictatorship of the patient population. The patient advisory committee, for example, could be organized to consist entirely of patient members, and decisions of the committee could be accepted as final and binding. The committee might, of course, seek the advice of staff members, but this consultation would be voluntary, not obligatory; decisions could be made without staff participation and exempt from staff veto.

Such a drastic shift of power might conceivably result in a tyranny in which a few patients assume the authoritarian position previously held by the senior staff. Such innovations might result in the appearance of a novel therapeutic ideology ("let us achieve well-being by helping one another, without depending on the help of doctors, nurses, or others"), or in an ideology in which the explicit emphasis is on power rather than well-being ("we have lost up to the present; let us now unite to fit ourselves to compete more effectively in the struggle for power; let us train one another, gaining the experience and mastery necessary to win by participating in our own power-sharing institutions"). Whatever the ultimate outcome, it would be extraordinarily informative to study what would happen if each of these models were realized (a hospital where power was genuinely and explicitly held by the collectivity, and a hospital where patients held such power without formal staff participation).

Conditions for Increased Power Sharing

Although such shifts of power might be feasible under some conditions, much would depend upon both the stability and the pathology of the patient population. Such changes would probably work best in a hospital where most patients remain in treatment for relatively long periods, insuring the participation of a core group thoroughly familiar with the workings of community institutions. Chances would be best where the pathology of patients does not include too many sociopathic personalities (individuals deprived in power and other values who refuse to acknowledge inner conflict, insisting that they in no way participate in their own victimization).

This prediction is strengthened by events at the YPI after the period of the present study. The research group which had been investigating the families of schizophrenics turned its attention to the families of sociopathic patients and undertook the comparison of families of schizophrenic and sociopathic patients. As part of this research, more sociopathic patients were admitted to the YPI. The hospital had previously accepted such patients cautiously, being sure that its current patients of this type had been successfully absorbed into the community before admitting more.

The abrupt increase in the number of sociopathic patients seriously interfered with hospital power-sharing institutions. Their provocative behavior, and the behavior which they evoked from other patients, disrupted the hospital to the extent that the senior staff reacted with dictatorial measures, at times suspending any attempt to share power. This observation invites detailed investigation to clarify how the balance of patient pathology in the hospital population determines and affects the nature of the power structure and perhaps limits the extent to which power sharing is possible without serious destruction of other values. The sociopath relies upon a mechanism dangerous to democratic process; he is compelled by inner conflict to insist upon transforming every situation into a direct conflict of wills, instead of anticipating such potential confrontations and seeking to keep them at a minimum by searching for objectives or strategies on which agreement can be attained. The sociopath refuses to use his intelligence to invent or endorse policies which integrate the situation. On the contrary, he exacerbates human relations as a chronic protester against the constellation of developmental circumstances in which he lost the family power struggle. If many sociopaths are present, they tend to dominate debate and to struggle with one another for control of the situation, often threatening to disrupt the procedures of orderly discussion and provoking the chairman to inflict deprivations on them. However, individuals sometimes learn to modify their strategy and identify themselves with latent demands, thus winning the support of others, an experience which may contribute to the eventual change of their basic orientation.

The expectation that the greater sharing of power with patients would result in more risks, perhaps in the jeopardizing of both the safety of patients and of the larger community, and in interference with the therapeutic program, requires investigation. It is possible that such shifts in power would result, not in more freedom for patients or in greater risk, but rather in a conservative, restrictive, and authoritarian hospital. When power was first extended to the patient -staff advisory committee, for example, observers were impressed with the care exercised by patients in avoiding risks and facilitating therapeutic objectives. At times it appeared to staff participants that the committee was too conservative, not taking chances which the staff might have (for example, supporting a patient in his first tentative moves toward resuming work or spending less time in the hospital), or insisting upon more evidence that a patient was ready for greater freedom than the staff would have felt justified in demanding. Furthermore, the reluctance of patients as a group to undertake responsibilities involving risk has often been documented. The true impact of great shifts of power is unknown; genuine power sharing of this order has not been innovated or studied.

The Strategy of Prototyping

The YPI innovation is of methodological importance since it is a means to knowledge that stands somewhere between experimentation and official intervention. An outstanding characteristic of experiments is not only that results are carefully manipulated according to plan, but that social practices are split into component variables. Although experimentation has many advantages, it is often important to work with whole social practices. Such an approach is the most appropriate to the reorganization of hospital environments. The aim is to enable patients to improve their mastery of social practice; if this is to be done, the practices around them must be effectively arranged. The innovation at the YPI can be summarized as a set of power-sharing practices initiated for the purpose of improving the eventual mastery of appropriate social practices by all concerned.

We use the term "prototype" to distinguish the method from experimentation or other strategies of knowledge. The YPI innovation enables us to provide a brief outline of what is involved.

Three phases of prototyping are distinguished: *pre-introduction, introduction,* and *post-introduction.* When can it be said that a prototype is "introduced?" The question is of great importance in assessing the consequences of an innovation. The traditional alibi of disappointed innovators, the allegation that "like Christianity it has never been tried," implies some lack of sincerity of purpose or competence. If we are to obtain comparison-worthy findings from a prototypical situation, it should be possible to demonstrate that at least some minimum degrees of agreement and competence were present. Let us reserve the term "introduced" to designate this level of consensus and innovation.

Patient-staff meetings were introduced at the YPI in 1956. The YPI staff was willing, even eager, to get ahead with the plan; as the transcripts of meetings presented demonstrate, it quickly achieved a stable level of operation.

It is not implied that every staff member was affirmatively committed to the innovation in 1956 or that intensities of commitment were equal. For instance, members of the supervisory staff were often noncommittal or negative. It is impractical to insist that every influential participant in a prototypical situation must be "for" the project. *It is enough to require that a program be regarded as "introduced" when new practices are initially stabilized, and when influential elements support it with the expectation that the prospects of success are rather favorable.*

In prototype research, *it is useful for its managers to make it easy for ideologically alienated and characterologically incapable leaders to withdraw.* At the YPI there was no necessity of easing out any staff members; by 1956 the trend of the hospital had become sufficiently clear to bring about a spontaneous process of selection accomplished by discreet withdrawal and by recruitment of individuals in harmony with the tendency to create an explicit therapeutic community. Some supervisors, for example, primarily concerned with the individual psychotherapeutic relationship, strongly opposed the introduction of group therapy or patient-staff meetings on the ground that the individual treatment relationship might be undermined. But even at the conscious ideological level, there was no disposition to deny the legitimacy of undertaking a program of investigation.

No less serious than ideological reservations to a prototype are characterological limitations. The YPI innovation was an exacting trial for psychiatrists, experienced and relatively inexperienced, and all other staff members. The program probably would have proceeded faster if some individuals had been transferred. In these cases a conflict which was deeply rooted in character interfered with the performance of the appropriate role. It is not necessary that everyone be of one mold for a prototype to be useful, but before a sound judgment can be made of the prototype it must be in the hands of persons who possess the capability as well as the conscious demand to give it a try.

It is not to be assumed that all staff members active in the YPI innovation are acceptable models of democratic character, or that a prototype must use personnel standards which are impractically high. As the results indicate, the innovation encouraged everyone to engage in continuous and candid self-appraisal and to expose himself to an almost unique variety of appraisals emanating from others. *Understanding and insight are among the advantages of well-conceived prototypes in society.*

Another strategic principle is *continuing concern with the clarifying of goals and objectives.* The YPI innovation is representative of many creative prototypes which at the beginning are not fully worked out—they take shape as experience accumulates. The record shows that the details of the YPI innovation were not planned in advance. The goal of creating a more fully therapeutic environment was present from the beginning, but implications for the various categories of participants were not anticipated. No one undertook to write a code of instructions for the staff or to assess the value impacts of the patient-staff meetings.

When we speak of goals and objectives we have three points in mind: the values sought, the essential pattern of innovation, and the specific criteria of success. The idea of a patient-staff conference had not initially been refined to include any particular number of meetings, nor had the agenda been given careful thought. The pattern was allowed to stabilize during the first year, as the chairman found himself faced with particular challenges. The degree to which the YPI innovation was in harmony with trends that had begun to grow stronger before patient-staff meetings were instituted has been described. The record confirms an advantage of prototyping: it permits favorable trends in a situation to be identified and furthered.

As the prototype becomes more explicit it is easier to select definite criteria of success or failure. However, in complex human situations a given list of specific criteria is never to be taken as exhaustive. As an innovation evolves, some initial objectives sink into obscurity, and new objectives emerge or rise in importance. In prototyping, objectives are modified or changed if, as the endeavor proceeds, new considerations are recognized as important or basic assumptions and expectations prove invalid. This flexibility, with the expectation that objectives may change in time, further distinguishs prototypes from experiments.

The YPI innovation was less thought-out in advance than it might have been. One result was that comparatively simple records of some importance were not provided for. The significance of the power process, for example, was not anticipated in detail. The seating patterns in meetings might have been closely observed as a means of describing shifts in the alignment of cliques and factions among staff and patients. The potential consequences of a prototypical innovation are limitless; there is no ceiling on records that may be potentially relevant. Important limitations, however, must be recognized in devising a data program for any specific project. *Data taking should not interfere with the innovation.*

Secrecy is not necessary, and it is dangerous in research of the kind we are advocating. It is unnecessary to keep secret the fact that recordings will be made of patient-staff meetings or interviews. In the past, alleged reluctance to agree to record taking has been greatly exaggerated; where confidence exists in the good faith and competence of investigators, problems rarely arise. Such secrecy breaks down the confidence essential to therapy. It must be assumed that attempts at secrecy will not escape eventual detection.

The criterion of noninterference with the formation of a prototype is by no means a deterrent to sound data gathering. On the contrary, the principle makes it necessary to assess alternative possibilities with care. The YPI innovation actually proved to be an act of emancipation, willing or not, for nurses and other staff members who formerly devoted time to making records which were rarely used for treatment or for scientific analysis. As described, ritualized modes of reporting were terminated.

A successful prototype not only leads to new and improved prototypes, but paves the way for experimentation. Prototypical programs tend to merge with experiments when a design is adopted that calls for the systematic matching of "innovations" against "control situations." For example, the size of patient-staff groups might be varied according to a fixed schedule; written constitutions could be introduced with somewhat contrasting provisions; seating arrangements might be assigned according to different plans.

Prototypes often suggest experiments which at first sight seem remotely related to the original situation. For instance, value-practice analysis of the YPI may lead to experiments designed to locate the "focal experiences" which influence individual predispositions to prefer one value above another. Other experiments might explore the effect of providing participants, patients and staff alike, with an explicit value theory.

Strategically, it is essential to encourage confidence in the importance of the prototype, without permitting new norms to be applied with fanatical intensity. At the beginning, the YPI program was low keyed. It did, however, soon win popularity among patients. The patients made overtures to patients elsewhere, proposing the innovation of patient-staff meetings at other hospitals. YPI patients also took responsibility toward newcomers, transmitting the new norms as part of an established pattern. It is, of course, conceivable that fanatical individuals may seize upon the new norms of a prototype and seek to exploit them as an instrument of repressive and censorious power. The director of YPI was successful in keeping the therapeutic aim in the foreground and in avoiding fanaticism. The ideology of the innovation made explicit demands for candid disclosure of motives, and for responsible participation in all hospital relationships. The patient-staff meetings were identified as important steps upon which patients and staff could congratulate one another. But this atmosphere of mutual congratulation was never transformed into a witch hunt against nonconformists.

When a prototype is contemplated, several strategies of disclosure are available to the leadership. YPI experience supports the principle that *although candid disclosure of goals and expectations is to be encouraged, this does not require innovators to stimulate opposition by stressing all contingencies.* If every conceivable opponent were fully alerted in advance to every hypothetical damage that might be done to his interests, very few prototypes could be innovated. In the absence of the knowledge obtainable from a prototype, speculation in advance must be conducted in the orbit of established views. Clearly, a major vindication of research is that it provides new and relevant intelligence.

The YPI case emphasizes the importance of strategies calculated to overcome adverse predispositions. *Initial indulgences are important.* When we reflect upon the many variables which in any social situation militate against change, this principle gains significance. The hospital's earlier experience with an ineffective patient government contributed to the necessity that the staff demonstrate by word and deed that what patients said in patient-staff meetings influence decision. Otherwise the innovation would have been perceived as "another fraud."

When objectives are incompletely specified, it is not always easy to distinguish between a given stage of partial stability and the terminal goal. Hence the importance of a principle that *cautions against permitting interests to crystallize at a transitional stage short of the goal.* During the period of innovation at the YPI, every new step was taken in the face of misgivings or opposition by some staff members who wanted to leave well enough alone. The proposed principle is a built-in challenge to engage in candid self-appraisal in the light of clarified goals.

As experience accumulates in the installation of prototypes, many additional principles will be developed as guides to basic strategy. The principles, it is to be noted, are of two closely interconnected kinds, principles of content and of procedure. Both are pertinent to the problem-solving tasks of individuals or groups: content principles formulate what is worth bringing to the focus of attention; procedural principles state the suggested order in which content is to be considered. Prototyping is an act of participation in human affairs which places heavy demands for insight and understanding upon those who engage in new ways of life.[1]

The Permeating Significance of Power in Man and Society

When we draw together the experiences at the YPI, a major factor in the life of man and society takes on renewed significance: power. However numerous the connotations of the term, a central bull's eye of meaning is well understood. Power implies volition and contextual importance. In every human relationship, whether bilateral or many-sided, power is active or latent; in every collective context that achieves stability, a volition-adjusting set of practices can be identified. These practices taken in the aggregate are the public and civic order of the group in question, whether the group is pluralistic or territorial.

When we examine the power history of each individual, the broad significance of this value becomes apparent. Strictly speaking, a mental hospital such as the YPI only encounters young people after years of exposure to the values and institutions characteristic of a complex culture, class, interest, and personality environment. The

1. See Harold D. Lasswell, *The Future of Political Science* (New York, Atherton Press, 1963), chap. 5; A. R. Holmberg, H. F. Dobyns et al., "Community and Regional Development: The Cornell-Peru Experiment," *Human Organization,* 21 (1962), 108–24.

individual acquires the predispositions with which he comes to the hospital on the basis of all kinds of value indulgences and deprivations. All his expectations, demands, and identities, together with every operational routine, have been acquired in interaction with the previous situation.

These predispositions have been shaped primarily in conflicting interaction within the family. They have also been shaped in struggles with others, including friends and colleagues in school, work, and the other communities in which the patient unsuccessfully sought to participate. They are influenced by any previous experience with psychiatrists or hospitals as well. Most important, however, is the fact that the patient who enters the hospital is the loser in a long protracted, at times subtle, at times violent, power struggle within his family. The family is no longer willing to tolerate the individual; he is expelled. On admission to the hospital, the expellee is identified as a "patient."

We emphasize power and describe the events which precipitate hospitalization as a power struggle which the patient has lost because this conception most adequately conforms to the facts. The most important choices made in the family are power decisions which concern the most meaningful issues to the persons involved. The critical family choices influence the extent to which each family member is an effective decision-maker and the extent to which all values in the family social process are shared.

The patient is a target of severe sanction in the family decision process. He is ejected as a burdensome and threatening deprivational influence of such magnitude that the life of the family cannot proceed without his removal. The sanction is the culminating outcome of a process that has gone on for years in which both patient and family have suffered severely. A naked confrontation of wills may finally result in the explicit defeat of the patient and his exclusion. The family is no longer able to rely on internal strategies to cope with the challenger; the disrupting participant must be excluded.

The character of the power struggle in the contemporary family reflects the transition of this institution from an authoritarian structure to one which emphasizes power sharing. In ancient Rome the larger community granted the father absolute control over his progeny; this included the use of capital punishment to enforce decisions. Paternal absolutism has been drastically curbed in our culture; deference to parental control has been undermined. The prevailing ideology encourages all family members, including children, to assert themselves more vigorously. Hence the contemporary family is confused and conflicted in seeking to exercise power: its objectives and strategies are ambiguous and contradictory. The democratizing trends in the larger society have engulfed the lesser units—the families—spreading the uncertainties, anxieties, and conflicts which characterize our epoch of transition. Although some families achieve relatively smooth working arrangements, each system remains provisional and exploratory. They are surrounded by, and interact with, families and other institutions stricken with inner contractions that generate the civil crises which may end in the expulsion of the losers.

We have reviewed the change in the power structure of the YPI and indicated that, although some patients and staff members were willing and able to participate in the decision process, the predispositions that were brought into the hospital situation contained inner contradictions to the practice of power sharing. Previous experience of socialization in American society was not sufficiently in harmony with the proclaimed norms of democracy to equip patients or staff to demand of themselves, or one another, that they take full responsibility in the clarification of common goals and the conduct of collective policy. Our discussion of the YPI model has considered more radical or drastic ways of changing authority and control in a mental hospital, drawing attention to lines of research that are essential if present-day uncertainties are to be followed by sounder understanding. It remains to take a further step in the consideration of policy alternatives for attempting to cope with troubled people.

Suitability of the Medical Model

Would democratization of the hospital render it a more suitable solution to the problems of those defeated in the family? Would the transformation of the hospital into a community where power is effectively shared succeed in adapting the medical-therapeutic model to the needs of this group and offer a more promising solution to their problems? Would it make the hospital more therapeutic?

We must weigh the possibility that the traditional medical model is, in fact, inappropriate to deal with the problems of those who have gone down to defeat in the struggle for power. Our analysis suggests that when a hospital is transformed in the direction of a democratic community, many traditional medical elements are discarded or modified to such an extent that they are no longer recognizable; indeed, what persists as "medical" appears to be less clearly justifiable. Perhaps a new specialized environment, elaborated from a new perception of the problem, might do a better job than the hospital. In its efforts to adapt itself more usefully to patient needs, the YPI put aside much that is conventionally medical, and emphasized instead self-exploration and participation in education, work, and political forums.

The most important implication of YPI experience may be to suggest a thorough reexamination of the suitability of the medical-therapeutic model for coping with the behavioral problems of the defeated: Why physicians? Why nurses? Why the designations "patient" and "illness"?

Answers to these questions will clarify the conditions that must be met if the medical-therapeutic model is to be regarded as obsolete and then abandoned. Medical institutions provide the patient and other participants in the family context with value indulgences which contribute to a partial resolution of their difficulties. The loser in the family power struggle, though evicted from the original arena, is admitted into an environment in which his role as patient obtains for him the indulgences customarily accorded the physically ill. Furthermore, the medical model provides indulgences in power, respect, and other values for his family and for those who seek to serve him in his predicament. Any new institution, geared specifically and more comprehensively to the use of strategies to cope with the effects of deprivational power-experiences in the family, must find other ways of furnishing the indulgences the medical model provides the sufferer and his allies if the hospital (and other elements in the medical model) are to be replaced.

Self-exploration will remain crucial to all effective processes which may eventually be invented or adapted to cope with the predicament of the defeated, whether the emphasis is put on well-being or power. Indeed, the clear delineation of perspectives, strategies, and preferred outcomes (What do we most care about? What do we want? What forces within and outside of ourselves must we master in pursuit of these objectives? How can they be mastered? How can we mobilize our energies and resources and get what we want?), augmented by opportunities for participation in power-sharing practices and institutions, would seem to constitute the core of the process, essential to its effectiveness. In the contemporary psychiatric hospital the task of self-exploration is carried on primarily in individual psychotherapy. The procedures are modifications of our most completely understood and refined method for such exploration, psychoanalysis. Considerations involved in applying psychoanalytic techniques to the psychoses were described earlier. The therapist is a more active participant and is brought into more direct contact with the patient than in the conventional treatment of the psychoneuroses. Some of these modifications increase the contribution made by psychotherapeutic work to the patient's capacity for equality of participation in social and power-sharing practices. The relevant changes depart from those aspects of psychotherapeutic procedure which may be experienced by the patient as depriving him of power (for example, the imbalance suggested by the patient reclining as the analyst sits up, or the inequality of participation implicit when the patient free-associates and the therapist refrains from sharing his own thoughts). It is possible that other modifications of psychotherapeutic technique might contribute to the patient's capacity for full participation. How to maximize this objective without jeopardizing elements of psychotherapeutic procedure which have been clearly established as useful, and without introducing contrived and artificial practices, is a delicate problem for further investigation.

The use of the medical-therapeutic model for coping with the predicament of the defeated is, in part, fostered by the medical orientation of psychoanalysis and psychotherapy in the United States. The application of psychoanalysis to work with the psychoses has been carried out largely within the framework of a specialized branch of medicine, and in medically supervised hospitals and clinics, the only institutions in which psychotherapy of the psychoses has been systematically undertaken. It is conceivable that procedures of self-exploration, undertaken in specialized environments which do not conform to the medical model, would undergo further developments impossible within medical and hospital contexts. The possibility of stimulating such experimentation is a potentially worthwhile and important consequence of developing specialized environments which depart from current approaches in psychiatric institutions.

The primary objective of modifying the setting in which individual psychotherapy is pursued would be to facilitate individual treatment. Regardless of how optimally psychotherapeutic the milieu may become, the success or failure of treatment depends on what is achieved in the individual psychotherapeutic relationship.

Conditions for Staff Learning and Sharing

It is to be expected that more comprehensively therapeutic psychiatric hospitals and other specialized environments which do not conform to the medical-therapeutic model will gradually be de-

veloped for meeting the needs of behaviorally disordered individuals. Is the role of the resident physician presently adapted to the
formidable challenge of providing creative intellectual leadership
which will guide research and corrective action in these emerging
contexts?

This study of the YPI documents the resident's preoccupation with
being approved of and otherwise indulged in affection and respect
by his seniors, and his readiness to accept deprivations of power if
affection and respect indulgences are forthcoming. In examining
his perspectives, we have seen the importance of the resident's previous years of experience in the authoritarian societies of medical
school and hospitals where traditional, hierarchical models were
emphasized for interactions with superiors, colleagues, and patients.
Although earlier experiences may have prepared the occasional physician to participate in a democratic society, medical training and
the constricted character of extra-professional experience during
those years limit his capacity to comprehend the meaning of participation in such a society and hamper his efforts to undertake or
grant full citizenship.

The resident's ability to learn, to pursue psychotherapeutic work
with unfettered curiosity and a flexible investigatory attitude, as
well as his capacity to understand and actively assume the responsibilities of community citizenship, are strongly influenced by the
character of the setting in which he works and by experiences with
seniors—especially if they subject him to arbitrary, ambiguous, or
hypocritical conduct. The resident is troubled when left uninformed
about matters affecting his vital interests, for example, when he
receives little feedback from teachers and bosses who are evaluating
his competence. The resident's responsibilities and the extent of his
power are often not clearly delineated. The limits of power sharing
in his hospital work are not explicated; the hierarchical constraints
to which he is subject in making decisions that concern his patients
are both ambiguous and obscure. The resident, in common with his
patients, experiences discrepancies between ideology and practice
as demoralizing, corrupting, and undermining of his quest for
dignity as a human being.

In examining the nurse's predicament, we become aware of the
threat implicit to her in change. She accepts the conventional role-
defining tasks with which she had been occupied and her hierarchically inferior position in the authoritarian hospital. The efforts of
the YPI staff to reexamine and modify the strategies employed in
coping with the predicaments of their patients have resulted in con-

fusion about the nurse's role and functions. Routines and procedures which helped her to cope with the stresses of work with severely disturbed patients have been discarded. She feels ill-prepared for the increasingly emphasized demand that her work consist primarily in direct participation with patients in the therapeutic community. Her interactions with patients are rarely inspected; they are neither guided nor informed by training for work in a psychotherapeutic hospital. The nurse continues to look to the doctors for respect and appreciation. She attempts to define her role as their colleague and helpmate, but this solution is virtually impossible because of the limitations of her professional training. The pursuit of the ideal of a comprehensively psychotherapeutic hospital demands a high level of sophistication from all participants, including nurses, and must provide experience, training, and opportunities for continuing professional development which enable the individual to participate with an investigatory and self-examining attitude.

The Policy Sciences of Democracy: The Strategy of Power Sharing

A fundamental issue of public policy is at stake when any specialized group, such as psychiatrists, is authorized under various conditions to dominate others by making decisions of enormous importance for their physical and mental well-being and for their freedom of participation in the familial, political, and economic institutions of society. We have called attention to the fact that the traditional assumptions used to justify these islands of presumably benevolent coercion are no longer to be taken for granted. Research is indicating that power-dominance in the mental hospital perpetuates the problems passed on to the hospital from the home, and that schizophrenic manifestations are culturally acquired strategies by which young people who have been severely defeated in the family present themselves, as it were, for perpetual exemption from full participation in society.

Public policy clearly indicates that new and radical lines of inquiry are needed if we are to discover the environments that are adapted to the renewal of self-development by damaged youths and adults. In the same way, the findings emphasize once more the civic importance of identifying those family systems failing to incorporate children into a pattern of life that permits the home to function effectively, and those systems contributing to the formation of adults who can function responsibly in the decision processes of society.

These implications belong to the policy sciences of democracy, a conception that is becoming more articulate with the growth of knowledge and the attempt to improve the effective realization of human dignity. The policy sciences of any civilization postulate the overriding value goals of the public order and give extended attention to the process of decision and to the processing of information of any kind into policy.

Phrasing the matter more formally, the policy sciences of democracy are mainly concerned with (1) the analysis of decision processes and (2) making contemporary knowledge available for public purposes. The present study is directly concerned with the former task, although, as indicated above, it also considers questions of public policy in dealing with troubled and troublesome people.

In situations where power is narrowly held, as in the traditional mental hospital, by what strategy can power be effectively shared with least disturbance? How can such islands of exemption from democratic practice as the mental hospital be brought closer to the proclaimed ideal of widely shared participation?

The power-sharing innovation at the YPI belongs to that category of cases in which the initiative came from the top rather than from the rank and file. When senior physicians decided to assess the sharing of power as a strategy of treatment, they were not struggling desperately to make belated concessions to revolutionary pressures spearheaded by political organizations within or beyond the hospital community. The evidence suggests that the decision developed out of scientific inquiry. Exploratory studies of the therapeutic community conception strongly supported the conclusion that it was not necessary for physicians to accept many of the traditional exemptions from democracy in order to benefit the patient. Earlier professional expectations had protected the staff against inner conflicts now generated by the discrepancy between the demand to act democratically and the imperative to fulfill therapeutic obligations. The issue arose when a responsible professional challenge was made to traditional assumptions.

The YPI "revolution from above" successfully inaugurated a pattern of changed decision-making and execution in which patients participated effectively. The revolution was not complete, but it was substantial. What light do the results throw upon the strategy of guided democratization?

The study of the YPI has the merit of exhibiting in a highly circumscribed context the characteristic factors that work for or against the successful completion of a program of power devolution. Although the revolution from above was genuinely effective in many respects, it was also self-limiting. An examination of these inter-relationships is significant for the strategy of political development, especially in nation-states where the most important elite elements in a program of change are personally committed to the sharing of authority and control.

The YPI case emphatically underlines the potential impact on ideology and behavior of whoever controls the focus of community attention. As a result of the innovation, the director had far more frequent communication with the hospital community than ever before, and under circumstances in which he had an advantageous power position. The director was able to exercise unprecedented control over the activities of residents, nurses, other staff members, and patients. As the overwhelming source of value indulgence and deprivation in the hospital, the director was made even more formidable by the power to act immediately and publicly on issues that arose.

Whatever the intentions of the innovators, the structure of the new arena made for a redefinition of the polarities of power among the participants. The director and the patients increased their weight in the decision process. Intermediate staff members were somewhat eclipsed by coalitions that arose between patients and the director. Coalitions formed among patients in the meetings, which entered into competition with one another for the support of the director. Staff members who held subordinate, hence intermediate, positions were literally "in the middle." Although they were also involved in the tacit formation and re-formation of coalitions, the director could cut the ground under any individual or group by not coming to its aid or by joining the opposition. Despite the loosening of the reins of power, the director vigorously retained ultimate authority.

These phenomena have parallels in the history of political units. National monarchs in conflict with other large landholders and members of the nobility often turned for support to broader strata of the population. In contemporary politics the elite elements who favor scientific and technological modernization are often opposed by oligarchies of wealth, respect, and other value assets. If modernization and democracy are to go together, the central elites must build coalitions able to sustain such programs.

The technological revolution that introduced new instruments of mass communication has brought into the political process an instrument of enormous potential impact. If television is effectively controlled by central authority, it provides the elite with access to the focus of attention comparable to the situation obtaining at YPI patient-staff meetings. If top leadership is determined and capable, instruments of communication can be used to establish contact with the entire population. Realistically coordinated with other instruments of policy, the direct-contact media can propagate doctrines of modernization and democratization and control the tempo of change toward more active and inclusively oriented participation.[2]

Many competent observers have been impressed with the greater alertness to the potentialities of modern media of communication demonstrated by communist elites than by leaders of noncommunist states.[3] Although the ideology of communism emphasizes material factors in social development, the strategy of communist parties and governments reveals their understanding of the importance of controlling the focus of attention as an instrument of power. Although microscopic, the YPI case provides a striking demonstration of attention control as a fundamental strategy of ideological and behavioral control.

The importance of attention control in the extent of the YPI director's power should not be overstated; the director's impact on the hospital community was decisive long before the meetings were inaugurated. Expectations were changed from initial scepticism about the genuineness of power sharing by the personal participation of the director and by decisions taken as a consequence of discussion. It was the transformation of the routines of life that brought conviction. On the national scale the central government is often in sufficient control of economic assets, for example, to provide inducements and indulgences that corroborate declarations of doctrine over the mass media.

The YPI case illuminates another dimension of any program of power sharing. How can responsible, rather than irresponsible, participation be encouraged? Remarks by the director about the un-

2. A research design for measuring the impact of television on audiences has been outlined with reference to one major problem in Arthur J. Brodbeck and Dorothy B. Jones, "Television Viewing and The Norm-Violating Practices and Perspectives of Adolescents: A Synchronized Depth and Scope Program of Policy Research," in L. Arons and Mark A. May, eds., *Television and Human Behavior: Tomorrow's Research in Mass Communication*, (New York, Appleton-Century-Crafts, 1963), pp. 98–136. On audience structure, participation, and response, see J. T. Klapper, *The Effects of Mass Communication* (Glencoe, Illinois, The Free Press, 1960); E. Katz and P. F. Lazarsfeld, *Personal Influence: The Part Played by People in The Flow of Communications* (Glencoe, Illinois, The Free Press, 1955).

3. Ithiel de Sola Pool, "The Mass Media and Politics in The Modernization Process," in Lucian W. Pye, ed., *Communications and Political Development* (Princeton, New Jersey, Princeton University Press, 1963), chap. 14. See also, T.C. Yu, "Communications and Politics in Communist China," ibid., chap. 16.

willingness of patients to take responsibility illustrate a recurring theme of champions of self-government. It is commonplace to discover once more that those excluded from power often appear reluctant and hopeless when challenged to take the opportunities and burdens of self-direction. YPI patients were expellees from the family arena where they had failed to share power effectively; such successes as they had obtained in critical life situations were often negative in character. Victories were not triumphs of responsible service to common goals; rather, they were typically destructive, though often indirect, attacks on the prevailing system of family order.

The YPI experience does not justify any simple-minded confidence in the future of power sharing in the social process, even in a body politic whose ideological orientation is in this tradition. The YPI case demonstrates some measure of irresponsibility on the part of both the power-deprived and the power-indulged, even when the latter are consciously committed to the demand for democratic practice.

The data obtained in the YPI prototype are directly relevant to the thousands of institutions engaged in psychiatric treatment and have far-reaching implications for the future of psychiatric training, treatment, and research. And if the power-sharing goal is taken seriously in connection with these enterprises, an appreciable advance will have been made in filling in land that communicates with what has hitherto been an island of relative exemption from democratic requirements. YPI experience can contribute to self-knowledge of latent and unconscious opposition to professed ideals of human dignity. Insight and understanding can provoke strategies of self-modification.

The strategies of power devolution demonstrated at the YPI underline the importance of emphasizing the ideological as well as the organizational dimension of social innovation. The senior staff did not allow the discussion of particular topics to proceed without explicit reference to the ideology of the hospital. This accounts in part for the prominent role of rectitude in the value profile of patient-staff meetings. The goal values championed by the ideology were actively applied to the invention, evaluation, and selection of policy alternatives. Hence each participant in the hospital community was challenged to take the belief system seriously enough to consider its application to daily life. Under such circumstances, the value imperatives of the YPI were prevented from degenerating into idle ritual.

It may be suggested that the problem of achieving an effective link between the language of doctrine and actual conduct is much easier at the YPI than elsewhere in society, especially in the wider community. Well-being is the obvious value of prime importance to a psychiatric hospital, but in the context of the wider community it rises and falls in relation to the vicissitudes of every value.

Problems of ideology and conduct occur in large territorially based communities in two situations: (1) When public questions are being decided as part of the community's specialized decision process; (2) when individuals and groups, concerned with their own policy problems, consider the implications of what they do for the larger community. The YPI experience bears most directly upon the second set of situations.

Pluralized groups in society are usually oriented toward a goal value to which they assign primary importance. The formation and activities of the group are justified in terms of this major objective, which is clarified, justified, and pursued in a context of ideological expectations, demands, and identities. The YPI focuses upon well-being, with heavy deference to enlightenment and skill. We take it for granted that private businesses bend their energies toward wealth, and that churches concentrate on rectitude. "Society" is specialized to respect; the family stresses affection.

From the viewpoint of the public order of territorial communities, the *strategies employed in the YPI innovation suggest how pluralized participants in modern society can integrate their policy objectives and procedures with policy goals they share with the wider context.* At every echelon the officials in an organization can deliberately bring their immediate subordinates more fully into the decision process. They can go beyond these to the rank and file, as the YPI included the patients in patient-staff meetings. In the case of large organizations, television and other mass media make attention control possible.

The YPI innovation supports the view that a number of conventional doubts about the limits of democratic participation cannot be corroborated. For many people the most dramatic result of YPI experience is the demonstration that even when seriously troubled, human beings can mobilize themselves enough to be cogent, realistic, and contributory to the process of decision.

Harmonizing the Ideology and Behavior of Democracy

Considered in the perspective of the policy sciences of democracy, the YPI innovation is to be seen as part of a vast movement in our society that works in opposition to the discrepancies that remain between the ideology of human dignity and actual conduct. The YPI prototype documents the fundamental importance to the individual of countering any trend toward self-isolation and alienation by seizing opportunities to participate with others in building and sustaining a social context in which he believes. In contemporary society, many religious organizations are already attempting to encourage individual and group study of moral questions in a setting that incorporates many of the insights and procedures developed in psychoanalysis and psychotherapy. In secular as well as religious circles, new associations are being formed to give support to troubled and disturbed individuals. The practice of personal counseling is on the increase in educational and welfare institutions, and engages the professional talent of psychiatrists, psychologists and sociologists. These influences are finding expression in industrial management and public administration, civilian and military.

The fact that the senior staff of a psychiatric hospital was motivated to investigate the consequences of power sharing indicates the strength of factors in personality and culture that tend to harmonize the actualities of conduct with the imperatives of ideology. As the YPI innovation transformed some of the basic structures and functions of the hospital community, the wider significance of the enterprise became progressively clarified in the minds of the senior staff, and of many residents, patients, and observers. The innovation did not conform to an experimental blueprint whose every detail was thought out in advance. The articulate aim of the director and his immediate circle was to do a better job of treatment as well as teaching in the hospital. Accepting the challenge of the potential importance of every human interaction in the total context of the community, the director and his principal collaborators allowed themselves to reappraise every feature of the social process in which staff, patients, relatives, and other participants were involved.

They reexamined the physical resources, social assets, and liabilities of the YPI, conducting the examination with an overriding goal that gained definition as the search proceeded. The conception of shared responsibility of doctor and patient rendered unacceptable the traditional roles of powerful authority and dependent patient.

All the strategies employed by senior physicians, residents, nurses, and every other responsible participant in the situation were appraised in the light of the clarified conception of the objectives of the total operation. From the beginning of his contact with the new hospital, the patient was involved in a program modified to challenge him to recognize his opportunity—and hence his obligation—to contribute to his own improvement and to the health of others. *Gradually it became more evident that the implications of this goal were more searching for all concerned than had originally been calculated. If the patients were to accept responsibility for a joint power position and to avoid either rebelliousness or chronic dependency, they must be presented with models of joint, responsible power participation and rewarded for their incorporation of this style of life.*

Clearly *political* change was required: nothing less than the transformation of an authoritarian hospital into a therapeutic community in which power was genuinely shared. The subsequent innovation of power-sharing practices was initially disruptive and eventually reintegrative of every aspect of hospital life. In reply to the growing demand that behavior conform to aspiration, all roles and operations gradually assume new form and direction. Among the many institutions revitalized by the vast social transformation of our time, the psychiatric hospital occupies a conspicuous place. In the hospital, as in every other institution that has come into the domain of change, the truly revolutionary step is to achieve the discipline required to transpose the ideology of democracy from a profession of faith to a way of life.

Appendix

These transcripts are made available for the purpose of providing comparative material that may be useful in conducting further individual cross checks on the categories employed in the present analysis.

YPI Patient-Staff Meeting December 16, 1957

BETTY 1: Where's Dr. Fleck?

DICK (patient) 2: He won't be able to be here today.

BETTY 3: Why?

DICK 4: He's dead.

BETTY 5: He's dead? (Pause. People continue to enter the room and sit down.) Hi, Mel, Mel (noise obscures) . . . came to school with me. (pause)

DR. BENNETT 6: Our new patient is here today, for those who don't know her, Edna Edwards (patient).

BETTY 7: She's going to the . . . with me. (pause)

CHAIRMAN (Dr. Rosenberg) 8: Keith?

KEITH 9: Yes?

CHAIRMAN 10: Did you raise your hand, ah?

KEITH 11: I didn't raise my hand. I rather see you sittin' up there 'n Fleck but ah I wouldn't get that excited. (laughter)

UNIDENTIFIED PARTICIPANT 12: That's just tough luck. (pause—laughter) That's the building. (pause)

MIKE 13: (mumbling) Probably one of us is going to talk.

BOB 14: . . . to say . . . (pause)

DICK 15: I just wanna say since everybody's moved off the second floor . . . that the place is pretty depressing. (pause)

CHAIRMAN 16: Keith moved down today. Kent went back up. (name obscured by noise) left last week. He moved down toward the end of last week.

KEITH 17: Sorry, I'm going to smoke cigarettes. (pause—some snickers)

CHAIRMAN 18: Lee?[1]

DR. LONG 19: This is my second Christmas I will be around here and ahm there are similarities in some respects between last year and

1. The chairman addresses Dr. Long by his first name.

this year. Everybody seemed to me at that time at to be rather undecided whether they get depressed or not—or depressed since some people succeeded to go home, they tried very much to do so. Other people ah didn't yet quite know what they should do and how they should handle it. If I remember correctly we hadn't had many meetings around that time to discuss this . . . (cough) . . . I was wondering if it wouldn't be something very worth while to talk about.

VIC 20: Well that's the I think, the most ah depressing thing ah to have to ask to go home for Christmas ah to put you in-in-in a position where you're denied. Really one of the most basic things of our culture, and if if we can't make our—some sort of home here, if one can call it that. It's very hard (voice rises in register) to ask to go home ah for Christmas. Because it is ah, it's ah and it's something that I, I think we all much rather had to act out about it—say to hell with the staff er other than just ask. At least that's how I f—I feel.

DICK 21: Well, there's one other—other thing that may steer off the subject, but ah the last meeting up here impressed me as being— showing a great deal of resistance on the part of the patients who were—saying—about themselves and it seems like, so far I've seen two different kinds of resistance where everybody starts laughing at various things, the meeting kind of falls apart at the seams or else nobody says anything. And ah I was interested in what happened over the weekend on the second floor after we had a meeting these past weeks. The place was ab-abnormally quiet—no noise at all.

EDWARD 22: Yesterday I went up on the second floor between the hours of 11 and noon and the thing that impressed me so much that I turned to the aide and spoke to him about it for a minute. The idea that the people up there just sit away and sit away and sit away . . .

NEAL 23: Have it a little louder, please.

EDWARD 24: Excuse me, I said yesterday when I went upstairs on the second floor I was impressed with the idea—it wasn't just because yesterday was a quiet mood up there, but the way the hospital allows the patient to sit away and sit away and sit away, and I can repeat that for the next fifteen hours, and each one would be synonomous with, say, the amount of hours that I've had to sit away. And I often wonder what is the wisdom, Dr. Rosenberg, in allowing and letting people just sit there in the same environment, ever continuously. Now I know you're going to say to me there's O.T. and there's checkers, (someone laughs) and there's gin rummy, and then there's O.T. and there's checkers, and there's gin rummy. But my impression of the hospital is for many people a kind of reinstitution back into ah the going business of living and it's just not therapy that does that. And when Dr. Long mentions about depression of the nature of the floor around this time, I think we can tie the whole conversation in together, and I'd certainly like to know more of the—say the clinical reasons as to why the hospital makes the patient upstairs sit away and sit away and sit away.

CHAIRMAN 25: What patients did you have in mind? (pause)

EDWARD 26: Well, for example, Adam. For example, Frank Field (patient).

UNIDENTIFIED WOMAN PARTICIPANT 27: Sandra, she goes to O.T. and she knits.

EDWARD 28: Dick.

UNIDENTIFIED WOMAN PARTICIPANT 29: He writes. (pause)

CHAIRMAN 30: Bob.

BOB 31: I, I found that when I went up there yesterday about the same time Edward did, they're just taken in by the atmosphere. Because I didn't—I couldn't do anything. I could just sit there. I-I tried to instigate some ah ah some activities, you know, somebody want to go down to the gym or something and everybody was feeling so depressed nobody wanted to do anything. And so while I was up there I couldn't do anything but sit. Now Edward tried the same thing. He came in and he tried to liven things up with a joke and ah tried to talk to people and—nothing! Ah—it's just a—very depressing atmosphere up there.

CHAIRMAN 32: Howard.

HOWARD 33: I was just wondering if it ah if it's really the hospital's responsibility to take someone and push them into doing whatever they're interested in. (pause)

CHAIRMAN 34: Neal.

NEAL 35: (very loudly) Ah Edward knows more about this than I do, but it seems to me that ah all of us on the outside have had some trouble—I call it a driven quality of trying to do too much, and finally the outside got too much for us. And I think that there's a time for action and reflection. And one thing about the second floor, it may depress first floor patients, but that's just too bad. I think ah second floor patients do what's right for them and most of the time it's just taking it easy. And I think playing cards and listening to music, and I know my scrabble games with Frank, even though I haven't concentrated, I think it's all a part of just letting down and being able to talk easily, not only to doctors but to nurses and relate to other patients, to relate well so you can get these things out in therapy, and then the first floor's a different situation. Ah, all this talk about opening up the second floor, I—Dr. Olson is hot for it, I

wonder about it. I think it's maybe the place for—reflection and taking it easy. Now Edward must know as a combat soldier ah knows how "R. and R." works. And I think that's what the second floor is.
CHAIRMAN 36: Fred.
FRED 37: I think, Neal, that in a sense you've made a generalization at the beginning of what you said. Ah, it is only true for yourself and for a few other patients up there. I think that really it isn't so much a, a question of forcing people to do what they're interested in. I admit that sometimes when you're up there, it's hard to find something that's interesting, but rather it's a matter of forcing—stopping them from doing what they're interested in. I think when Vic was speaking about going home, this was one of those things.
CHAIRMAN 38: Vic.
VIC 39: Ah well, outside of insulting, I thought Neal's ah defense of the, the second floor was just fine, because I know an awful lot of us have been interacting in ah the last week and it hasn't been exactly on the outside. We haven't been running around—it doesn't seem too exciting. But, ah to me personally, the friendships that I've been allowed by time and by the second floor setup to ah understand ah has been tremendously thrilling and much more thrilling than that in doing, than any action, that I've ever done in my life. Ah and the second floor is a place for that—for sitting down and just contemplating the subject—first of all . . .
CHAIRMAN 40: Dick.
VIC 41: Witha . . .
DICK 42: I know the only thing I thought about what Neal said is that ah it's more or less a completely individual thing—and it-it doesn't in any way re-reflect what I think about the second floor. And I think ah as far as Neal goes, most of it is an act too.
NEAL 43: Can't hear you.
DICK 44: I said most of what you did was an act, what you said is an act.
CHAIRMAN 45: Mike.
MIKE 46: I'd like to bring up two points in this. I don't see why we're confining our remarks about patients on the second floor, since there are patients on the first floor who sit, myself included, Greta (patient), ah, Mrs. Hill (patient). The second thing is that when I first went to [another psychiatric hospital], I met a girl up there who continually sat and said nothing, which was terribly disturbing to me. I-I I went to her one day and I said "Why do you sit?" and she said, "I just sit." And it seems to be some kind of a pattern that all people have. They sit and recline in their treatment. (Much

coughing and noise in the group.) And I noticed at [that hospital] there is no—effort to push and, yet this girl, while I was there, came out of this and became active through her own efforts, not through the efforts of the staff or someone, no one guided her. This was ah something that she had to go through.

CHAIRMAN 47: Keith.

KEITH 48: When I think about the situation on the second floor—I just moved out today, but up until that time ah it strikes me, there's —the number of patients that are ah they wanna become active and wanna live as close to a normal life as they can, and a number of patients that want to sit away, like Edward says, ah I think are about evenly divided, but I certainly can—but correct me if I'm wrong, but as far as I—I know, I think ah it's just about half and half up there. Half the people just wanna sit around and half of 'em wanna live as close to the normal life as they can. I think for the people who wanna sit around, they got it made up there, they can just goof off. But I think for the people that wanna, you know ah, act and ah do something with their lives, or try to, I don't think there is enough to do and I think, ah, the hospital might take some activity, like Howard says, if ah, you know, do somethin' that they're interested in. I don't know how much they're, you know they should be pushed. And I know also that a lot of resentment is gonna be incurred by ah pushing them to the, to ah, you know, any degree. That's somethin' that ah the staff would have to decide. But it does strike me that they could do a lot more for the people. I'm thinkin' of Fred, I'm thinkin' of Frank Field, and I'm thinkin' of ah a couple of 'em like that—Dick here, that ah wanna, you know, do things 'n go places and so on. I think that ah this hospital could be more for them. I dunno exactly how. (pause)

DR. LONG 49: I would like to go back to Vic's comment, to say how very difficult it is to—difficult for patients who go home, that it's so "natural" that Christmas is coming up, and one is joining one's family. I think this may be quite difficult or extremely humiliating. But ahm I found it is, perhaps, a lot more difficult for us the other way ah to say that despite the fact that Christmas is obviously a holiday symbol, that may ah really not feel very comfortable with our home. We may go home but we don't really feel like it because we know that it's going to be something that is not exactly pleasure. And I think these are the problems which are much more disturbing than that the hospital says you are not supposed to go or you are supposed to go. I wonder what some of the others feel about this. (pause)

EDWARD 50: Well, that's exactly my point when I—what Dr. Long said it can be spread to about any situation from practically anybody here, and that is, granted that, that there is that friction between you and—there is a friction between you and your home. Okay. So nature makes you pay a price for it. And the way I look at it is, how much of a price do you finally have to pay in the form of living hours where the hospital then literally just sits you down. Then why don't they have a more active life here? That's what I mean by sittin' away for hours. I know that—all seconds in one form or another, we've all had troubles and problems with mother, father, sister and brother and et cetera, but why should you be so eternally confined on the second floor, and why not make the environment more active just in New Haven as a general rule?

FRED 51: I know this argument I agree with. I've stated it myself many times here. But I sort of think it's a hopeless argument in a sense, because nothing's really ever been done, nothing probably ever will be. I think that the staff has made up its mind in its own way, sometime in the past, and it's sort of a senseless thing to bother to talk about it because as long as you're up there you're gonna just rot and that's it, period.

CHAIRMAN 52: Bob?

BOB 53: Ah maybe Fred's, Fred said ah there's nothing to be done about it, I think this is a more or less individual thing with each patient. Ah as a group you can't say, well, the second floor group should be allowed to do this as a group or that as a group, or something else. But I think when a patient wants to do something or two or three patients want to do something, I think if it's at all possible, that the opportunity shouldn't be denied them. I, in the past ah week or so ah have come across this myself even on the first floor, everybody gets it. Ah I don't think it's just on the second floor. Neal says he likes the idea of being able to sit down and collect his thoughts an-and sort of be at peace with the world and ah whereas Fred likes to get out. Well Fred is getting out, right now, he's been going out, he's-he's allowed out with another patient. He's been going out to movies and so on, and I think he went out just a little while ago with another patient. Ah (clears throat) I was asked to a party ah I don't know if should bring this up or not, but I was asked to a party, ah Saturday night—for Saturday night, and ah when I spoke to my doctor about it, he said ah he thought it would be ah, okay, ah, the only problem would be that I'm allowed out with two other patients, I'd have to find a couple of other patients that would ah want to go with me. Well, ah, this I did, and then ah later that evening it came back to me that the staff had voted against it, or-or had discussed it and it was decided that it would be better at this time if I didn't go because ah, this party was at ah the Children's Home, ah, and it was phrased as "inter-institutional activity" to me, and they didn't want this at this time. Well, I don't know why. And I don't know why they came to this conclusion that I couldn't go and why the opportunity to do this—to go out and go to a party, meet people and dance and have fun—was denied me. Ah I'd like to know ah, at this time if the staff has any ideas why this was. But ah the whole thing is that it's an individual thing, I don't think you can say th-that a whole group but fer—the opportunity comes for the individual to do something I think ah it shouldn't be denied them, if it's possible. And I'd like to get a couple of ideas right in this meeting, if possible, as to why I couldn't go to this party.

CHAIRMAN 54: Did you discuss it with Dr. Ingraham (resident physician)?[2]

BOB 55: Ah I didn't discuss it with him, no, I just got the decision, ah, this was it. But he's usually pretty vague with me anyway ah . . . when I try to get him to—the subject changes or else it just comes out, well, no explanation, but the just the fact that well, "At this time we don't feel that it's right," this is what I get and with my therapist, Dr. Judd, he usually isn't at the, at the meetings—staff meetings and usually doesn't know what it is, he doesn't know the procedures and why the—why the decisions are made. I'd like to have an idea. It may be a little bit easier for me to ah resign myself to staying in, ah, if I could see the staff's point of view on this, even if I don't agree with it, at least if I can see what they were thinking. Because I've been asked to go again next week and ah . . .

DR. LONG 56: Bob?

BOB 57: Mmmhm.

DR. LONG 58: What kind of a party is this?

BOB 59: Mmm?

---

2. Dr. Ingraham, one of the residents, is Bob's "administrative doctor," and Dr. Judd, a clinical psychologist on the hospital staff, is Bob's therapist. Whenever a patient in the hospital has a therapist other than a resident (a psychiatrist or psychoanalyst practicing in the community, or a psychiatrist, psychologist or social worker on the hospital staff other than a resident), the patient is also assigned a resident as his "administrator." The "administrative doctor" writes any orders for medications or "privileges" (going out of the hospital, shifting from one ward to another, etc.), meets with the patient himself regularly, and brings up any issues concerning the patient in staff meetings and other hospital forums. Patients are only assigned psychiatrists practicing privately in the community when it is expected that they will leave the hospital soon and then continue their therapy with this "outside doctor."

DR. LONG 60: What kind of a party is this?

BOB 61: It's a dance. Ah at the Children's Home they have ...

UNIDENTIFIED PARTICIPANT 62: (in undertone) Children ... (Whispering in the group obscures Bob's next words on the recording.)

BOB 63: ... and there's a girl at the Children's Home, I guess it's been about seven weeks now, I-I met her about seven weeks ago and ah I became pretty friendly with her, and ah she asked me if I'd go. And I asked her if she'd go to the movie with me and ah, well, both of these things were out of the question after the meeting.[3] Ah but people from town go, some of the boys there ask girls from the town, and so on. I just couldn't see any reason why, why I shouldn't've been allowed to go. She was disappointed, and I was very disappointed, because doing something like this means an awful lot to me, going to a party and ah meeting people, and dancing and having fun. It-it's-it's something I haven't done in three months. (pause)

DR. LONG 64: If I may just add, I asked you this question because I hadn't been here on Friday and I didn't know ah what the situation was. (pause)

BETTY 65: Bob?

BOB 66: (laughing) Yeah?

BETTY 67: Which—is this Children's Home, in New Haven, or in Philadelphia, or where, because once I went to a nursery school called the Children's Home—where I met the doctor who sent me here a long, long time ago. Which Children's Home is this, Bob? (laughter)

ADAM 68: It's Philadelphia.

BOB 69: It's in New Haven, Betty, I don't know if the girls there are ...

BETTY 70: Well, it—well it's not the one where I met [my doctor]. (Pause)

DR. OLSON 71: I'd like to ask ah a few more questions Bob, could you ah ah possibly give us some information about this? It seems that in the Children's Home is expected to be a rather a young group of ah people there, ah, you—how old is this girl and ah (much noise, talking, and laughter in the group throughout the following exchange.)

BOB 72: The girl, the girl that asked me, the girl that asked me is 13—the girl said it's an orphanage. There are girls there younger I suppose, and there are girls there, older. Keith ah, I think met some of the girls at the roller skating rink ...

---

3. Refers to the staff meeting about which Dr. Ingraham had told Bob, at which it was decided that Bob could not attend the dance.

KEITH 73: Yeah.

BOB 74: There was one ah . . .

KEITH 75: The one that asked ya is good lookin'.

BOB 76: She is pretty. (Keith laughs) The one that Keith chased before was slightly younger.

KEITH 77: Yeah.

BOB 78: A couple of the girls there are sixteen, seventeen and eighteen, the girls that were at roller skating rink.

KEITH 79: But that one's thirteen (laughs).

BOB 80: But this is no difference . . . the general group I associate with in my age, when I go there it is within . . .

KEITH 81: Right.

BOB 82: . . . my age ah by two or three years each way.

KEITH 83: There, There-there are a lot of ah—I-I'm laughin' because the girl was thirteen and sh-she is good lookin'. There are—there are ah, there a lot of ah it's because they're an abstract picture, they range from ah, I guess somethin' like thirteen to about seventeen or eighteen. I think there was a, a girl there who was seventeen or eighteen, that-that blonde you wish you could know.

BOB 84: That blonde is twenty-seven.

KEITH 85: Twenty-seven. (pause, laughter)

UNIDENTIFIED PARTICIPANT 86: A fossil!

BOB 87: I think they range all the way up to twenty-one, because it is an orphange, I think they go right up to legal age.

CHAIRMAN 88: I think it ranges up to sixteen, Bob. (Talking and whispering in the group obscures Bob's next words.)

BOB 89: . . . sixteen, because, because ah . . .

KEITH 90: They allow 'em at sixteen here.

BOB 91: Katey spoke of two of the girls as being there ah and ah . . . a couple of the guys that were there at the center, ah, from the center, were oldern' that.

KEITH 92: How old was the small one in the purple sweater? (laughter)

BOB 93: Pardon?

KEITH 94: The small one in the purple sweater?

BOB 95: You asked me . . . in the purple sweater. (pause)

ADAM 96: Well—it seems to me that ah when Dr. Long asked his question and when Dr. Olson asked his question to Bob that there ah that they're—were—perfectly ah natural good questions, but ah I think when the group—when Dr. Olson ah asked Bob that—anyway what I want to say is that ah when the group ah laughed, it ah . . . it made Bob, or it made ah it made Bob feel ah ill at ease, I think, and therefore—it ah . . . (pause) . . . I don't think the group should have laughed at that. And ah . . .

GLORIA 97: Well, I know that Dr. Ingraham told the meeting . . .

ADAM 98: . . . and ah . . . (laughter)

GLORIA 99: Oh, excuse me. Ah, can I talk when he finishes?

ADAM 100: . . . and I think that—well, I don't think that the group should ah (laughter) should've laughed.

GLORIA 101: Well, ah I know that I have been complaining to the staff about coming up to patient-staff because I felt that I wanted to get—when I wanted to get home from school, I wanted to go into my room instead of going to patient-staff, if I wanted to. And the door is locked to me and I can't go into ah I guess I have strict orders from Len [hospital janitor] or something not to let me into—into Cedar One when I want to, because it is compulsory to go to staff. And from this discussion I can certainly understand why it is compulsory to go to staff, that it certainly helps all the patients a great deal and I-I wouldn't miss this for the world.

ADAM 102: Yeah. (pause. snickering)

EDWARD 103: Ah, Bob, you said that your doctor discussed it with the staff. Were you at the meeting, Dr. Ingraham—I mean, Dr. Olson, when it was was discussed?

DR. OLSON 104: Yes, I was.

EDWARD 105: And no—information then, apparently, was revealed about the age of the people.

DR. OLSON 106: Ah, I dare say that ah my question was ah just to bring this point out.

EDWARD 107: Which meant that it was discussed.

DR. INGRAHAM 108: Perhaps I can add some information to this, ah, (clears throat) just go back over it, I think ah the first point is that ah had Bob gone to this dance by himself, this would have been a new order for him and ah this was something that we did not discucuss, neither Bob nor I nor the staff, so that there was a question of his going out with several other people, ah, the question of-of ah three people from the Institute going to the Children's Home for a social activity would have involved, I think, ah what would've amounted to an inter-institutional ah activity, ah, even though it may not seem that way. I think if a group of people here goes there, this would be a matter of policy which had not been discussed ah, as far as we know, by the Children's Home, and we don't know how they would feel about it. Ah I would also like to add that ah ah Bob gave me to believe that the girl's age was about fifteen, so that ah Dr. Olson's question I think had some note.

BOB 109: I told everybody what her age was.

FRED 110: I think this is the usual fare we hear around this place whenever you ask to do anything. I think it comes out in different ways, one way or the other. (laughing) I think it's so stereotyped, as a matter of fact I've said that when I come to this meeting, before I come I know what's gonna be sp-spoken about. I mean it's so stereotyped in a sense. Ah in a sense, I had something of the same answer when I ah asked to go home for Christmas, it was a little different ah for variety, I suppose—in the answer that you gave me.

KEITH 111: What could be the harm of a couple of patients from here going to that party? I mean you can throw around words like, you know, inter-institutional activities, this and that. I don't see where there'd be any harm to it. I really don't. I mean so that—I mean w-why would the two institutions have to contact each other and make a federal case out of it, why couldn't just three people go? I think the thing is—Bob, is it somethin' like an open house generally speaking?

BOB 112: Yeah, it's in ah the people there invite the people that they ah, the girls invite their boyfriends, or boys that they would like to invite, and the boys do the same.

KEITH 113: I don't see, I can't see where any harm would come of it although I don't know everything about it. But ah I think this oughta be be discussed by the staff, I'll say that. I don't think it oughta be just let go at that. If there are enough people that ah care to go.

MIKE 114: I-I find myself at this time being rather resentful against the staff, that they should—need to resort to some sort of ah mystic ah formula, well the interrrr-institutional something-or-other . . . I think . . .

GLORIA 115: Yeah, what's that mean?

KEITH 116: I don't know.

MIKE 117: . . . it'd be terribly frustrating to me, even though it-it's not my problem.

UNIDENTIFIED GIRL 118: What is it?

UNIDENTIFIED GIRL 119: The Children's Home.

MIKE 120: It has been my problem such as the business with the, with the nurses. This ah supposed ah inter-institutional or something, no one has ever gotten down to the point, you know, of saying, well, I might myself be hurt if I were to be rejected by one of these girls, or ah I might ah not really know how, after having spent ten months here, how I should ah act in the society of-of women. None of this is ever brought out. Just some junk about fraternization or something. (pause)

CHAIRMAN 121: Dr. Olson.

DR. OLSON 122: It would seem here ah that for instance where the advisory committee might have been useful, I wonder ah what the patients do think about this, whether they think it would be a good idea, aside from the considerations here, it seems that ah, ah there has been no suggestion about if it would be a good idea—a good way of, ah, dealing with this as a problem. I-I think that ah Mike has ah has accused the, the staff of ah hiding behind a smoke screen of ah gobbledegook ah . . .

HOWARD 123: What? (Mike laughs)

DR. OLSON 124: Ah, but what ah suggestions do you have? What do you—do you think that it would be a good idea for ah, for Bob to ah to go to this, this dance, and then why?

MEL (patient) 125: Well, I think, I look at it this way, going back to ah Mike's point, I don't think that—I think it varies among the individual [sic] ah whether ten months in the—or ten months in here in the hospital would ah affect his relationship with one of the— (pause—whispering)

CHAIRMAN 126: Mike.

MIKE 127: Ah, I don't have a suggestion as to whether or not Bob should go to this dance, but I do have a very strange feeling that if it were me I would go to my doctor and say doctor, can I do this, that's the problem I'm facing. I'm asking to go out and fraternize with women and suddenly I'm having another problem that is not really mine shoved into my face that someone will say, no, you'll—you'll, my psychiatrist, for instance, who has not done this to me, but it could happen, would say, "Well, because we feel you shouldn't fraternize." This—the minute that that it is said to me, I-I say to myself, "God damn the authority that should—that should so confuse the issue that I'm hung! I can't get out from underneath. All I want to do is go out and instead they throw things at me."

CHAIRMAN 128: Howard.

HOWARD 129: Ah I don't know that they're putting a problem that you don't ah, Mike? I don't know that-that they're adding problems to you, I think that ah when you don't look at ah everything that is involved ah and they suggest someth—a possibility of something else being involved in this, I don't think that is adding problems, to use the phrase, or anyway, I think they should be thoroughly looked into rather than just—okay, you say it's a problem, to hell with it.

TOM 130: Well, with the, with what (clears throat) Dr. Ingraham was concerned about, about the ah attitude of the authorities at the orphanage about whether these patients from here should come is quite important. I imagine Bob could understand that, and I imagine that Dr. Ingraham could contact the people at the orphanage, ask them, and then it seems very simple. I don't quite see why Bob is so upset by it. It's just a . . .

GLORIA 131: In-instead of the patients discussing every aspect, obviously, Dr. Ingraham and Dr. Olson have an absolute bevy of ideas as to why Bob can't ah go to this and perhaps they could say the real reason behind it instead of inter-institution which is a big fancy word which doesn't mean a damn thing, it's something that perhaps both of them are institutions, I don't see how that has any bearing on what Bob is trying to get across at all.

KEITH 132: Hear, hear.

CHAIRMAN 133: Fred?

FRED 134: I was just going to say that I would agree with Mike wholeheartedly. (pause)

CHAIRMAN 135: Bob?

BOB 136: I was tryin' to ah—I agree with Mike, I-I know he—this is what I'm tryin' to get across, this thing he says about being hung. Ah I got two other things now, I'm—when I go down to the canteen[4] I've gotta go with one other patient. This is—what's it for, why can't I go down alone? Ah the-the authorities—it's got me stumped. If I wa—I want to go down to the canteen and get a cup of coffee or-or-or some chewing gum or something and I can't find another patient, well I can't go down. Ah when I wanna go out, I gotta go with two other patients, ah, if I can't find two other patients that wanna go out and go to see this movie, I wanna go out and get a hamburger, I can't go out. Ah, technically I have privileges, when you come right down to it, I don't.

MIKE 137: You know this, and I-I ah asked why I'm so affected, I—having my family for twenty years or so—they'll refuse to allow me to do something and not give me any substantiation as to why I can't do it. It's terribly frustrating to sit down and to continually punish myself for something that is not and never has been so. It's—like someone's pulling at me and o-or throwing stones at me without —any reasoning. Ah, I'm—I resent having a doctor say something to me that has no substantiation, that is pure unadulterated mysticism. I'm supposed to sit here and understand what some gook said to me—(laughter) . . . why should I have to, what's the necessity of—of having a psychiatrist say to me, well, ah you s—your head is square. How am I supposed to figure out this? What does this mean in-in

4. The "canteen" is a lounge for medical students containing cigarette, coffee and candy vending machines on a basement level of the building which houses both the medical school and the hospital.

terms of me? And you mean I'm the only person in this hospital who has this resentment of having doctors say, "Well, in time, son, you'll be fine." What does this mean? It's a lot of crap.

CHAIRMAN 138: Kent.

KENT 139: Well, ah, (clears throat) the fact that this, what Bob is driving at, his situation has improved ah so much in the past weeks, it never seems to enter into the Bob's calculations, the fact that he's allowed out with ah two other patients is only, only one point of view which is that he's not allowed out with one other patient. It's never looked at from the point of view that he now ought to go out unaccompanied, the fact that he can go down to the canteen with one other patient, there's no doubt that he can't go down alone instead of ah, not at all. This has come up over and over again.

DR. LONG 140: I just wanted some of the points of my thinking around the area which Bob e-expresses much more clearly, that it would be better for all of us ah to have the full trust of other people I think what it amounts to, our conversation here, why wouldn't we "trust" quotes, unquote, Bob to do certain things or another patient to do some other things. But ah I would think that in our society this works a little bit differently. If somebody has not behaved or ah to work out his relationship with other people in a fashion to ah stimulate trust, then a hospital like ours which takes the responsibilities for some . . .

CHAIRMAN 141: Lee, just a moment. Bob I-I think you ought to be listening to this. I think it's directed at you.

BOB 142: I-I heard it, I heard it.

DR. LONG 143: . . . for someone who, who had a problem in a society of this kind, and then we take over this responsibility, ah, where we have to be sure to give him a fighting chance, that is when he is here, it wouldn't be correct of us, I think, to allow something which we know he had difficulty in handling, because that's not giving a fighting chance to anybody. That's cruel.

FRED 144: I-I, I've often gotten the feeling, I think that in a sense I would agree with Bob in a lot of places, but I think it's kind of interesting that he always seems to be the focal point for giving more privileges. In other words, it is—or this is often the case, I've noticed, and it seems to me, for example, when I bring up something, I bring up I want to get a job, everybody laughs. I bring up the idea of maybe the idea of maybe I'd like to go home for ah Christmas, I get ah sour faces. I—it seems to me as if I'm sort of stewing in my own juice (laughter) so to speak, and ah like—I'd like to have some of these things, I really would. I have just only asked for them for about six months, that's all, a short period. And ah what's that, you've had t-two and a half years, after all you're gonna be around this place for another five, ah might as well learn to live with it, you know. A great place.

CHAIRMAN 145: Mike.

MIKE 146: Well, I'm quite aware that this hospital attempts to take responsibility for the patients, and in doing so, they place on me rules that are designed to protect six year olds, and I'm not a six-year old. I'm twenty-seven years old, and there's a hell of a big difference. And I know that other patients resent this. I know other patients are having a hell of a hard time even after ten months of sitting down and saying I'm in a place that has rules designed for, for six year olds! Y-you can go to fantastic extremes as doctors of protecting the patient. We have to sit here and take this until eventually, as I am today, exploding, I've had it! I hate these rules! I'm not a six year old! However much you can say, "Well, we have rules, they protect you," you can be complacent about this and you can go on being complacent, but we are the people who suffer because of it! Hell, I don't even have a diaper—after all these years. (laughter)

ZEKE 147: Well, I think the example that, that . . . Bob brought up, ah, if you think about it a little more, ah I don't think he was being deprived of any ah great thing here, because there are a lot of reasons why ah his going to the orphanage ah ah might not have been a very good thing, and I can think of a lot of practical reasons. One is that ahm, I know he asked me if I wanted to go with him, and, and the things that came to my mind were, I didn't know anything about these people I ah—they probably would be a lot younger than me. I didn't know whether the people at the orphanage would, would, would like me to be there o-o-or resent my being there. And ah I suppose . . .

CHAIRMAN 148: Howard.

HOWARD 149: I was just, I was just wondering ah could you accept the rules when you were six?

GLORIA 150: Oi!

UNIDENTIFIED GIRL 151: Oh, (laughing) my God.

MIKE 152: I don't remember whether I could accept the rules when I was six. I do remember that when I was six years old, for some reason or other I had some kind of an aggression and I started throwing stones at people, and my mother, in an effort to teach me not to throw stones, gave me a large pile of stones and said, "throw them at me until I'm bloody." And I did it. This when I was six. The fact still remains that while here I can recognize quite fully that there are some patients whom it's necessary to protect, but it does not hold true for me. And it doesn't hold true for such people as—as Mr. Newton (patient), whom I know resents these things. Mr. Ives, I feel, resents this. He is a man now and there are some things that you just don't have to go to your doctor and (hits table) repeatedly, repeatedly, (hits table) consult him, say, "Doctor, can I go out alone and buy myself a—a hairbrush." (hits table) This is fantastic!

CHAIRMAN 153: Dick.

DICK 154: Well, I just don't see what's so unclear about, inter-inter-institutional activity. I don't think it's—too hard a word—for people to understand.

CHAIRMAN 155: Gregor.

GREGOR 156: Well, I was just going to say one thing that seems to have been overlooked here, a lot of people feel that Bob has been ah given a dirty deal here. Well, and he's come out and—he didn't talk to his doctor openly about it, so that his doctor believed he was going out with a fifteen year old girl who was a thirteen year old girl. And I think if that's the case, he wasn't being very open with his doctor, he doesn't have any ah grievance.

HOWARD 157: Ah, I think ah a person can learn to live within the limitations that ah is—are set for him, that there is more of a possibility of these limitations being widened. If you can't accept it aaaa it doesn't seem that ah he should get them.

MIKE 158: You know I'm rather angry about this. About three months ago, Mrs. ah Morton (closed ward chief nurse), refused something to Howard and he got so terribly angry and resentful because of this. This is completely forgotten, this resentment. The same thing happened to me last night . . .

UNIDENTIFIED PARTICIPANT 159: What?

MIKE 160: Mrs. Ordway [nurse] sticks to the rules to the extent (hits table) that its—she says to me, (mimicking) "You can't go into the kitchen for anything you like. You're a six year old." And I'm not (hits table) a six year old! (pounds table) The-these rules a-are taarrue! (hits table) (laughter)

UNIDENTIFIED MAN 161: It's true. It must be true. (pause)

EDWARD 162: Well, it's very easy to see, in reviewing this, how the camp got divided. And I'd like to point out the position. And I think that this nomenclature will do us all a lot of good. (someone hits table) I think you used your fist. (laughter) This weekend for me was not two-hundred per cent . . .

UNIDENTIFIED PARTICIPANT 163: Only 100. (laughter)

EDWARD 164: . . . so it's very possible that in coming back to here I had a kind of a sore spot in me, and when I went upstairs Sunday I immediately felt it all over again, all that denial, as I saw everybody else sitting around, and possibly that's why I brought it up. But then those people who are much sorer within themselves, I don't mean only in the sense of angry but a sore that just hurts, 'cause they have had the opportunity then, as this conversation evolved into the idea of permission, expounded pretty heavily on the idea that they couldn't have anything because of the environment around them. However Dr. Long then said was that it would be a very poor action on the hospital's part to allow a patient to have the complete freedom while he was relearning and re-seeing how to go about and get something for himself. Now to end it, the differences then between Howard and myself and a lot of other people here, who possibly are more openly hostile, is that Howard has experienced something, I think, Mike, that you haven't yet, and that is he has begun to feel for himself.

GLORIA 165: Ohh no!

EDWARD 166: Just begun. So maybe he can bank on the quality of a little more relaxation and have the quality of a little more tolerance.

CHAIRMAN 167: Neal, did you?

NEAL 168: Ah, I was just going to say when the age thirteen was brought up, we all will remember Elizabeth Taylor in "National Velvet" . . . in particular captured the Nation's heart at thirteen. (laughter) Now I think this is not funny! (stern voiced) If it's true. Ah, I think Bob has a desire to help people and there're no people more helpless than orphans. And ah I don't know anything about the details, but I'd just let that be kept in mind.

CHAIRMAN 169: We'll continue on Thursday.

YPI Patient-Staff Meeting of June 16, 1958

CHAIRMAN (Dr. Fleck) 1: Rose.

ROSE 2: You always say the meetings are at two-thirty, you can make sure it starts at three, and then 'till quarter of four . . . (door slams), now say it starts at two-fifteen to make sure it starts at two-thirty.

GREGOR 3: It seems to me that it's just the first floor patients that are late, so the first floor nurse ought go around and tell people to come up early. (pause)

CHAIRMAN 4: The first floor nurse is still busy rounding them up, so she can't speak about it. Ah, Mrs. Morton, you want to say something for her.

MRS. MORTON 5: Well, I would say, if I were on first floor, they're all capable of telling time, and they all know that this is meeting day, and they should get here themselves. (pause)

ROSE 6: Do we have to wait to start the meeting before everybody comes in? (door slams)

CHAIRMAN 7: Well—it's a difficult question, really. (pause. more people come in) We're talking about why people are late, Abner—and what we can do about it.

ABNER 8: That's interesting. (laughter)

CHAIRMAN 9: Can you tell us why you were late?

ABNER 10: Well, ah, I forgot what time it was. There's nobody around to tell me. (laughter)

BETTY 11: What about your watch? (pause, someone clears throat)

ABNER 12: It's fast.

ROSE 13: Can I bring something up? As I got it, as far as staff meeting was concerned—because Friday I saw my folks before I got permission to Saturday, because I took off—I am completely restricted to second floor, because they don't trust me. (Voices are heard down the hallway as a group of patients approaches the conference room.) I explained this, or tried to, the few minutes I had to see Dr. Olson this morning, and I tried to explain it to Dr. Bennett. But Saturday when I was out on the terrace, except for the time that I was playing the piano, I was rather tense, and a number of other people were. There's no way I could get any relief from it. So I asked Dr. Bennett if I could go in special[1] for the afternoon. I talked to him about it and told him why, and he completely ignored me and said no. So then I just walked out the door, with a student nurse following me, and I told her that I couldn't take it any more, that I had asked to go in special, and my request hadn't been granted. I told her I had telegraphed my punches hours before in asking. And then—the past few days when I've thought about it, I realized I kinda caused some trouble on Saturday for the student nurse, and myself and my family. But I'm wondering, did Dr. Bennett not listen, not put me in special because I was supposed to exercise control myself, or was I just supposed to—be tense, watch other people be tense, and get no help whatsoever? (pause) (The conference room door opens and more latecomers enter.) I certainly asked for it, and I meant that in both ways. (pause. noise in hall)

1. "Special" is the isolation area on the closed ward. It consists of four individual rooms, the doors of which may be locked, a central lounge with overstuffed chairs and television, and a hallway. The area was renovated in 1953; this included air conditioning, installing a system for piping music into the individual rooms, and tile murals on the walls of the rooms. After the renovation, residents began sleeping in "special" often during summer nights on duty.

CHAIRMAN 14: Anybody here can help Rose? (pause)

ROSE 15: I wish Dr. Bennett or one of the doctors would tell me why I couldn't go into special for a couple of afternoons, a couple of hours that afternoon, instead of having to take off to look for some relief. I haven't—except for Monday night when I took off, until Saturday I hadn't been out of this hospital in almost five weeks. Now all I wanted to do before I decided to go home was to go for a walk. I've asked to go for a walk, I've asked to see a dentist because my teeth have been hurting for two weeks. I asked for a couple of other things that would make me feel a heck of a lot better, and the requests are always vetoed. (pause)

CHAIRMAN 16: Keith.

KEITH 17: . . . nobody has anything to say about Rose's problems. I don't because I don't know enough about it. Ah, I have something that I'd like to bring up, is it all right? (pause)

CHAIRMAN 18: Ah—no, I have—we have some older business on the table yet, that we were waiting for you to settle what shall we do about coming late to meetings.

KEITH 19: String 'em up. (laughter)

CHAIRMAN 20: Two gentlemen came in on the left; I would like to hear from 'em. (Mumbling. The door slams. Giggling.) What?

BOB 21: Why don't you just plan on starting the meeting five minutes early?

CHAIRMAN 22: Well, is that your private opinion, or is this what everybody thinks, that we should have the meeting at two-thirty-five?

KEITH 23: 'Spose some people are starting around two-forty.

BOB 24: (mumbling) . . . all this ah . . . (pause)

ROSE 25: And you're not discussing people being late might I ask a question and ask why I haven't gotten any help on Saturday, why isn't Dr. Bennett saying anything about it, or—other staff members and how they felt—how they said they felt at staff this morning, and how the other patients feel.

CHAIRMAN 26: (irritated) You heard your answer, Rose, and there doesn't seem to be anybody in the room who wants to help you, and there doesn't seem to be anyone in the room who wants to help me.

ROSE 27: This is some meeting. (pause) I don't know how you feel, but I feel lousy.

CHAIRMAN 28: Shake hands. (laughter, pause)

DR. BENNETT 29: Well, I guess ought to say something. (laughter) Well, I think that ah—these days it's very difficult for Rose to hear any answers, which is one reason I didn't reply. Ah, just as she didn't hear anything I said Saturday. Ah, so let me just say from my own observation, Saturday, I didn't feel there was any reason for Rose to be in special. The alternative was not just running away, because that wouldn't've happened except for an oversight. Ah . . . I didn't feel that she was different then than she is most of the time now. CHAIRMAN 30: Yeah, that—I suspected that was the answer. Now I do wonder whether I'm in the same boat, though, whether I don't hear either. (pause)

ROSE 31: Well—I don't—I don't agree with you Dr. Bennett, because I spent two days in my room as much as possible, and only talked when I felt the need to, to people whom I felt would listen, and try to help if they could. And I came up with a couple of things that—I should've come up with five weeks ago so s-still wouldn't be here now. So I don't agree with you that—yesterday and today I've been like I was before. And I think that—taking off as I did on Monday night really helped. And I feel that ah I wish I hadn't had to take off—without my realizing that at the moment when I asked you to go to special, I was telegraphing my punches. And I didn't even know it myself. So I suppose I shouldn't expect you to know, but you're the doctor, I'm not. (pause)

TOM 32: I think that answers ah the reason why people don't say anything about Rose is that every time you say anything what you get is string of plausible explanations mostly consisting of, well, that was yesterday, and I'm much better now. And ah really no attempt at all to understand what anybody says to Rose, but just ah crystallize what she's saying with a string of prepared phrases. (pause)

CHAIRMAN 33: Will you tell us why you were late, Howard?

HOWARD 34: What say?

CHAIRMAN 35: Will you tell us why you were late?

HOWARD 36: I was sleeping.

CHAIRMAN 37: Nobody wake you?

HOWARD 38: What's that?

CHAIRMAN 39: Nobody wake you?

HOWARD 40: Somebody tried. (pause)

CHAIRMAN 41: Well, I'm trying to get an answer in what we can do about this in coming to the meetings. (pause) Keith.

KEITH 42: Fred and I went downtown; we got back at twenty after two. It took me ten minutes to comb my hair. (laughter)

ADAM 43: That leaves ten minutes unaccounted for. (pause)

CHAIRMAN 44: Rose.

ROSE 45: I'm interested in what Tom was saying, before you asked Howard why he was late. Think someone oughta continue the discussion because it's rather important, at least to me and it is to the peace and quiet, and . . . out of the degree of tension on the second floor.

CHAIRMAN 46: Gregor.

GREGOR 47: I think Rose has a very hard time on the floor trying to find somebody to talk to and to tell her story to. She has the story down pretty pat, and she'd like to find as many people as she can to tell her story to. Here she's got us trapped because we've got to sit here and listen to her. And I don't think it's very fair to do it. If people aren't going to listen to you voluntarily, I don't think it's fair to take advantage of the fact that you're in this meeting to, to get your story out.

CHAIRMAN 48: Pat.

PAT 49: I'd like to point out that yesterday I said . . . the same thing that Tom just said now to Rose. But she obviously didn't hear me yesterday.

ROSE 50: I heard you, honestly, it depressed me quite a bit. It's one of the things I've been thinking about for two days. As far as Gregor is concerned, I can't see that he should talk, because we were—a couple of times we've been sitting in the dining room and Sandra and I or someone else have sat down and played the piano. And Gregor bare feet and all, has come and really slammed that door, when we've been trying to relax or be quiet, and have as much peace and quiet on the second floor as we could have—(Laughter)

CHAIRMAN 51: George.

GEORGE (patient) 52: I would like to point out that I, I think he's quite in his, in his, in his, in his rights about that, that I don't think any—anybody that does go in and does play there should have the common courtesy to close that door, so that people who are on the wards, ah who might not wish to be plagued by the sound of me or Rose, or anyone else, can can have a little peace and quiet. Though I don't know the final standards. (pause)

CHAIRMAN 53: . . . thing that Alice had?

ROSE 54: Well, he slammed the door, we didn't.

CHAIRMAN 55: Keith, you want to bring up something?

KEITH 56: Yeah, ah I was home this weekend, and ah, this mornin' I went inta Bob's room, and ah he said that ah on accounta this and on Saturday night Dr. Ingraham had seen fit to change his privileges so that now he can only go out with two other patients. I'm thinkin' of myself when he's tellin' that this is tough luck to try and find two other patients, and so on and—not entirely in agreeance with the decision that was handed down, and so on. But behind that he told the other little facet of this decision that was handed down which is that he cannot go out, I mean the two patients he goes out with can't be Fred and me, like it could be me and somebody else, or it could be Fred and somebody else. But it can't be both Fred and me together. Ah and I resent that. (laughter) While I'm resenting it, I want to know why it is. Because ah yeah, . . . the last incident involving any infraction of regulations involving Bob and myself, it was—I think revolved around February, when we separated from the group, and so on. And nothin' like that has happened since when we would go out, you know, ah . . . pretty regularly. So ah I'm curious to know about that and so on, it's ah often we have the same things to do, and it's pretty convenient for us ah to go out ah with each other. So ah I'd like to hear, you know, an explanation of that from—maybe from the staff, and see what ideas they got about it, 'cause I resent the hell outta of it. I mean, you know, seem to me like I've been told who the heck I can go out with. (Pause)

CHAIRMAN 57: Well . . . before anybody else may want to say something about that, I want to say something first, ah I consider your coming late to the meeting sort of, if not a violation of the rules, certainly behavior that isn't . . . to going out with anybody—from this hospital.

KEITH 58: Well, I musta been about four minutes late, I confess to.

CHAIRMAN 59: In other words, this indicates to me that people who do this, especially that do it continually are not apt to take full responsibility for themselves.

KEITH 60: You consider that I do it continually?

CHAIRMAN 61: I dunno, I haven't kep track, but I . . .

KEITH 62: I wouldn't say so.

CHAIRMAN 63: I do know this, that there is a group missing every time, and there's to some extent—similar—si—ah, the group has similar people in it, not always the same. Of course, some people are honestly late sometimes. But ah . . .

KEITH 64: I don't think that I am. . . .

CHAIRMAN 65: I do, I do conceive of it as a whole attitude toward the hospital, toward what goes on, that is not conducive with ah making one very optimistic about any privileges, ah . . . in the sense of going out alone, being responsible for one's self, and so forth.

GREGOR 66: I don't see why you have to confuse the two issues, one is the question of coming late, and the other, the other is why Fred, Bob, and Keith can't go out together. So that why don't we just talk about the-the second issue, to forget about the other first.

CHAIRMAN 67: I'm sore that nobody, that nobody gives me the courtesy of an answer. Of course . . .

GREGOR 68: Why blame it on every other question that comes up?

CHAIRMAN 69: Bob.

BOB 70: I was late today for one reason, I wasn't very ah I wasn't looking forward to coming up to the meeting because this morning when Dr. Ingraham walked in and ah smilingly told me that my orders were being changed and so on (laughter) . . . at the same time he told me he ordered me to come up to this meeting. It had a bad association. And so I would ah I wasn't very anxious to go, I was just as ah was comfortable sitting down there talking with some people in the living room, who I guess weren't anxious to come up for one reason or another either. So I was about four or five minutes late, that's my reason. I haven't been late for a while, either. I missed one, so I . . . late for a while.

CHAIRMAN 71: Well, that's one of the difficulties we have all over the hospital, there's somebody anxious or uncomfortable or little diffident, about doing something, we act out. And ah this is just why I think this is an—just as an important issue as all the things that happened over the weekend. (pause) Now what can we do about it? (pause) Rose.

ROSE 72: Well, I haven't got any suggestions as to what to do about it. I just get—the impression that you say, you're like a parent or a teacher saying, well, now you've been bad, now how do you think you oughta change, or to be punished? (pause)

CHAIRMAN 73: Dick.

DICK 74: I'd like to suggest that's a, that's a pat answer also. It doesn't help—much. (pause)

BOB 75: I don't have my watch with me, so I don't know how long the meeting's been going, but I know already we've had at least five full minutes of silence in between talking, so ah that's one reason why people might not be anxious to come up to the meeting. So if you're five minutes late, big deal, throughout the whole meeting we have at least fifteen minutes of silence—through the whole thing. This meeting is very uncomfortable for some people—at times to—don't answer ah some of the things are uncomfortable for them. (pause, someone scoots a chair)

CHAIRMAN 76: Keith.

KEITH 77: If nobody has any objection I would like to try and get to the bottom of this business that I brought up before. I haven't heard anything from the staff about it beside the fact that I was late to this meetin' by four minutes. (pause)

CHAIRMAN 78: I don't know, I think ahm . . . the bottom when you talk about the attitude that goes into coming late, that goes into various other things. This morning we spent a half an hour solid on all the things that happened over the weekend. One after another indicating that somebody gets upset or does something that ah is inadvisable, hurts other patients and the like. Now this is the atmosphere right now, and ah so it goes. Now I think these things are at the bottom of ah why Bob's orders get changed, why yours might get—may get changed, and why maybe everybody should get a change.

KEITH 79: Nobody said anything about changing my orders, just a . . .

CHAIRMAN 80: I just did.

KEITH 81: Oh, you just did. (mumbles) That's nice. (laughter. pause)

BOB 82: I hear you laugh, but I don't think it's funny (laughing).

KEITH 83: What am I laughin' about? (pause)

TOM 84: Well, since we have . . . more or less a resistence to talking about it as a—what, I think what you're talking about, especially at this period when people are likely to be upset about a lotta things, to react to it by doing things sort of ah slightly hostile toward someone, or toward the hospital—toward the group in general. But you present it, ah through a medium of personal irritation, where it seems that you're irritated about something—and ah partly that nobody said anything and partly that other people do things like this in the first place. Whereas ah it isn't necessarily a personal attack on you. But it is something ah, I think you, you probably did talk about in the staff meeting, with serious consideration, that something should be done about it. (pause) I mean y-in a sense you're reacting the same way, you're getting irritated with us just as we're being (laughing) irritated with you. You're threatening us just as we sorta threaten the hospital with. . . . (pause) We could all go a moratorium on this and then start over again, and talk about—answering. . . . This isn't really a group problem, I don't think, it's sorta a lot of individual cases that all happen to be together, that everybody reacts in somewhat the same way—due to their anxieties now. You get—what you get out of most people is a defensive reaction, what you get outta Bob, and you get outta Keith, you get outta practically everybody, a reaction of ah tending to put up a defense, rather than look at the problem.

CHAIRMAN 85: Dick?

DICK 86: (whispers) I don't wanna . . .

DR. BENNETT 87: I get a bit unhappy with the role of ogre that I and I think the rest of the staff seems to be put in at these meetings. I mean, the way I hear it, it is as if some people want to go out to have a good time, that's their purpose in going out. And they go out and they have a very good time, they come back and, as a result of that they're punished by not being allowed to go out. Because it seems to me that it's much closer to the facts, that people are feeling tense and restless and in some way of discharging this, go out not really out of a sense of happiness, or a desire to do something, but more as a means of releasing some kind of tension. And then outside find themselves ah in some difficulty controlling themselves, like Rose says, for example, that she just wanted to go for a walk, and yet when she went for a walk she demonstrated that she couldn't control herself. Ah, Saturday when I was on, Bob went out and came back ah about four o'clock in the morning with Fred, I believe. Now I, I find it hard to see that as people just out for a good time, to have a good time while they're out. It seems to me rather a symptom of, of ah ah some difficulty they're having, and that by controlling them ah I, and whoever is responsible for their orders, is not depriving them of something which is an inconvenience for them, but helping them to control this kind of tension and unrest which they're feeling.

GLORIA 88: I don't see how you can put things in categories and generalize so much as you're doing right now. I think they're different reasons for each patient acting the way they (clears throat), excuse me, the way they do. And that ah I know that my reasons ah for acting a little differently now are completely different going out are completely different than what you just described. Ahm and they have nothing to do with that. I don't see how you can general . . .

CHAIRMAN 89: Is everybody having a gloriously good time?

GLORIA 90: No, I'm not, I don't say that I'm having a glorious time, I never pretended that I did.

CHAIRMAN 91: Well, this is the only point that Dr. Bennett seems to make . . .

GLORIA 92: No . . .

CHAIRMAN 93: . . . that people have a good time, as they apparently appear sort of pretending.

GLORIA 94: Well, t—ahm . . .

CHAIRMAN 95: Not you, but ah this is ah I think correctly, observed by Dr. Bennett, that ah we're not irritated because people are having a good time.

GLORIA 96: (whispered off-side) Something wrong with that. I mean is ah having a good time acting out. I mean, for instance, they say "don't act out" because, then you can't retain—ah your therapy, and it's ah diffused ah through your acting out, and is ah good, having a good time releasing some of this tension, couldn't you go down to calisthenics and ah I never did, but if you do, I imagine you release a lot of energy and things like that. Is that, is that ah that diffuses something that could be used in therapy? I don't understand the distinction. (pause)

TOM 97: Well, I don't think in going down to calisthenics you're releasing hostility toward the hospital.

GLORIA 98: Going out may . . .?

TOM 99: Well, that's possible. I'm not saying that it's necessarily so, but it is possible.

GLORIA 100: (low voice) You sk . . .

CHAIRMAN 101: Rose.

ROSE 102: Well, I know I certainly was ah expressing hostility or something toward Dr. Bennett and toward my own doctor and toward the hospital. I, I dunno, I tried explaining this to Dr. Olson and I tried explaining it to the nurse when we walked down to the station that—had I been allowed to go out individually accompanied for a walk to a dentist and not have the feeling of being completely hemmed in, I don't think that I would've taken off either time that I did last week. I guess I'm still a bit angry that my orders didn't read such that I could go out or do something, act like a human being, especially at times when my tension and other people's tension was the greatest on the ward. I don't even go to calisthenics. Can't go to O.T. (pause)

MRS. HEMINGWAY (patient) 103: I nearly ran away Sunday night. I thought this hospital was the worst place I ever saw in all my life on Sunday night. I didn't have anybody to talk to since Dr. Olson was on, and I don't like Dr. Olson. I don't trust him. George talked me out of it. This really was a terrible place on Sunday.

CHAIRMAN 104: Dick.

DICK 105: Well, I think, I-I think that although, that although people have their own problems—and I don't think that everybody has the same reasons for doing things. I think that the tension does —I mean it does communicate itself, and you do get a general feeling of, of-of, of ah wanting to, you know, do something off-beat. And ah I know I felt that way. I just ah mean—I don't see how you can pull people back into, to line with ah ah just hanging some more rules over their heads or something. (pause)

CHAIRMAN 106: So . . . we'll try and do something.

TOM 107: Well, for one thing it doesn't help, I think, if the patients try to justify the things they do as perfectly reasonable and—helpful —without considering that it is an expression of tension or hostility or things like that. It doesn't help anybody just to try to justify things, white-wash them, especially without a remedy.

CHAIRMAN 108: Well, . . . of arguing this point of one—not one definite possibility, one that isn't open to Rose, because right now nobody can can communicate with Rose the way George apparently could with Mrs. Hemingway. Obviously nobody could communicate with Bob on ah the night before or whenever it was, and so right now—ah tension is infectious and ah sometimes doctors may be able and sometimes ah the help may come from elsewhere, but it cannot come, first from ah one particular source or ah or isn't one particular rock in the place who can always be relied on, and is always present around the clock.

MRS. HEMINGWAY 109: I think the way George talked me out of running away might be very interesting to the staff. (clears throat) He didn't object to it at all, as a matter of fact he was, was willing to lend me some money because I didn't have any. But he said that, that if I did, what was I proving, and second of all, it was okay with him if I ran away, he'd even help me if I wanted to, but I'd lose my privileges is all I'd get out of it. But he offered no objection. And it was very clever. (laughter)

DR. BENNETT 110: The points that have been made can set up a long time . . . (laughter)

CHAIRMAN 111: Abner.

ABNER 112: I met Mrs. Hemingway's family on Saturday morning and . . .

MRS. HEMINGWAY 113: Only some of 'em, Abner.

ABNER 114: Well, some of 'em, yeah. Ah and ah we ah talked about ah what ah the group that she was in ah had been discussing . . . and ah, but ah that this—I remember it was ah talked about, that the patient-group could grow angry and therefore ah not even—try to set any speed record comin' up here. Ah that they ah I remember on September 23rd ah I ah, I I, I-I deliberately missed a meeting because ah of res—because I was ah chained to the second floor.

CHAIRMAN 115: Rose.

ROSE 116: Well, I know that if someone like George said anything to me, I mean if the student-nurse had been a little bit more involved, and said something to me and tried to help Saturday morning and afternoon, I know I wouldn't've taken off, 'cause I, I really didn't prove anything. I would've been just as—it helped a little but not enough, so it wasn't really worth it.

CHAIRMAN 117: Even the nurse didn't use the right technique?

ROSE 118: Well, she did and she didn't. She talked to me, and she said she couldn't sanction it professionally, she couldn't really understand it 'cause she wasn't in my place. She did say, however, that ah she's a fairly well-adjusted person, but mental hospitals and the tension around here starts driving her bats too (laughter). And this is a he—a normal—student-nurse goes back to the dorm—at the end of the first day, the first day she said she went back and because of the tension around here she was tense. And yet I'm supposed to suppose, and Warren was as . . .

WARREN 119: Why—why do you bring my name into it? (laughter)

ROSE 120: And then myself and everybody else who had trouble over here. We're supposed to curb the tension without any help from anybody else. That's what gripes me.

ADAM 121: . . . why don't you build a big silver statue of George and put it out . . . (laughter) or pass out pictures to everybody to look at who felt like running away? Might do some good, or help a few people. (laughter)

ROSE 122: Help sell them. (laughter)

FRED 123: I think the only reason why—well, I won't say the only reason because there're been many reasons why in the past I've ah broken rules, but I feel certain this time ah one of the basic reasons for it ah I was feeling sort of bored. And I get this way a lot of times but I find that just doing the right things, things within the rules and what-not, ah there's just so many things you can do in this town. I mean you kin ah go to Savin Rock, you can go to the beach and you can ah maybe go to the library, maybe listen to some music. You get tired of doing these things day in and day out, sometimes you get a kick out of ah just breaking the rules a little bit, for some reason, I don't know what it is, at least I do. And so occasionally I'll do it. (pause)

CHAIRMAN 124: I get the impression that this falls into the category of what Tom said before . . . when we're making light of all these incidents.

FRED 125: Well, I'm not trying to make light of it, ah . . .

CHAIRMAN 126: Perhaps it's been more than boredom, or the ah ah label of . . . and we're getting confused if you can, ah, it's usually so in my experience, there are . . . the more difficulties behind this and besides ah Fred, you know that ah . . . other things happen besides going to Savin Rock.

FRED 127: Well to be quite truthful we were in the middle of ah to be quite truthful we were in the middle of nowhere, about thirty miles away from the hospital at four o'clock in the morning. We were just about ready to sleep in a cow field. (laughter) And I'm telling you I was . . . when I got back here I was damn glad. (pause) I'm not tryin' to make light of it. (pause)

CHAIRMAN 128: Mrs. Jennings.

MRS. JENNINGS (patient) 129: It seems to me that in the last couple of weeks there has been ah quite a let down in the amount of organized activity that's going on around here.

CHAIRMAN 130: Quite a let down?

MRS. JENNINGS 131: The a let-down in the amount of organized activity going on around here. Very few ah trips out for people who have to go out accompanied, and not many trips even just over to Clarks Dairy, and places like that, just to get people out of the hospital. And Sunday particularly has always been a pretty deadly day because there's nothing planned, except church. (pause)

CHAIRMAN 132: Well, aren't there new activities scheduled? (pause) Rose.

ROSE 133: Well, I agree with—Mrs. Jennings. 'Cept that I found things to do yesterday and I can't see why other people can't either—(laughter) I wasn't doing a heck of a lot of talking, at least I didn't think so comparatively. (pause)

CHAIRMAN 134: Any of you on the activities committee?

BETTY 135: I, I am on the activities committee (laughter) . . . Miss Tyler isn't here. Let's see who else, Jack [patient], Mel, Mike, Mrs. King [patient] are on it with me. I think Jack's here, I see, Mrs. King isn't here. I don't know if Mel or Mike are here. Yes, I don't know about Mel. (laughter)

MEL 136: Well what I heard was that the activities committee scheduled activities up until the 23rd of June. And then that the, this new committee would ah make out some more. (pause)

CHAIRMAN 137: What was planned for yesterday?

MEL 138: I didn't look.

UNIDENTIFIED WOMEN 139: Nothing was planned.

CHAIRMAN 140: Maybe this has something to do with the members on the committee, they're not very . . . (laughter)

MISS NEWTON 141: Well, maybe we should make up a new one.

BOB 142: I spent forty-five minutes today talking to my doctor about that. There's two weekends, no, three if you want to count the ones going to the theatre that some people want to see, going to the beach and the movies on Wednesday night, we've had two dances in two months. (pause)

CHAIRMAN 143: Rose.

ROSE 144: Yeah, but when they are activities like the supper-dance that Bob is referring to, half the people went out that Saturday night.

KEITH 145: Saturday night is no time to have it in this place.

BOB 146: Why do we have it Saturday night?

ROSE 147: I don't know, I'm not on the committee.

MRS. HEMINGWAY 148: I spoke to Miss Tyler and to Miss Underwood and to Pat about this very thing, that-that the . . . is that so many people go out for the weekend in their home or whatever it is they're going to do they they ahm, also that the paid personnel has to get time and a half if they work on a weekend. It seems to me that if they could have an extra student nurse so that those people that are remaining in the hospital and have nothing to do, could go out at least to the movies, and that would ease a lot of this off and would give you something to look forward to. Because there isn't anything to do on Saturday or Sunday, and you can't go out because there's never enough staff.

CHAIRMAN 149: No, there isn't enough staff routinely unless it's planned in advance.

MRS. HEMINGWAY 150: I don't see why we can't have a-a, a movie group go outside to the movies on either Saturday or Sunday night, I guess Sunday night would be better.

CHAIRMAN 151: I don't know either. But ah unless the patients organize this kind of thing . . .

MRS. HEMINGWAY 152: If there'd be a student nurse, if they—because there may be six . . . somebody has to be accompanied.

CHAIRMAN 153: Unless the patients organize this kind of thing it's just not going to happen. Mrs. Ordway?

MRS. ORDWAY 154: Y-you did go to the movies this Sunday.

MRS. HEMINGWAY 155: (interrupting) This last Sunday. But it's the first time, but it's the first time since I've been here.

MRS. ORDWAY 156: Well, we do try on Saturdays and Sundays to.

MRS. HEMINGWAY 157: (interrupts again) It's not your fault; you don't have enough staff.

MRS. ORDWAY 158: I'm not saying that, but we do try, if you come and ask us to let you go out for a walk, and—and . . . if it's at all possible.

MRS. HEMINGWAY 159: But most of the—sure, you're willing a-and I know you're willing but there just isn't anybody around to do it, you know, because they're so short on weekends. It's not your fault and it's not the patient's fault—there just isn't anybody here unless Miss Underwood will assign students especially for that day.

MRS. ORDWAY 160: Especially during the week some of the activities such as roller-skating and bowling on Monday nights, very few people ah are willing to go. We go around every Monday night and ask who wants to go roller skating. There is never a group because nobody wants to go.

MRS. HEMINGWAY 161: I don't like to roller skate, I've got a crippled leg.

MRS. ORDWAY 162: That's what I mean.

CHAIRMAN 163: Dr. Bennett.

DR. BENNETT 164: There's one difficulty that I'd like to make clear to you, and I really don't know how to get about it, but ah the people who usually go when there is something like this on the weekends are those who aren't feeling so badly, leaving behind those people that really feel pretty lousy and ah quite tense and ah who in turn are quite deprived by the loss of those who feel somewhat better. In other words it makes it more difficult for them. Ah now I think it's unfair to keep everybody in, but at the same time I think there is a problem in this, that it does make things worse for a sizeable group of rather tense and upset patients.

CHAIRMAN 165: Well, exactly, and I don't think that a movie even is something that needs to be planned except that we sometimes need extra people for certain patients. The activity I have in mind, and the activity a functioning and . . . as a committee commensurate with the abilities of the patients in general ah I would see to it that activities were in the hospital, not away from here, activities that do not require extra personnel necessarily. I would think the committee of the patients could function on the spur of the moment, whereas nurses cannot be hired on the spur of the moment and schedules rearranged. Miss Underwood?

MISS UNDERWOOD 166: I was going to ask Miss Oakland if ah, ah she thought that there was ah real restriction of people going out Saturday and Sunday afternoons, there's really quite a bit of activity going on that way.

MISS OAKLAND 167: Ah, well, on Saturday they[2] have a cook-out. . . .

MISS UNDERWOOD 168: But in general. It seems to me as I go through the wards there's a good deal going on over the weekend as it is.

UNIDENTIFIED NURSE 169: On Friday, ah I think two nights a week there's usually a . . . group to the movies.

MISS OAKLAND 170: That's why they went Saturday because they couldn't go ss-Friday night.

MISS UNDERWOOD 171: And we wonder about the advisability of ah the . . . here, a couple of groups going out and of having the need for

2. The use of the designation "they" clearly distinguishes patients from staff. This designation is used less often now, mostly by nurses.

more of that and not trying to have more of the activities in a . . . differentiated way within the hospital.

CHAIRMAN 172: Zeke.

ZEKE 173: Well, I think a lot of the . . . activities in the hospital itself . . . take the people out for a walk or, or a lot of the time anyway, actually there's small group activity right here in the hospital.

CHAIRMAN 174: Well, the tension, according to the law of the patients within the hospital . . . by taking a few people out. Ah, Bob.

BOB 175: I was going to say the same thing, maybe you could ah what I was thinking of were activities in the hospital say on more evenings in the week, you know, because I go out very often and I go out and spend money that I don't have—in other words I borrow money from anybody who's going, and I have a perfectly lousy time, most of the time, because there's nothing to do, really, outside, or inside activities.

CHAIRMAN 176: Rose.

ROSE 177: Well, I agree with Dr. Bennett that the people that are tensest are the ones that on the weekend are left by themselves. And if these people, out instead, like Bob says, he has lots of time, if they could—leave their going-out to night when—during the week when —they don't want to stay for activities, maybe they could stay in weekends, and between now and the change of doctors[3] the next two weekends, and see if we could—either the patients who aren't on the advisory committee or the committee itself get together and make sure that for the next two weekends at least there'd be a number of activities, because they're going to be the tensest. (pause)

GLORIA 178: Well, what about other people? I mean ahm what do you mean left alone? You're left in the hospital alone with forty-two people surrounding you, plus a doctor on call. No one's ever left alone in this hospital.

ROSE 179: I'm talkin' about what Dr. Bennett said about the people who are tensest being the ones who can't go out, and people from the first floor and people who feel much better ah they go out and leave the tense ones just to fend for themselves.

CHAIRMAN 180: Mrs. Morton.

MRS. MORTON 181: The thing that bothers me the most in listening to this is the fact that with many people that there is never a spon-

---

3. The first explicit mention of a fact which strongly influences much of what is said in this meeting; the "change of doctors"—the replacing of the resident therapists by new, unknown residents—will occur two weeks after this patient-staff meeting, on July 1.

taneous thing started on evenings when there's nothing planned. I'm wondering if you ever get a group of this size, even outside, that hasn't some time or other, a spontaneous plan, arrangement of games, dancing or singing or music. It seems to me that everyone here expects someone to outline everything they have to do. And I should think there's plenty of them here that are able to arrange and organize some of this for themselves.

CHAIRMAN 182: Fred.

FRED 183: I think the basic reason for that is that, that for a long time, not so much now, ah everything had to be planned around this place. Ah and if you didn't plan on something, you got hell for it. Ah I mean, for example, you ah, when you, when I—when I had privileges to go out with two other patients, ah, geez, I've have to plan three days in advance practically to make certain that I'd have somebody to go out with. And I think in little subtle ways, it's hard to describe, it's always damn . . . in some way they, things have to be planned around this place, because if you do something spontaneous, I dunno ah, I guess people are a little conscious of it. (pause)

CHAIRMAN 184: Bob.

BOB 185: I try and ah well, I try all the time to get things going like volley-ball games or something like that, people who on Saturdays all play and with much enthusiasm because this is generally done on Saturdays after the cook-out, are going to other times, ah sit around and watch television, or listen to records or something but for volley-ball or that sort of thing, if you try to get something spontaneous, it doesn't work. (pause)

ABNER 186: Ah oh, ah I remember ah that night ah where they ah had—were going in a group to see that ah, see this ah, see a particular movie and ah they had enough things for a change, because the aide for this entertainment had to go home to his wife who was sick and therefore the group wasn't going and, that's where, where I got irritated.

CHAIRMAN 187: Fred.

FRED 188: I think spontaneity is one thing that, is one thing. But I've been here for three years now, or almost three years, and ah just about everything there is that I could do within the rules has been done at least ah a hundred times. And ah you get bored stiff with it, you do it, and you do it, and you do it, it doesn't have any more kicks. I think even the spontaneity to a degree is becoming habitual. And ah I think if they could find some new things to do, everybody could use their imagination then maybe we'd get outta this hole, or this mess.

CHAIRMAN 189: Gloria. Gloria.

GLORIA 190: I can't agree with you, Fred. I mean, ah, a man gets up and goes to work, ah goes to the same work every day, comes back, sees the same wife, the same kids, the same dog, all the time and ah (laughter) and ah, I mean even if you're seeing the same thing, it gets sort of dull after a while, so he gonna get—divorce his wife and run off with some other woman or ah . . .

ADAM 191: Divorce his dog.

GLORIA 192: . . . commit a murder for kicks, but ah, you know some things you—I don't—I can't agree with you there.

CHAIRMAN 193: O.K.

Index